INDUCTIVE PROBABILITY

International Library of Philosophy and Scientific Method

EDITED BY A. J. AYER

INDUCTIVE

PROBABILITY

by

John Patrick Day

Senior Lecturer in Philosophy in the
University College of North Staffordshire

LONDON
ROUTLEDGE & KEGAN PAUL
NEW YORK : THE HUMANITIES PRESS

First published 1961
by Routledge & Kegan Paul Ltd.
Broadway House, 68–74 Carter Lane
London, E.C.4

Printed in Great Britain
by Richard Clay and Company, Ltd.
Bungay, Suffolk

78256

To the Memory of
JOHN LANGSHAW AUSTIN

CONTENTS

vii

CONTENTS

PREFACE

It may, therefore, be a subject worthy of curiosity, to enquire what is the nature of that evidence which assures us of any real existence and matter of fact, beyond the present testimony of our senses, or the records of our memory. (D. Hume)

Everyone has some idea of the meanings of the terms 'probable' and 'improbable'; yet no attempt to make precise the exact nature of these concepts can be said to have been successful. (R. H. Nisbet)

The scope of the following essay, and my reasons for writing it, are indicated by the preceding quotations. On the one hand, the interest of the knot of problems usually treated of under the rubric *Probability and Induction* is at least as great in our day as it was in Hume's. On the other, the fact that there is no sort of agreement among those who have tried to unravel it about what the right solution of these problems may be, leaves ample room for another attempt upon them.

My primary objective throughout is to provide a true constructive account of the matter. But I also engage in a good deal of critical discussion, in which are included fairly numerous quotations and references. For the literature on the subject is interesting and extensive; and though this book is in no sense a history of philosophical doctrines about Induction and Probability, I hope that these discussions increase its educative value. In all of them, the ideal I aim at is that which Leibniz set himself in his examination of Locke's *Essay concerning Human Understanding*: '*Mon but a esté plustost d'eclaircir les choses, que de refuter les sentimens d'autruy*'. Consequently, they are selective and not complete, since I am concerned to make only those points, both critical and constructive, which illuminate the general view of probability and induction presented in this book.

Probability is a concept which is used not only by ordinary men but also by specialists, notably mathematicians, statisticians, men of science and of law. The philosopher of Probability must consequently consider these professional uses as well as the lay ones.

But if, like me, he is not himself a specialist in any of these disciplines, he thereby exposes himself to the charge of not knowing what he is talking about. However, I think that this objection is less forbidding than it sounds. In the first place, the works of these specialists are not esoteric, but open to inspection by philosophers as by other men. Nor, what is more important, are they by any means unintelligible to the lay reader who is willing to try to understand them. It may be urged that these considerations show at best that Philosophy of Probability *can* be written by outsiders; but that it nevertheless must in the nature of the case be written better by those who know these disciplines from the inside. But I think that it is possible to make out a case at least as strong for the opposite opinion. Witness some wise words of Venn's, who comments on the then prevailing tendency, which he considered disastrous, to leave the study of Probability entirely to the mathematicians, in the following terms: 'No science can safely be abandoned entirely to its own devotees. Its details of course can only be studied by those who make it their special occupation, but its general principles are sure to be cramped if it is not exposed occasionally to the free criticism of those whose main culture has been of a more general character.' [J. Venn, *The Logic of Chance*, Preface to 1st ed., London, 1866]

As to style, I have tried to write in a manner that will be intelligible, not only to professional philosophers, but also to the student and the general reader; that is to say, above all, clearly. However, these problems are generally and rightly regarded as among the hardest in Philosophy, and there is no denying that this difficulty of the subject-matter precludes easy understanding. But—to adapt Aristotle's remark about precision in Ethics—it is a mark of the educated man that in every subject he looks for only so much simplicity as its nature permits. My use of formulas poses a special stylistic difficulty. They are however very simple, and need deter no-one. They are moreover introduced, not from pedantry or any belief in the intrinsic value of formalization, but for definite reasons which will be given in due course. [1.2, end; 6.2]

I acknowledge indebtedness in various degrees to all the authors listed under *References*. [pp. xiiiff.] Those from whom I have learnt most are Hume, Mill, Venn and Peirce among older writers, and Johnson, Keynes, Broad, Kneale and von Wright among contemporary ones; but it will be found that I am unable to accept the solutions that they propose. My view of the nature of Philosophy derives from Wittgenstein; but I do not consider this a matter of the first importance, since it seems to me that philosophical investigations are conducted either well or ill by those who take false as well as by those who take true views of what Philosophy is. The history of philosophical opinions about Probability and Induction bears out this judgement at least as well as the history of opinions about other of the leading problems of Philosophy. This preface is not the place in which to state or defend my view of what philosophizing rightly consists in. But I make some explicit remarks on the matter in 1.2 and 6.2, in addition to which the view is of course implicitly involved in the entire essay.

Finally, it is a pleasure to thank the following for reading the book in typescript and for making helpful suggestions about how it might be improved: the Editor; and R. F. Atkinson, the late J. L. Austin, R. B. Braithwaite, A. G. N. Flew, G. Ryle and S. E. Toulmin.

J. P. DAY

Keele, Staffordshire,
6 July 1960

REFERENCES

I abbreviate my principal references as follows:—

Apelt: E. F. Apelt, *Die Theorie der Induction*, Leipzig, 1854.
Aristotle: Aristotle, *The Organon*, I, tr. H. P. Cooke and H. Tredennick, London, 1938.
Ayer: A. J. Ayer, *Language, Truth and Logic*, 2nd ed., London, 1946.
Bacon: *The Philosophical Works of Francis Bacon*, reprinted from the texts and translations, with the notes and prefaces, of Ellis and Spedding, ed. J. M. Robertson, London, 1905.
Bentham: J. Bentham, *Rationale of Judicial Evidence*, Vol. I, ed. J. S. Mill, London, 1827.
Black, C: M. Black, *Critical Thinking*, New York, 1946.
Black, H: M. Black, 'How Difficult Might Induction Be?', *Problems of Analysis*, London, 1954.
Black, I: M. Black, 'Inductive Support of Inductive Rules', *Problems of Analysis*, London, 1954.
Black, J: M. Black, 'The Justification of Induction', *Language and Philosophy*, Ithaca, N.Y., 1949.
Black, P: M. Black, ' "Pragmatic" Justifications of Induction', *Problems of Analysis*, London, 1954.
Braithwaite: R. B. Braithwaite, *Scientific Explanation*, Cambridge, 1953.
Broad, D, I: C. D. Broad, 'The Principles of Demonstrative Induction (I)', *Mind*, July 1930.
Broad, D, II: C. D. Broad, 'The Principles of Demonstrative Induction (II)', *Mind*, October 1930.
Broad, P: C. D. Broad, 'The Principles of Problematic Induction', *Aristotelian Society Proceedings*, Vol. XXVIII, 1928.
Broad, R, I: C. D. Broad, 'On the Relation between Induction and Probability (I)', *Mind*, October 1918.
Broad, R, II: C. D. Broad, 'On the Relation between Induction and Probability (II)', *Mind*, January 1920.
Carnap: R. Carnap, *Logical Foundations of Probability*, Chicago, 1950.
Eaton: R. M. Eaton, *General Logic*, New York, 1931.

REFERENCES

Hampshire: S. Hampshire, 'The Analogy of Feeling', *Mind*, January 1952.

Hare: R. M. Hare, *The Language of Morals*, Oxford, 1952.

Hempel, I: C. G. Hempel, 'Studies in the Logic of Confirmation (I)', *Mind*, January 1945.

Hempel, II: C. G. Hempel, 'Studies in the Logic of Confirmation (II)', *Mind*, April 1945.

Hume, E: D. Hume, *An Enquiry concerning Human Understanding*, ed. L. A. Selby-Bigge, Oxford, 1902.

Hume, T: D. Hume, *A Treatise of Human Nature*, ed. L. A. Selby-Bigge, Oxford, 1896.

Jeffreys: H. Jeffreys, *Theory of Probability*, Oxford, 1939.

Jevons, I: W. S. Jevons, *The Principles of Science*, Vol. I, London, 1874.

Jevons, II: W. S. Jevons, *The Principles of Science*, Vol. II, London, 1874.

Johnson, I: W. E. Johnson, *Logic*, Part I, Cambridge, 1921.

Johnson, II: W. E. Johnson, *Logic*, Part II, Cambridge, 1922.

Johnson, III: W. E. Johnson, *Logic*, Part III, Cambridge, 1924.

Keynes: J. M. Keynes, *A Treatise on Probability*, London, 1921.

Kneale: W. Kneale, *Probability and Induction*, Oxford, 1949.

Kneale, II: W. Kneale, 'Probability and Induction (II)', *Mind*, July 1951.

Lalande: A. Lalande, *Les Théories de l'Induction et de l'Experimentation*, Paris, 1929.

Laplace: P. S. de Laplace, *A Philosophical Essay on Probabilities*, tr. F. W. Truscott and F. L. Emory, New York, 1951.

Leibniz: L. Couturat, *La Logique de Leibniz*, Paris, 1901.

Lewis: C. I. Lewis, *An Analysis of Knowledge and Valuation*, La Salle, Ill., 1946.

Lewy: C. Lewy, 'On the "Justification" of Induction', *Analysis*, September 1939.

Locke: J. Locke, *An Essay concerning Human Understanding*, abr. and ed. A. S. Pringle-Pattison, Oxford, 1924.

Mace: C. A. Mace, *The Principles of Logic*, London, 1933.

Mill: J. S. Mill, *A System of Logic*, 8th ed., People's Edition, London, 1898.

Mises: R. von Mises, *Probability, Statistics and Truth*, tr. J. Neyman *et al.*, London, 1939.

Nagel: E. Nagel, 'Principles of the Theory of Probability', *International Encyclopaedia of Unified Science*, Vol. I, No. 6, Chicago, 1939.

REFERENCES

Nicod: J. Nicod, *Foundations of Geometry and Induction*, tr. P. P.
              Wiener, London, 1930.
Nisbet: R. H. Nisbet, 'The Foundations of Probability', *Mind*,
              January 1926.
Peirce: *The Philosophy of Peirce: Selected Writings*, ed. J. Buchler,
              London, 1940.
Philodemus: *Philodemus: On Methods of Inference*, ed. and tr. P. H. and
              E. A. de Lacy, Philadelphia, 1941.
Poincaré: H. Poincaré, *Science and Hypothesis*, tr. G. B. Halsted,
              Lancaster, Pa., 1946.
Popper: K. R. Popper, *Logik der Forschung*, Vienna, 1935.
Price: H. H. Price, *Thinking and Experience*, London, 1953.
Ramsey: F. P. Ramsey, *The Foundations of Mathematics and Other
              Logical Essays*, ed. R. B. Braithwaite, London,
              1931.
Reichenbach: H. Reichenbach, *Experience and Prediction*, Chicago,
              1938.
Reid: T. Reid, *Essays on the Intellectual Powers of Man*, ed. and
              abr. A. D. Woozley, London, 1941.
Russell, H: B. Russell, *Human Knowledge: Its Scope and Limits*,
              London, 1948.
Russell, P: B. Russell, *The Problems of Philosophy*, London, 1912.
Ryle, C: G. Ryle, *The Concept of Mind*, London, 1949.
Ryle, I: G. Ryle, 'Induction and Hypothesis', *Aristotelian Society
              Sup. Vol. XVI*, 1937.
Stocks: J. L. Stocks, 'Epicurean Induction', *Mind*, April 1925.
Strawson: P. F. Strawson, *Introduction to Logical Theory*, London,
              1952.
Thomson: J. F. Thomson, 'The Argument from Analogy and our
              Knowledge of Other Minds', *Mind*, July 1951.
Tippett: L. H. C. Tippett, *Statistics*, London, 1943.
Toulmin, Ph: S. Toulmin, *The Philosophy of Science*, London, 1953.
Toulmin, Pr: S. Toulmin, 'Probability', *Aristotelian Society Sup. Vol.
              XXIV*, 1950.
Urmson: J. O. Urmson, 'Two of the Senses of "Probable"',
              Analysis, October 1947.
Venn, L: J. Venn, *The Logic of Chance*, 3rd ed., London, 1888.
Venn, P: J. Venn, *The Principles of Empirical or Inductive Logic*,
              London, 1889.
Waismann: F. Waismann, '*Logische Analyse des Wahrscheinlichkeitsbe-
              griffs*', *Erkenntnis*, Vol. I, 1930–1931.
Weinberg: J. R. Weinberg, *An Examination of Logical Positivism*,
              London, 1936.

Whewell: W. Whewell, *The Philosophy of the Inductive Sciences*, Vol.
                II, 2nd ed., London, 1847.
Whiteley: C. H. Whiteley, 'On the Justification of Induction',
                Analysis, Vol. 7, No. 3, 1940.
Wigmore: J. H. Wigmore, *The Principles of Judicial Proof*, 2nd ed.,
                Boston, Mass., 1931.
Williams, D: D. Williams, 'On the Direct Probability of Inductions',
                Mind, October 1953.
Williams, G: D. Williams, *The Ground of Induction*, Cambridge, Mass.,
                1947.
Wisdom: J. O. Wisdom, *Foundations of Inference in Natural Science*,
                London, 1952.
Woozley: A. D. Woozley, *Theory of Knowledge*, London, 1949.
Wright, L: G. H. von Wright, *The Logical Problem of Induction*, *Acta
                Philosophica Fennica*, Vol. III, Helsingfors, 1941.
Wright, T: G. H. von Wright, *A Treatise on Induction and Prob-
                ability*, London, 1951.
Yule: G. U. Yule and M. G. Kendall, *An Introduction to the
                Theory of Statistics*, 12th ed., London, 1940.

References to these works are generally given by page-numbers, and
are placed between square brackets, as are cross-references also. The
preceding list is also offered as a select bibliography of the subject down
to the beginning of 1956, when the following essay was completed in
draft. I mean by this that, as I have found at least part of all these works
helpful, but not equally helpful, in composing this book, so other
people too may find at least part of at least some of them helpful in at
least some degree.

1 THE PHILOSOPHICAL PROBLEM OF INDUCTIVE PROBABILITY

1.1.1 *The Meaning of 'Induction'*

By 'inductive probability' I mean the probability of inductions. What then are inductions? 'Induction' is a technical term of Philosophy, so that there cannot be a problem of explaining its meaning in the same way as there is a problem of explaining the meaning of non-philosophical terms such as 'probable' or 'evidence'; its meaning is what philosophers stipulatively define it to be. Nevertheless, there is a problem of a sort, since philosophers do not all agree about the stipulated definition of the word.

Conformably with the practice of at any rate some philosophers, I define 'an induction' as 'a generalization or a proposition derived from a generalization'. This requires an explanation of the meaning of 'a generalization'; not a stipulated definition thereof, for 'generalization' is not a philosophical term. The explanation must be given, in my view, in terms of the notion of an evidential-statement. Consider the formula, (1): $E(p, q)$, read 'The fact that q is evidence that p'. I use p, q, r, etc., as proposition-variables; in this formula it is convenient to call q the evidencing-statement-formula and p the evidenced-statement-formula. I call this formula the categorical evidential-statement-formula. It would also be possible to construct an hypothetical evidential-statement-formula, to be read 'If q that is evidence that p'. But in this essay it

B   I

will be convenient to confine our attention in the main to categorical formulas. Notice, however, that indicative sentences are often used to make hypothetical, not categorical, evidential-statements; e.g. 'Dark cloud is evidence of coming rain'.

Take now a special case of formula (1), namely the formula, (2): $E(fAg, f'Ag)$, read 'The fact that all observed f are g is evidence that all f are g'. I use f, g, h, etc., as attribute-variables, and symbolize 'observed f, g, h, etc.' as f', g', h', etc. A is the universal quantifier, read 'all'. I call (2) an inductive primitive evidential-statement-formula. Its evidenced-statement-formula is a generalization-formula or primitive induction-formula, and statements substituted on it are generalizations or primitive inductions. This is an illustration designed to explain the meaning of 'a generalization', not a definition. For it is too narrow to serve as a definition. For, as will be shown, there are variable-generalizations as well as attribute-generalizations. Moreover, it illustrates only one type of attribute-generalization, namely, the universal subject-predicate type; but, as will also be shown, there are other types of attribute-generalization. I take as paradigm exemplification of formula (2) the evidential-statement: 'The fact that all observed balls in this urn are hollow is evidence that all the balls in this urn are hollow', and abbreviate this statement: 'The fact that all observed BU are H is evidence that all BU are H'.

Consider next the formula, (3): $E(gx, I(fAg) . fx)$. I use x, y, z, etc., as individual-variables; fx and gx are to be read respectively as x is f and x is g. . symbolizes conjunction, read 'and'. As for the constituent formula $I(fAg)$, this indicates that fAg is an induction-formula and not e.g. an observation-statement-formula. I call (3) an inductive derivative evidential-statement-formula. The difference between a derivative and a primitive evidential-statement-formula is that the evidencing-statement-formula of the former contains as constituent an evidenced-statement-formula, whereas that of the latter does not. Then, the evidenced-statement-formula of (3) is a derivative induction-formula. This again is an illustration, not a definition, being too narrow to serve for the latter. An exemplification of formula (3) is: 'The fact that all BU are H and that this is a BU is evidence that this is H'. It may be objected that the formula that this statement exemplifies is rather: $E(gx, f'Ag . fx)$. But on this question I agree with Mill. Doubtless there is what he calls 'inference from particulars to particulars'; i.e. inductive inference in which we move from fx to gx without first making the generalization $I(fAg)$. But, though they need not be so regarded, such inferences may always be regarded as passing through the generalization; and it is convenient so to regard them. I.e., we have first an inductive inference in accordance with formula (2); and second a deductive inference in accordance with the formula: $I(fAg).fx \supset I(gx)$. $\supset$ symbolizes implication, read 'if'. [Mill, 121 ff., 187 ff.]

My distinction between primitive and derivative inductions closely resembles Nicod's distinction between primary and secondary inductions. '. . . suppose that an induction has among its premises the conclusion of another induction. We shall call it then a *secondary induction*. *Primary inductions* are those whose premises do not derive their certainty or probability from any induction.' [Nicod, 212] Cp. also Mace's distinction between 'direct' and 'indirect' inductions. [Mace, 259, 285] All generalizations are primitive inductions and conversely; and since generalizations are of course general, all singular inductions are derivative. This is not to deny that there are general derivative inductions; consider e.g. statements exemplifying the evidenced-statement-formula of the formula, (4): $E(fAg, I(hAg).fAh)$. But it is to deny that general derivative inductions are (rightly called) generalizations.

It will now be convenient to comment on some other definitions or explanations of the meaning of 'an induction'. Some say that one sort of induction is induction by complete enumeration. Our word 'induction' is derived from Aristotle's technical term ἐπαγωγή, by which he means the establishing of universal statements by a consideration of particular cases falling under them. One, but not the only, way in which he says that this is done may be illustrated as follows. [Aristotle, 512 ff.; Kneale, 7 ff.; Mace, 245 ff.] I know by observation that $f'Ag$ and that fAf', and assert that fAg. Then, a statement substituted upon this last formula is an induction by complete enumeration. This doctrine has endured. E.g., in the 16th century Zabarella represents inductions by complete enumeration or 'perfect' inductions as one of the two species of inductions. '. . . there is no one who does not know that Induction is a logical instrument by which from particular notions a less known universal is demonstrated; and that this is of two kinds, perfect, which concludes necessarily because it embraces all the particulars, and imperfect which does not conclude necessarily because it does not embrace all the particulars'. [*De Doctrinae Ordine Apologia*, 1594; quoted in Venn, P, 343] And in recent times Johnson has recognized them under the name of 'summary inductions' as one of the four species of induction that he distinguishes. [Johnson, III, xiv] But I do not propose to call universal statements so established 'inductions' for the following reason. If, knowing that all the BU I have observed are H and that the BU I have observed are all the BU there are, I say that all BU are H, my statement is a description of BU. But my account of the meaning of 'an induction' is in terms of a generalization; and descriptions, as I shall argue more fully later, must be clearly distinguished from generalizations. The essential feature of the latter is that they assert something about unobserved instances of a kind on the evidence of observed instances of that kind, that they 'go beyond the evidence' or involve a 'leap' as it is often put; whereas the former logically must be about observed instances only. Hence, too, an induction is a conclusion of an inference or argument, whereas a description is not.

The passage from Zabarella raises two further points that deserve mention. He states that inductive inference is always from particulars to a universal conclusion. This doctrine also derives from Aristotle and is widely held; it is used to distinguish induction from deduction, the former being said to proceed from particular cases to a universal conclusion, the latter conversely. [Aristotle, *Posterior Analytics*, 81 b] On my account of inductions, this is false; cp. formula (3). It is not true even of primitive inductions either, for we shall see that some generalizations are not universal, i.e. not of the form *f*A*g*. Again, Zabarella says that an induction is always 'less known', i.e. less certain, than its evidencing-statement; but we shall see that this too is false, since sometimes both have the same degree of certainty, namely, when both are true.

The other way in which Aristotle says that universal statements can be established by observation of particular cases is by what Johnson calls 'intuitive induction'. [Aristotle, *Posterior Analytics*, 71a, 81b; Kneale, 30 ff.; Mace, 248ff.] The kind of universal statements that can be so established are necessary ones, e.g. 'All coloured things must be extended'. To establish such a statement by intuitive induction apparently means this. I 'see' that this particular thing that is coloured must be extended; but I simultaneously also 'see' that all things that are coloured must be extended. The operation is sometimes called 'seeing the general rule in the particular case'; Aristotle himself speaks of 'induction exhibiting the universal as implicit in the clearly known particular'. I do not myself believe that we ever establish universal necessary truths in this way. And even if we do, I do not propose to call universal necessary truths so established 'inductions', for two reasons. The first is the same as one of those for refusing to recognize 'summary inductions' as a sort of inductions; namely, that on my definition an induction is a conclusion of an inference, whereas intuitive induction involves no inference. We do not argue or reason 'This coloured thing must be extended, therefore all coloured things must be extended'; we 'see the general rule in the particular case'. The second reason is this: if intuitive inductions are to be called inductions, then some inductions are necessary truths. But on my definition of 'induction' no inductions are necessary truths, since generalizations are not necessary truths. This needs explaining.

Necessary truths must be distinguished from necessary consequences. What I call 'deductive derivative inductions' are by definition necessary consequences of primitive inductions or generalizations. But they are not on this account necessary truths; they would be so only if the generalizations of which they are necessary consequences were necessary truths. However, it may be urged that they sometimes are. It may be said: We say that all men must die; this primitive induction is therefore a necessary truth; and when we deduce from it and the additional premiss that Tom is a man that Tom must die, this derivative induction is therefore a necessary truth too. But this still confuses necessary consequences with necessary truths. 'All men must be mortal' is not like 'All men must be male'. In the latter, 'must' does indeed signify that the statement is a necessary or analytic truth. But in the former, 'must' signifies that the statement is a necessary consequence merely, say of 'All animals are mortal' conjoined with the additional premiss 'All men are animals'. And since 'All animals are mortal' is a contingent or synthetic truth, its necessary consequence 'All men must be mortal' is not a necessary truth either.

It may also be thought that mathematical induction is a species of induction in my sense. [Kneale, 37 ff.] But this is not so. The essential difference is this. Mathematical inductions are deductions

5

or theorems, mathematical induction being a process of deduction. But primitive inductions are not deductions, as Hume points out. [Hume, E, 35] His point is this. 'A deduction' and 'a valid deduction' mean the same thing. To say that p is a deduction is therefore to say that the conjunction of the contradictory of p, $\sim p$ (read 'not-p'), with the premiss from which it is inferred, q, is self-contradictory. It is to say that $q \cdot \sim p$ is self-contradictory. But to say that p is a primitive induction is not to say that the conjunction of its contradictory with the evidencing-statement from which it is inferred, q, is self-contradictory. It is not to say that $q \cdot \sim p$ is self-contradictory. Thus e.g. $fAg \cdot f'I\bar{g}$ is self-contradictory, but $f'Ag \cdot fI\bar{g}$ is not. ($\bar{f}$, $\bar{g}$, etc. are read, 'non-f', 'non-g', etc.; the quantifier I is to be read 'Some'.) Hume's distinction differentiates deductions from primitive inductions, but not from derivative inductions, since some of these are deductions from primitive inductions. Nevertheless, mathematical inductions are not derivative inductions either. For the axioms or premisses from which they and the theorems of Pure Mathematics generally are deduced are not generalizations. Mill, indeed, asserts the opposite. [Mill, 147 ff.] According to him, the axioms of Pure Mathematics are precisely empirical generalizations of the widest scope; so that by his account mathematical inductions and mathematical theorems generally are derivative inductions. But his account is not acceptable.

The question whether mathematical inductions are a sort of inductions in my sense of 'an induction' must be distinguished from the question whether inductions in my sense are allowable in Pure Mathematics. The answer to the latter question seems to me to be as follows. When the process of induction is applied to empirical objects, it is both a method of discovery and a method of proof. '. . . Induction may be defined, the operation of discovering and proving general propositions.' [Mill, 186] Actually, this definition is both too narrow and too wide; too narrow in that it excludes singular (derivative) inductions, and too wide in that it admits e.g. deductions as well as inductions; Mill really means 'generalizations', not 'general propositions', as indeed he himself later says. [Mill, 200] When I establish that all observed BU are H and generalize from this fact that all BU are H, I simultaneously discover the composition of the population and prove that it has that composition. But in Pure Mathematics, where the process of

6

induction is applied to non-empirical objects, say numbers, it is allowable as a method of discovery only. The reason is that in this field induction is not regarded as the right sort of proof; here, deductive proof or demonstration is alone accepted, one species of which is mathematical induction. But that induction is a common method of mathematical discovery is not disputed; thus, by his own account Newton discovered the binomial theorem in this way, though he left it to others to provide a satisfactory demonstration of it.

In the light of these considerations we can answer a connected question, Are there non-empirical inductions? Or are all generalizations necessarily 'generalizations from experience', in Mill's phrase; and is the expression 'empirical generalization' consequently pleonastic? Granted that numbers are not empirical objects, it appears from the foregoing discussion that there are non-empirical inductions. But in this essay I shall discuss empirical inductions only. For my topic is inductive probability, and this relates to the probative, not to the heuristic, aspect of induction. But we have seen that in non-empirical domains, such as Pure Mathematics, the probative aspect of induction does not apply. Consequently, philosophical problems about the inductive probability of mathematical theorems do not arise.

According to Jevons, 'all inductive reasoning is but an inverse application of deductive reasoning', specifically of 'probable deductive reasoning'. [Jevons, I, 307 f.; 239 ff.] Jevons follows Laplace, who attempts to justify induction by an inversion of Bernoulli's theorem, in the proof of which he uses Bayes' inversion formula, otherwise called the principle of inverse probability. [Laplace, 15 f.] Somewhat similar attempts are made by e.g. Keynes and Broad, Jeffreys and Williams. I shall consider Williams' theory later [4.2]. There is an important difference between his account and the others' in that he makes no use of the principle of inverse probability, and indeed claims it as a leading merit of his theory that it dispenses with this principle and so avoids the difficulties that it involves. [Williams, G, 99, 192; Keynes, 148 f., 174 ff., 367 ff.; Kneale, 201 ff.] Detailed discussion of argument along these lines is therefore deferred to my examination of Williams' theory. But the general question should be raised here, Is Jevons' formula an acceptable account of inductions as I have defined them? It is not, for a reason already given; that some inductions, notably primitive ones, are not deductions at all, and hence are not probable deductions.

Two further important points need making in this connexion. The sort of probability that this line of argument purports to prove that some inductions possess is what I call 'casual probability' and is called by others 'the probability of chances' or 'mathematical probability'. [Hume, T, 124 ff.; Russell, H, 362 ff.] From this it follows that according to these accounts, the probability of inductions can be measured in the strong sense of 'to measure'. But both these connected theses are unacceptable. For I shall argue that 'probable' as applied to inductions has a different meaning from that which it has when applied in matters of chance, and that the probability of inductions cannot be measured in the strong sense, it being one of the chief differences between casual and other sorts of probability that the former alone are measurable in this sense. Finally, there is surely much force in Kneale's suggestion that a main reason for philosophers' conflation of inductive inferences with this sort of deductive inferences is a similarity between the criteria of their soundness. For in both cases it may be said that they are sound if and only if the examined sample is large or numerous and fair or random. Whether this is in fact a satisfactory formulation of the criteria of the probability of inductions we shall be in a position to judge later. [2, 3, 4]

Still in connexion with Jevons' formula, it is desirable to say next something about the relation of inductions in my sense to the inferences discussed in that part of the Theory of Statistics which is called the Theory of Sampling. The essential point for the present is this; the type of reasonings discussed by statisticians under this head is almost exclusively what Jevons calls 'probable deductive reasoning'. And this, I have said, must be clearly distinguished from induction in my sense. Yule and Kendall, e.g., discuss almost exclusively 'random sampling' rather than 'purposive' and 'stratified' sampling. And the former involves nothing but probable deductive reasoning, for it turns wholly upon the practical application of the Calculus of Probabilities.

However, it is no longer correct to say, as Jevons does, that the type of probable deductive reasoning used in inferring from a sample to its population is always 'inverse'. For the modern tendency among statisticians, as exemplified by R. A. Fisher and his school, is not to use the principle of inverse probability but to consider only 'direct' probabilities. As I said above, this abandonment of inverse for direct probabilities is a salient feature of Williams' philosophy of inductive probability, as it is in a somewhat different way of Kneale's also. Williams summarizes the present position thus: 'Statisticians, partly ignorant of and partly disillusioned with the inverse rule, have been avoiding the concept of an inductive probability, preferring an *ad hoc* notion of "reliability", or Professor Fisher's "fiducial" criteria, or the cognate theory of "confidence" of Professors Neyman and Pearson. . . . One device was simply to rechristen the direct Bernoullian probability "the reliability" of the opposite inference. The methods of Fisher and Neyman, triumphant in Britain and America now, while renouncing any logical or philosophical rationale, calmly accept or reject statistical hypotheses concerning a population in accordance with what Fisher calls the "likelihoods", that is, the relations of direct probability which run from the respective hypotheses to the sample observation; and Mr. Kneale has lately appended these floating rules of thumb to his own prescriptions of inductive "policy".' [Williams, D, 466 f.] His account is perhaps a bit over-simplified, and yet, I think, essentially correct. But whether the probable reasonings are inverse or direct, they are deductive and not in any sense inductive. I shall say more on this topic in connexion with Williams' theory [4.2] and with the question of the meaning of the probability of proportional (or statistical) hypotheses [1.2]. The latter question forms part of the wider question of the meaning of what I call 'hypothetic probability', which I distinguish from both casual and inductive probability. These later discussions will serve, I hope, to elucidate the foregoing introductory remarks.

Some say that inductive inference in my sense does not exist, and that what may appear to be so is really what I call, after Peirce, 'hypothetic inference' and what others call the hypothetico-deductive method or system. [Peirce, 379] Whewell e.g. writes: 'The doctrine which is the *hypothesis* of the deductive reasoning, is the *inference* of the inductive process. The special facts which are the basis of the inductive inference are the conclusion of the train of deduction. And in this manner the deduction establishes the induction. The principle which we gather from the facts is true, because the facts can be derived from it by rigorous demonstration. Induction moves upwards, and deduction downwards, on the same stair.' [Whewell, 92] Similar views are advanced by Lalande, Popper and Wisdom. [Lalande, 234; Popper, 1 ff.; Wisdom, vii, 46 ff.] But it is proper to notice certain difficulties of interpretation. It is not clear whether the last two authors' thesis is that there is no such method of investigation as inductive inference, or that although there is such a thing it plays no part in the sciences. And Whewell does not actually say in the passage quoted that there is no such thing as inductive inference; on the contrary. What these authors intend can best be explained by a simple example. Suppose that I generalize, as we say, from $f'Ag$ that fAg. Then, according to these authors, I do not really infer from $f'Ag$ to fAg, though I may appear to do so, for there is no such mode of inference. What I really do is frame the hypothesis that fAg, immediately infer from it that $f'Ag$, observe that this consequence corresponds with the facts, and judge that the hypothesis is thereby in some degree confirmed. What is mistaken for inductive inference is simply the psychological process, whatever it may be, by which I arrive at the hypothesis.

On which these comments. It is false that we always investigate such questions as the composition of a population by hypothetic inference, though it is often possible to proceed in this way. We usually do it simply by generalizing from observation and without framing any hypothesis about its composition at all. It is also false that, whereas moving from fAg to $f'Ag$ is (called) inferring, moving from $f'Ag$ to fAg is not (so called); as the terms 'infer' and 'reason' are correctly used, both are called inferring or reasoning. These authors' denial of this probably rests on the prejudice that the only sort of reasoning is deductive reasoning. I conclude as against them that generalization is a regularly employed method of investigation; that it is (correctly called) a mode of inference or reasoning; that it is a different mode of inference from hypothetic inference; and that it is false that in inquiries in which we ordinarily describe ourselves as proceeding in the former manner we are 'really' proceeding in the latter manner. These points are elaborated later. In 5.2 I defend the assertion that inductive and hypothetic inference are distinct modes of ampliative or synthetic inference; from which it follows, not only that the former is not identical with or 'reducible to' the latter, but also that, contrary to what others say, the latter is not identical with or 'reducible to' the former. I also argue that the ancient quarrel between the inductivists and the hypothetists about whether inductive or hypothetic inference is 'the' method of science is pointless, since both methods are regularly employed in scientific and other investigations. The question of the relation of induction to reasoning is taken up in 6.1.

It may be objected that my definition of 'an induction' is too wide, that it would be better to use the term as synonymous with 'a generalization' and to exclude what I call 'derivative inductions'. This question was the subject of a controversy between Mill and Whewell, Whewell arguing for the narrower definition and Mill arguing for the wider. [Mill, 187 f.] I follow Mill for the reason, among others, that he here gives, that it is convenient to include among inductions inferences from particulars to a particular. But we have already noticed that such inferences may always be regarded simply as deductions from generalizations, so that generalization is the better part if not the whole of induction. This Mill allows: 'We shall fall into no error, then, if, in treating of Induction, we limit our attention to the establishment of general propositions'. [Mill, 188] Here again, he means 'generalizations' rather than 'general propositions' generally.

Alternatively, it may be objected that my definition of 'an induction' is too narrow, for the following reason. Consider the formula, (5): $E(gx, I(fMg).fx)$. The quantifier M is to be read 'Most'. Then, the suggestion for examination is that the evidenced-statement-formula of formula (5) should be called a derivative induction, as are the evidenced-statement-formulas of formulas (3) and (4). But the suggestion is unacceptable because, although formula (5) does indeed involve inductive evidence, it also involves casual evidence. To elucidate. Consider the formula, (6): $E(gx, fMg.fx)$. I call this a casual evidential-statement-formula. Consequently, formula (5) is what I call an heterogeneous evidential-statement-formula, being partly inductive but partly also casual. Consequently, its evidenced-statement-formula is not rightly called an induction-formula. By contrast, I call formulas (3) and (4) homogeneous evidential-statement-formulas, since they involve only a generalization and a deduction therefrom; their evidenced-statement-formulas are accordingly rightly called induction-formulas. And this brings out an essential difference between formulas (3) and (4) on the one hand and formula (5) on the other; in the former the evidenced-statement-formula is deduced from the evidencing-statement-formula, but in the latter it is not. The importance of these distinctions will appear later [2.2] when I compare the type of probabilification-judgement-formula corresponding to formula (5) with the type of probabilification-judgement-formula corresponding to formula (3). These considerations also show that the distinction between primitive and derivative inductions should not be confused with the distinction between primitive evidential-statements and derivative evidential-statements the evidencing-statements of which include an induction. All derivative inductions are evidenced-statements of derivative evidential-statements the evidencing-statements of which include an induction, but not conversely. For the evidenced-statement-formula of formula (5) is the evidenced-statement-formula of a derivative evidential-statement-formula the evidencing-statement-formula of which includes an induction, yet it is not a derivative induction-formula.

Finally on this head, we may notice what definitions of 'an induction' are consonant with mine. What Peirce calls 'ampliative' inductions and Johnson calls 'problematic' inductions are the same as what I call primitive inductions. And what Johnson calls 'demonstrative' inductions are the same as what I call deductive derivative inductions. [Peirce, 180; Johnson, III, xiv]

1.1.2 *Attribute-inductions and Variable-inductions*

The next topic for investigation is the division of inductions into attribute-inductions and variable-inductions, the first task in which is to distinguish them. By an attribute-induction I mean an induction that contains attributes, and by a variable-induction I mean an induction that contains variables. I here use the terms 'attribute' and 'variable' in the senses given to them in the Theory of Statistics, meaning by a variable or variable magnitude a quality that varies in degree and by an attribute a quality that does not so vary. Examples of attributes are the properties of being a BU and of being H, examples of variables are the properties of being long and heavy. This will serve for a preliminary explanation; questions arising out of the distinction between attribute-inductions and variable-inductions will be discussed shortly.

Consider the formula, (7): $E((Aa)(Ab)b=a, (Aa')(Ab')b=a)$, read 'The fact that for all observed values of a and b b is equal to *a* is evidence that for all values of *a* and *b* *b* is equal to *a*'. I use *a*, *b*, *c*, etc., as variable-variables. In the expression 'variable-variable', 'variable' in its first occurrence bears its statistical sense and in its second occurrence its logical sense; the two senses are of course quite distinct. And I mark the several degrees or values of variables by subscripts, as a_1, a_2, b_n, b_m, etc. Attribute-variables and variable-variables may be referred to collectively as predicate-variables. Then, the evidenced-statement-formula of formula (7) is a functional primitive induction-formula or a functional generalization-formula. A very simple exemplification of formula (7) is: 'The fact that for all observed lengths and breadths of this leaf, its breadth in cms. is equal to its length in ins., is evidence that, for all lengths and breadths of this leaf, its breadth in cms. is equal to its length in ins.'

There is a point here that requires clarification. It will be seen that, in this example, I substitute upon *a* 'length of this leaf in ins.', not 'length in ins.', and upon *b* 'breadth of this leaf in cms.', not 'breadth in cms.' It is convenient to treat these as permissible substitutions, because our formulas are thereby simplified; it is not necessary to include in e.g. formula (7) an individual variable, *x*, to symbolize 'this leaf'. And it is justifiable to do so because the reference to, say, this leaf is non-essential; the only thing that matters is the relation of functional dependence between the several values of the variables, and the thing, 'this leaf', serves only to 'carry' the variables. Indeed, in many functional generalizations there is no reference to a thing or things. Mace gives the following illustration. [Mace, 325 ff.] Consider the dependence of the electrical resistance of a wire on its material, its length and its cross-section. This is expressed by the formula: $R = kl/s$, where k is a constant that differs for different materials, as copper, platinum, etc. At this stage the notion of a thing or substance characterized by a certain attribute, e.g. 'copper wire', has been replaced by that of a constant. But we may envisage the possibility of carrying the elimination of substances and attributes a stage further. 'With further inquiry it might, of course, be possible to show that the different constants in the case of the different metals are determined by variations in some one determinable in terms of which the different metals may be described, e.g. some characteristic in atomic or molecular structure. In this case the various special formulae for determining resistance would be assimilated into a more general formula of the form $R=f(KLS)$ in which K as well as L and S is a variable.' I.e., we should have a formula containing nothing but variables. It seems to me that such 'pure' variable-formulas are rightly regarded as the type of functional generalizations, and this is why I think that formula (7) may rightly be regarded as symbolizing the example that I give. Formula (7) is a special case of the more general formula, (8): $E((Aa)(Ab)b=\phi(a), (Aa')(Ab')b=\phi(a))$, read: 'The fact that for all observed values of a and b b is some function of a is evidence that for all values of a and b b is some the same function of a'.

Take next the formula, (9): $E(b_n, I((Aa)(Ab)b=a) . a_n)$. It is to be understood that a_n and b_n are not themselves among the observed values of a and b on the evidence of which the functional generalization contained in the evidencing-statement-formula is asserted; were they so, that b_n is true when a_n is true would of course be a fact of observation, not something asserted upon evidence. The evidenced-statement-formula of formula (9) is then a functional deductive derivative induction-formula. It is also a functional interpolation-formula; for 'a functional interpolation' is correctly defined, I think, as 'a functional deductive derivative induction'. But 'a functional extrapolation' is not correctly so defined, and requires separate discussion accordingly. [See 3.2.] An exemplification of formula (9) is: 'The fact that, for all lengths and breadths of this leaf, its breadth in cms. is equal to its length in ins. and that its length at such a time was 3·5 ins., is evidence that its breadth at that time was 3·5 cms.'

Formulas (7), (8) and (9) will serve to explain the meaning of 'a variable-induction'. But we shall see that functional inductions are not the only type of variable-inductions any more than subject-predicate inductions are the only type of attribute-inductions. They are, however, the types of each that have received most attention from philosophers, not without reason, since they are in many ways the most important. Philodemus makes it clear that subject-predicate attribute-inductions, such as 'All men are mortal', were carefully studied by Epicurus or at any rate by his school. [Philodemus, 26 ff.] To him, or them, I therefore think properly belongs the style 'the Father of Inductive Philosophy', which, however, is usually conferred on Bacon. As for Aristotle's claim, it must be remembered that his ἐπαγωγή does not mean ampliative or problematic induction. But to Bacon belongs the credit for initiating with his Table of Degrees the study of functional variable-inductions, for I find no trace of this in Ancient Philosophy [Bacon, 315 ff.] Mill's Method of Concomitant Variations represents of course another historically important treatment of functional inductions. [Mill, 260 ff.] Alternative names for functional inductions are 'universalizations' [Mace, 261] and 'quantitative inductions'. [Jevons, II, 105] But this last name is in an important respect misleading, since it suggests that quantitative considerations arise only in functional inductions, or at any rate only in variable-inductions, and that attribute-inductions involve qualitative considerations only. We shall see shortly, however, that in fact attribute-inductions involve quantitative considerations no less than do variable-inductions.

1.1.3 *Types of Inductions*

It is desirable now to inquire whether attribute-inductions and variable-inductions are mutually exclusive and jointly exhaustive of the class of inductions. I shall take the latter question first, and shall aim to show that what seem to be all the chief types of inductions can be accommodated in one or the other sub class. This review will also serve a useful purpose by bringing out the variety of types of inductions, for my account of them to date has been rather thin.

To begin with attribute-inductions: I have distinguished so far the universal subject-predicate primitive type, i.e. the evidenced-statement-formula of formula (2), and the singular and the universal subject-predicate derivative types, i.e. the evidenced-statement-formulas of formulas (3) and (4) respectively. But there are others. Still within the subject-predicate class, consider the evidenced-statement-formulas of the formulas, (10): $E(fMg, f'Mg)$, and (11) $E(fm/ng, f'm/ng)$, in which the quantifier is to be read 'm-$n$ths'. I call these respectively non-numerical preponderant and numerical preponderant formulas. Preponderant belong to the wider class of proportional subject-predicate inductions, which I oppose to universal. It is noteworthy, however, that universal and proportional subject-predicate inductions are similar in an important respect; both assert that a proportion of all f are g. Proportional generalizations are universal in this sense, that fMg e.g. means 'Most (or 'The majority') of all f are g' and is in this sense about all f. And universal generalizations are proportional in this sense, that fAg means 'All of all f are g'. The difference between universal and proportional in this latter regard is just one of degree, as is particularly clear when fAg is expressed in the equivalent form $f100\%g$ and contrasted with e.g. $f60\%g$. There are important differences in these respects between fMg and fm/ng on the one hand and fIg and e.g. '$56f$ are g' on the other. For the last two are not about all f as the first two are; their meanings are not illuminated by their being rendered 'Some (or '56') of all f are g'. Nor can fAg or $f100\%g$ be regarded as just the upper limiting case of fIg or '$56f$ are g'. It is for these reasons that statements of the form of the last two formulas logically cannot be generalizations as statements of the forms fAg and fMg can. The resemblances and differences between the logical powers of the quantifiers A, I and M is a question of general logical interest; M, for various reasons, has received much less attention from logicians than the other two. I shall touch on the question again in 2.2. What I call 'proportional inductions' are often called, after Keynes, 'statistical inductions'; and what I call 'preponderant inductions' are sometimes called, after Mill, 'approximate generalizations'. [Keynes, 406 ff.; Mill, 386 ff.]

Distinct from the subject-predicate type are what I call 'associative inductions'; consider e.g. the evidenced-statement of the evidential-statement: 'The fact that among all observed BU being H is positively associated in a certain degree with being red ("R") is evidence that among all BU being H is positively associated in that degree with being R'. Degrees of association between attributes are commonly expressed numerically by means of a coefficient of association. Associative inductions evidently differ from subject-predicate inductions in involving more than two attributes, e.g. being R as well as being a BU and being H.

To turn now to variable-inductions: I have distinguished so far the functional primitive type, i.e. the evidenced-statement-formula of formula (7), and the functional derivative type, i.e. the evidenced-statement-formula of formula (9). But there are other types. There are what I call 'correlative inductions', illustrated by the evidenced-statement of the evidential-statement: 'The fact that there is a correlation of $+0\cdot73$ between all observed breadths of this leaf in cms. and its length in ins. is evidence that there is a correlation of $+0\cdot73$ between all breadths of this leaf in cms. and its length in ins.' Degrees of correlation between variables are commonly expressed numerically, as in this example, by means of a coefficient of correlation. Correlative generalizations are a subclass of the wider class of inductions involving statistical numbers, another subclass of which is e.g. the evidenced-statement of the evidential-statement: 'The fact that the mean weight of all observed BU is 5·6 oz. is evidence that the mean weight of all BU is 5·6 oz.' In discussing induction by complete enumeration, I stressed the difference between inductions and descriptions, and I shall revert to this topic shortly. But it needs to be emphasized again here. For descriptions of a sample by means of statistical numbers are a sophisticated sort of descriptions. And this has led some authors to overlook the crucial difference between making what may be called a 'statistical statement' about a sample, e.g. observed BU, which is what Keynes calls 'statistical description', and making a statistical statement about a population, e.g. unobserved as well as observed BU, which is what he calls 'statistical induction'. [Keynes, 327 ff.]

There are significant resemblances and differences between these several types of inductions. Universal and proportional subject-predicate, and associative, attribute-inductions all assert a complete or partial compresence of attributes. And universal subject-predicate attribute-inductions and functional variable-inductions assert respectively a complete compresence of attributes and a complete covariation of variables. But there is an interesting difference between these last two. To establish an evidencing-statement of the form $f'Ag$ nothing is needed but observation. But to establish an evidencing-statement of the form (Aa') $(Ab')b = \phi(a)$ it is requisite not merely to observe that degrees of a and b covary in some way or other, but to discover some function, ϕ, that describes the observed covariation, in other words what Whewell calls a 'colligating concept'. Now more than one and indeed indefinitely many functions may do this job of describing or colligating. This poses the practical problem of choosing one of them, and the philosophical problem of discovering the criterion of its preferability, say its 'simplicity'. The latter is an interesting problem, but it is distinct from that of inductive probability, notwithstanding that some suppose them connected. Discovering a colligating concept can hardly be described as difficult in the case of my example about this leaf, where

C   17

the very simple function $y = x$ will serve, in other words where an adequate colligating concept is a straight line bisecting the angle between the positive y and the positive x axes. I explain 'simple' as predicated of assertions of functional dependence later. [4.1] It is more difficult, as Kepler knew, where an equation of the form $x^2/a^2 + y^2/b^2 = 1$ will serve, in other words where an adequate colligating concept is the ellipse.

The operation of finding a mathematical description that approximately fits and colligates the observed facts must not be confused with induction; as statistical induction must be distinguished from statistical description, so too functional description must not be confused with functional induction. Saying e.g. that all observed positions of Mars lie (more or less) on an ellipse is description; it is asserting, on the evidence of this description, that all positions of Mars do likewise that constitutes the corresponding induction. Hence, 'Mars describes an ellipse' is not, as one might think, a description, but a functional induction. Mill seems to me to be right when he denies Whewell's contention that induction is to be defined as the colligation of facts and points out that this operation is descriptive. Whewell writes: '. . . in every inference by Induction, there is some Conception *superinduced* upon the Facts: and we may henceforth conceive this to be the peculiar import of the term *Induction*'. [Whewell, 50] Actually, he gives two different accounts of the meaning of 'induction'; namely, as the colligation of facts, but also, as previously noticed, as hypothetic inference. He seems to regard his two accounts as identical, whereas in fact they are incompatible. For the same point applies again. Hypotheses or conjectures logically must be about the unobserved. If I have established that some positions of Mars lie on an ellipse, I logically cannot suppose that they do so; though I can of course suppose that its unobserved positions also do so. But descriptions or colligations logically must be of the observed. If I have observed some positions of Mars I can describe and connect them by the summary description 'They all lie on an ellipse'; but I logically cannot so describe and connect its unobserved positions. This indeed Whewell himself allows, for he says that what are colligated are facts, i.e. observations. Hence, defining induction as the colligation of facts (the observed) is incompatible with defining it as the framing, deductive elaboration and testing of an hypothesis about the unobserved. So that we must reject Whewell's implicit claim that his two accounts are identical, and include his former as well as his latter one in our list of unacceptable explanations of the meaning of 'induction'. [Mill, 191 ff.; Whewell, 36 ff.]

Deductive derivative subject-predicate inductions and deductive derivative functional inductions or interpolations are alike in being deductively derived respectively from assertions of a complete compresence of attributes and from assertions of a complete covariation of variables. Again, functional generalizations may be regarded as a limiting case of correlative generalizations, in that where we have functional dependence between variables, there we have perfect correlation, or a degree of correlation 1, between variables. Similarly, universal subject-predicate generalizations may be regarded as a limiting case of associative generalizations, since where we have complete compresence of attributes, there we have perfect association of attributes. Finally, there is an analogy of relation between universal and preponderant subject-predicate generalizations on the one hand and functional and correlative generalizations on the other; for whereas the former pair assert respectively a complete and a preponderant compresence of attributes, the latter pair assert respectively a complete and a preponderant covariation of variables.

Some inductions are (called) laws. Consider the following examples. First, Kepler's first law of planetary motion: 'All the planets move in elliptical paths, with the Sun at one focus of the ellipse'. Second, Boyle's law: 'For a given mass of gas, at a constant temperature, the absolute pressure P and the volume V of the gas are related by the formula $P \propto 1/V$'. Third, the law attributed to Gresham: 'Provided that there is no scarcity of money, the circulation of bad money drives good money out of circulation'. It is convenient to call such laws 'inductive laws'. But although some inductions are called laws, some and indeed most are not rightly so called. 'All BU are H' e.g. would not be called a law. And although some of the statements and formulas that are called 'laws' are inductions, some are not. In particular, there is the important class of laws and principles that are non-empirical, i.e. contain theoretical terms or words that do not refer directly to observable things. A simple illustration is the principle of the rectilinear propagation of light: 'All light travels in straight lines'; for in this context 'light' does not designate an observable thing as it does in 'Switch off the light'. Further, some laws are not (called) laws of Nature; a law of planetary motion e.g. is not so called. But Newton's law of universal gravitation e.g., which explains Kepler's laws of planetary motion, is called a law of Nature. The difference is one of scope; a law of Nature applies 'universally' or to all Nature; it asserts e.g. that all matter gravitates in a certain manner. [Toulmin, Ph, 17 ff., 86 f., 99 f.]

These considerations suggest two questions. We have seen that some but not all inductions are called laws, which leads one to inquire what is the basis of the distinction. Part of the answer, I think, is simply importance; a law of planetary motion is important in a way that 'All BU are H' obviously is not. 'Law' is an honorific style that is not bestowed on any trivial regularity. Another necessary condition of an induction's being called a law is that it should be true, which it is rightly claimed to be when and only when the evidence for it is judged to be conclusive. [5.2] Hence, no induction for which the evidence is judged to be less than conclusive will be called a law. The second question is this; if an induction is important, true and in the required sense universal, is it always called a law of Nature? Braithwaite argues plausibly that a fourth additional condition is necessary to distinguish a law of Nature from what Kneale calls a 'matter of fact with accidental universality', namely '. . . that it occurs in an established scientific deductive system as a deduction from higher-level hypotheses which are supported by empirical evidence which is not direct evidence for [it] itself'. [Braithwaite, 302]

The main question for us, however, is whether the specimen inductive laws I have mentioned can be classified as either attribute-inductions or variable-inductions. Kepler's and Boyle's laws plainly fall into the second class, for they are functional generalizations, which are an especially important type of inductive law. It is worth noticing that Kepler's law is not only an ampliative induction but also an induction by complete enumeration, since it asserts something about all the planets. Gresham's law introduces a complication in the form of a reference to time; it asserts what Mill calls a 'uniformity of succession'. He opposes these uniformities to what he calls 'uniformities of coexistence', such as 'All ruminants are cloven-footed'. However, we can reasonably represent Gresham's law as an attribute-induction by paraphrasing it: 'All cases of the circulation of bad money when there is no scarcity of money are characterized by the subsequent disappearance from circulation of good money'. For, as 'All BU are H' is a subject-predicate generalization about things, so the paraphrase may be regarded as a subject-predicate generalization about events. And as the former may be regarded as asserting the invariable compresence of the thing-attribute of being H with the thing-attribute of being a BU, so the latter may be regarded as asserting the invariable compresence of the event-attribute of being a subsequent disappearance, etc. with the event-attribute of being a circulation, etc. It may be objected that such paraphrases are pointless, as are most, if not all, attempts to reduce statements of one form to another form that is selected for some reason as standard. But I am not entirely convinced by the objection. In the question now under investigation, at any rate, there seem to me substantial advantages in exhibiting all inductions as either attribute-inductions or variable-inductions; for only by some such means can one reduce all the variety of types of inductions to manageable proportions.

These observations on scientific laws and principles are of some importance in the Philosophy of Science. According to one well-known philosophy of science, the so-called descriptive interpretation favoured by Comte, Mach and others, all scientific laws and principles are descriptions. Karl Pearson e.g. writes: 'Scientific law is . . . a brief description in mental shorthand of as wide a range as possible of the sequences of our sense-impressions'. [K. Pearson, *The Grammar of Science*, 2nd ed., London, 1900, p. 112; J. O. Wisdom, 'The Descriptive Interpretation of Science', *Proceedings of the Aristotelian Society*, 1944] But this doctrine is objectionable on two scores. It overlooks a point made above, that some of the statements and formulas called scientific laws and principles are non-empirical and so logically cannot be descriptions of our 'sense-impressions'. More important for present purposes, it is not true even of the class of laws typified by my three examples. For these are generalizations or primitive inductions, not descriptions. And generalizations are essentially different from descriptions, since, whereas the former logically must be, the latter logically cannot be about the unobserved.

This last contention might be challenged on the following sort of grounds. Suppose that A asks B to say what he (B) imagines that his (A's) Aunt Agatha looks like, B having never seen the

woman; and that B accordingly makes some descriptive statements that happen to fit. Then A may say: 'Amazing; although
you have never seen her you have described her to a T'. But I do
not think that the objection holds. For B has not really described
A's aunt, which he is in no position to do. What he has done is to
utter some sentences which chance to be the same ones as he
would have used if he had been describing her, if he had been in a
position to describe her. He has also done what he was asked to
do, namely, to say what he imagines she looks like; which, however, is different from and indeed incompatible with describing
her; for to describe her he logically must have observed her, and
if he has observed her and has not forgotten he knows, and so
logically cannot imagine, what she looks like.

The thesis that all scientific laws and principles are inductions,
which might be called the inductive interpretation of science,
would represent an advance on the descriptive interpretation, but
would still be liable to the objection from the existence of non-
empirical laws or principles. Such a view, which is also that of
Hume, is advanced by Braithwaite. [Braithwaite, 9–12, 293] He
attempts to meet the difficulty about non-empirical laws by contending that some laws, e.g. that every hydrogen atom consists of
one proton together with one electron, though generalizations,
are yet not derived from simple observation of instances. But to
say that fAg is a generalization-formula but not from $f'Ag$ is surely
illogical, since 'a generalization' *means* 'a generalization from observed instances', 'a generalization-formula' being properly defined as the evidenced-statement-formula of such an evidential-
statement-formula as $E(fAg, f'Ag)$.

The doctrine often encountered in the literature, that there are
'higher-order' generalizations, seems to me unacceptable for the
same reason. [Strawson, 200] It is said that there are (at least)
first-order and second-order generalizations. If I observe some
specimens of lead, find them all malleable and generalize 'All lead
is malleable', that is a first-order generalization. Suppose I also
make the additional first-order generalizations 'All iron is malleable' and 'All copper is malleable'. Then, it is said, I may generalize
from these first-order generalizations to the second-order
generalization 'All metals are malleable'; it being understood that
I know that lead, iron and copper are metals but not all the
metals. But a generalization logically must be a statement about

22

unobserved cases on the evidence of observed cases. Yet the doctrine of second-order generalizations, of generalizations from generalizations, involves that some generalizations are statements about unobserved cases on the evidence of unobserved cases, or that we can generalize from the unobserved to the unobserved. And this seems wrong. In fact, in the case sketched, 'All metals are malleable' is a first-order generalization, or, to avoid pleonasm, a generalization. The evidence for it is not the conjunction of generalizations 'All lead, iron and copper is malleable', but the same evidence as that on which these are based, namely, the conjunction of descriptions or observation-statements 'All observed lead, iron and copper is malleable'.

The temporal considerations involved in Gresham's law need further discussion. It is familiar that inductions can be about the future and the past as well as about the present. Consider the following exemplifications of formula (3): (a) 'The fact that all BU are H and that this (unexamined) ball is a BU is evidence that it is H'; (b) 'The fact that all BU are H and that the next ball to be drawn will be a BU is evidence that it will be H'; (c) 'The fact that all BU are H and that the last ball drawn was a BU is evidence that it was H'.

In the induction in (a), 'is' does not mean 'is now', with an implied contrast with what it was or may have been in the past or with what it will be or may be in the future. The use illustrates rather what Strawson calls 'the omnitemporal (or perhaps 'quasi--omnitemporal') present'. But there are also inductions in which 'is' does mean 'is now', e.g. the induction in the (elliptical) evidential-statement: 'The fact that Tom is pale is evidence that he is angry'. This also illustrates an important type of evidential-statements and inductions, namely, those about other people's states of mind and heart. Hume signalizes the difference between this type and the type about e.g. the hollowness of this BU by distinguishing 'moral' from 'natural' evidence. But he maintains, rightly I think, that there is no essential epistemological difference between these types of evidential-statement, and that the distinction is only one of subject-matter, since what underlies both is simply the existence of uniformities. 'Moral' states and events, he observes, including decisions or 'volitions', are regular or determined by laws or generalizations just as are 'natural' states and events, and he makes this observation a main point in his classic discussion of liberty and necessity. [Hume, T, 399 ff.; Mill, 547 ff.]

As for (b), it is notorious that some philosophers tend to identify inductions with inductions about the future. This is presumably due, partly to the peculiar importance that predictions possess for us as practical agents, and partly to the authority of Hume, who sometimes makes such statements as: '. . . all inferences from experience suppose, as their foundation, that the future will resemble the past'. [Hume, E, 37] But inductions are about the unobserved, not merely about the future unobserved; the former includes also that which is past and not remembered, or spatially remote, or present in space and time but hidden. Hume indeed generally recognizes this, as when he refers to the principle: '. . . that instances, of which we have had no experience, must resemble those of which we have had experience, and that the course of nature continues always uniformly the same'. [Hume, T, 89] I shall have something to say about this 'uniformity of Nature' later. [4.2]

As for (c), it might be thought that this sort of induction typifies historical statements. It is indeed a very approximate truth that historical statements are typically singular statements about the past unobserved, whereas scientific statements are typically omnitemporal general statements about the past, present and future unobserved. But these historical statements are usually not inductive but hypothetic inferences; the latter mode of ampliative inference will be elucidated in 1.2. This brings out the important point that, although all inductive inferences are inferences about the unobserved from the evidence of the observed, the converse is by no means true. For we shall see that hypothetic inferences are also inferences about the unobserved from the evidence of the observed.

As final illustrations of the variety of types of inductions I cite existential and identity inductions, e.g. respectively: 'There is or was a watchmaker who made this watch' and 'Shakespeare was not Bacon'. It will suffice to consider the former, which is one of the stock arguments that are mentioned in pretended proofs of the existence of God from marks of design in Nature. If I infer from the present existence of a watch the present or past existence of a watchmaker who made it, what is the nature of my inference? It goes: 'The fact that all cases of the present existence of a watch are characterized by the present or past existence of a watchmaker who made it, and that this is a case of the present existence of a watch, is evidence that this is characterized by the present or past existence of a watchmaker who made it'. But this exemplifies formula (3); so that here again inductions that are apparently of a different type, namely existential inductions, may reasonably be regarded as attribute-inductions. Identity inductions likewise may be so classified by a similar device of paraphrase; it would be superfluous to show in detail how.

The foregoing observations will serve, I hope, both to illustrate the variety of types of inductions and to show how they can all nevertheless reasonably be classified as attribute-inductions or variable-inductions, in other words how these two classes are jointly exhaustive of inductions. It remains to be seen whether they are also mutually exclusive. I shall argue that, subject to qualifications of some interest and importance, they may be so regarded. [Yule, 11; Venn, P, 418 ff.]

1.1.4 *Attribute-inductions and Variable-inductions (concluded)*

The essential difference between attributes and variables is this: an attribute, e.g. that of being a ruminant, can only be present or absent, whereas a variable, e.g. that of being tall, can vary in degree. An animal cannot be more or less of a ruminant, but it can be more or less tall. It does not follow, however, that another difference between variable- and attribute-inductions is that the former involve quantitative considerations whereas the latter involve only qualitative ones. For both involve quantity, though in different ways. To make an attribute-generalization of the form $I(f\,m/n\,g)$, one must establish that $f'm/n\,g$; which involves counting the number of f' and the number of gf'. gf or $g \times f$, etc. represent logical multiplication, read 'both g and f' or 'things that are both g and f'. Attribute-inductions involve quantity in this way only. Of course, one can establish an attribute-generalization of the non-numerical form $I(fMg)$ without actually counting, by generalizing from one's 'general impression' that $f'Mg$; but the generalization is not the less quantitative for being less determinate. To make a variable-generalization of the form $I((Aa)(Ab)b=a)$, on the other hand, one must establish that $(Aa')(Ab')b=a$; which involves measuring the observed values of *a* and *b*. Variable-inductions involve quantity in this different way.

However, variables can be treated as attributes. Take the variable height: we can say if we wish that all men of 5' 10" or over are tall and all men under this non-tall, and so replace a variable by an attribute and its contradictory. But conversely, attribute-generalizations can sometimes be regarded as first steps towards variable-generalizations. We may regard the attribute-generalization 'Most tall men are thin' as an approximation to a variable-generalization, in this case a correlative generalization about men's degrees of height and degrees of girth. Some authors are so impressed by this consideration as to regard variable-generalizations generally as in a sense more fundamental than attribute-generalizations; an opinion in which they are confirmed by noting the peculiar importance of functional generalizations in the natural sciences and of generalizations involving statistical numbers in many sorts of investigations, e.g. the social studies. But others are led to the opposite opinion by considering just what is involved in, notably, functional generalizations. They observe that what a functional generalization asserts is that when certain values of the independent variable are present, certain values of the dependent variable are present. E.g. $I((Aa)(Ab) b=a)$ asserts that when a_1 then b_1, when a_2 then b_2 . . . and when a_n then b_n. So that the fundamental notion is that of compresence, covariation (or concomitant variation) being analysable in terms of it. They say, however, that what functional generalizations assert to be compresent are, not attributes, but what Johnson calls 'determinates'. For they regard variables, e.g. length, as 'determinables', and specific degrees or values of variables, e.g. '3·5" long', as determinates of these determinables. Hence, they represent my model functional generalization about this leaf as asserting the compresence of an indefinite number of determinates under two different determinables, length and breadth.

But again, although some attribute-generalizations such as 'Most tall men are thin' may be regarded as first steps towards variable-generalizations, there is a strong *prima facie* objection to regarding this as true of all attribute-generalizations. For many attributes seem to be in principle not replaceable by variables. Consider the attribute-generalization 'All BU are H'; it makes no sense to speak of being more or less a BU in the way that it does make sense to speak of being more or less tall. Even so, the objection can be met by regarding the presence or absence of such an attribute as being a BU as changes in a variable that can take only two values, o and 1; by this device all attribute-inductions may be regarded as approximations to variable-inductions and the notion of variation in degree represented as fundamental. On the other hand, Venn e.g. regards variations in degree as cases of 'partial presence and absence', the implication of which is that it is the notions of presence and absence which are fundamental. But as against this it seems plain that such expressions as 'very present' and 'fairly absent' make no sense.

These observations are interesting, and show at least that the distinction between attributes and variables is not rigid or absolute. But I do not think that they have any tendency to show that it is wrong to divide inductions into attribute-inductions and variable-inductions and to treat them as mutually exclusive. It is a fruitful and suggestive principle of division between inductions, and it is significant that it is in accordance with it that statisticians divide their topics of inquiry.

1.2 PROBABILITY-JUDGEMENTS, PROBABILIFICATION-JUDGEMENTS AND EVIDENTIAL-EVALUATIONS

The task of the Philosophy of Probability is to describe the ordinary or right use of 'probable'. But there is a distinction that needs to be drawn here lest confusion result. Kneale writes: ' . . . the business of the philosopher . . . is to clarify the meaning of the probability statements made by plain men'. [Kneale, 158] But this restricts the scope of the inquiry too narrowly, for the philosopher of probability must study the use of 'probable' not only by plain men but also by specialists, such as mathematicians, statisticians, scientists, historians, lawyers and critics. It seems likely that there is in this passage a confusion between 'the ordinary use of "probable" by (ordinary and extraordinary) men' and 'the use of "probable" by ordinary men'. However, this objection holds only against the passage cited, not against Kneale's book as a whole, the scope of which is not thus restricted; moreover, he restates the matter unexceptionably elsewhere. [Kneale, II, 310 f.]

The first main question is, What is (said to be) probable? I answer, with Keynes, A proposition. [Keynes, 5] But different answers have been proposed, and it will be illuminating to consider the chief of them. Some may prefer to answer, A statement. And this is correct so far as it goes, but too narrow. For it is not only statements or assertions that are called probable, but also, notably, suppositions. We say not only: 'What you say (assert) is very probable', but also: 'Your hypothesis (supposition) is rather unlikely'. Hence it is convenient to say that that which is probable is a proposition; for this semi-technical term does not connote that the form of words in question is asserted as opposed to supposed or otherwise entertained. The answer that what is probable is a belief is open to a similar objection. For that which is believed, or the 'object of belief', is a proposition; believed propositions are thus a species of propositions, as are asserted propositions; so that in saying that what are probable are propositions we include these species among others. It is nevertheless true, as I shall try to show shortly, that there is an intimate connexion between belief and probability.

Again, it may be said that what are probable are events. Nor is this wrong: we certainly say e.g. 'Rain is probable to-night'. But this answer is not opposed to mine, since this judgement has exactly the same meaning as 'It is probable that it will rain to-night'. And there are substantial advantages in concentrating on the latter form of words rather than on the former. Finally, some philosophers say that what are probable are inferences. Peirce e.g. writes: 'The character of probability belongs primarily, without doubt, to certain inferences'. He adds that to say that a proposition is probable is to say that it is the conclusion of a probable inference or argument. [Peirce, 158, 193] This doctrine is basic to his theory of inductive probability, which I shall discuss later. [4.3] Similarly, Hume and Reid speak of 'probable reasoning'. [Hume, T, 103; Reid, 432 ff.] But I think that this is a serious error. We do not in fact call inferences or arguments probable at all, not even in a derivative sense; i.e. we do not speak of a piece of reasoning, the conclusion of which is judged to be probable, as itself probable.

The next step is to recognize, as some contemporary philosophers do, that 'probable' is an evaluative and not a descriptive word. 'It is important to remember . . . that "likely" and "probable" are value-words.' [Hare, 60; R. F. Atkinson, ' "Good" and "Right" and "Probable" in Language, Truth and Logic ', Mind,

April 1955] Its derivation also indicates this fact; for it comes from the Latin *probabilis*, meaning 'approvable'. Again, some at least of the words we use as more or less synonymous with it are obviously evaluative; consider 'sound', 'plausible', 'reliable', 'reasonable', 'sensible', 'justified' and simply 'good'. On the last, consider Mill's famous but unjust remark: 'That all swans are white, cannot have been a good induction, since the conclusion has turned out erroneous'. [Mill, 205] Unjust, because he mistakenly supposes that, as we rightly say that 'All swans are white' was not a true induction because it subsequently turned out to be false, so we rightly say that it was not a probable (good) induction for the same reason. I shall discuss the relation of probability to truth later. [5.2]

1.2.1 *The Evaluative Meaning of 'Probable'*

Like 'good', 'probable' has both evaluative and descriptive meaning, as Hare puts it. Let us consider the former first. We may also agree with Hare that the evaluative force of judging p to be (very, fairly, etc.) probable is to commend it more or less strongly. But this is too vague to be helpful; we want to know further *as* what p is judged to be good and is commended. Similarly, if I am told that so-and-so is a good man, I shall want to know, if I do not already do so from the context of the remark, as what or seen in what view he is a good man; as full-back, tenor, philosopher or whatnot. The answer, I submit, is good as an assertion or statement. The evaluative meaning of 'probable' is tolerably well conveyed by the expression 'warranted assertibility'. To call p probable is to commend the assertion, as opposed to the mere entertainment, consideration or conjecture of p. Naturally, the assertion need not be made out loud or explicitly formulated in words. Degrees of probability are explicable thus: as 'It is probable that p' means 'One is warranted in asserting that p', so 'It is very probable that p' means 'One is eminently warranted (or justified) in asserting that p'. I also think that this is the respect in which probable propositions are verisimilar or likely; they resemble true ones in being rightly assertible. The reader may object that I ought to go on to explain the meaning of 'assertion' and 'statement'. But I do not propose to do so; for philosophical analysis, unlike time, must have a stop. Moreover, in one sense he knows well enough the meaning of these words; though I think that some quite interesting philosophical problems arise in giving an explanation of it. Most of them seem to me to be raised in articles by Lewy and Duncan-Jones, to which the reader is referred. [C. Lewy, 'Some Notes on Assertion', *Analysis*, December 1939; A. E. Duncan-Jones, 'More Notes on Assertion', *Analysis*, June 1940]

It is now desirable to consider some alternative accounts of the evaluative meaning of 'probable'. One view comes in effect to this: to call *p* probable is to call it good as an 'object of belief', i.e. to commend its belief. This view has eminent supporters. Keynes writes: 'A *definition* of probability is not possible, unless it contents us to define degrees of the probability-relation by reference to degrees of rational belief'. [Keynes, 8] I discuss his notion of 'the probability-relation' below. And Russell explains the meaning of one concept or sense of 'degree of probability' as 'degree of credibility', and explains the meaning of the latter expression in turn as 'the degree of credence given by a man who is rational'. [Russell, H, 360] It is worth remarking in this connexion that the meanings of adjectives ending in '-able' or '-ible' are apt to be slippery. Mill notoriously thought that 'desirable' was of the same logical type as 'visible'. The same point arises about 'credible'. As used by Russell, it is plainly an evaluative word; '(highly, fairly, etc.) credible' means '(very, fairly, etc.) good or worthy as object of belief'. This is revealed by the fact that he explains the meaning of 'degree of credibility' in terms of 'rationality' or 'reasonableness'; for 'reasonableness', as here used, is also an evaluative word. But neither point is altogether obvious. One might think that 'credible' is like 'visible' and means 'can be believed', and that 'reasonable' and 'sensible' are purely descriptive words. In fact, this essay is largely about such gerundive adjectives; 'probable' or 'approvable' itself is a member of this class, and I shall also have something to say later about 'reliable' and 'reasonable'. [4.3, 6.1]

Again, Braithwaite explains the meaning of 'the probability *of* an hypothesis' (as opposed to 'the probability *in* a statistical hypothesis') as the reasonableness of believing it. [Braithwaite, 120] The doctrine that 'degree of probability' means 'degree of *reasonableness* of belief' must be distinguished from the doctrine that it means 'degree of *belief*'; the latter is the view of Hume. Braithwaite's account differs from those of Keynes and Russell in that he denies the existence of degrees of reasonableness of belief as opposed to degrees of belief, which he thinks do exist and are measurable by betting-odds. [Braithwaite, 354 ff.] However, we surely do employ such locutions as 'a perfectly sensible (reasonable) belief', and 'it is not unreasonable (is fairly reasonable) to believe that . . .'.

The objection to these accounts of the evaluative meaning of 'probable' seems to me to be that they are circular. For I think that the primary meaning of 'belief' must be explained in terms of 'probable', so that circularity results if the evaluative meaning of 'probable' is explained in terms of 'belief'. To elucidate this will require some consideration of the uses of 'believe' and its approximate synonyms, 'think', 'be of the opinion that', etc.

First, What is believed? A proposition. Next, When is a proposition (rightly said to be) believed? Locke writes: 'The entertainment the mind gives this sort of propositions [sc., propositions judged to be probable] is called *belief, assent or opinion*. . . .' [Locke, 335] I think that the primary use of 'believe' is simply as Locke describes it; it is the word we use for the manner in which we entertain propositions that we judge to be more or less probable. My judging that it is (very, etc.) probable that *p* is the necessary and sufficient condition of my rightly saying, in the primary use of 'believe', that I (firmly, etc.) believe or am (strongly, etc.) of the opinion, that *p*. Notice, my judging that it is probable that *p*, not its being probable that *p*. In this use it is wrong to say either 'I believe that *p* although it is not in any degree probable that *p*' or 'It is (in some degree) probable that *p* but I do not believe that *p*'. On the latter point, cp.: '. . . we cannot hinder our knowledge when the agreement [sc., between 'ideas'] is once perceived; nor our assent, where the probability manifestly appears upon due consideration of all the measures of it. . . .' [Locke, 368] He implies that the impossibility is psychological, whereas it is in fact logical.

Now this may be denied. It may be objected that we can quite well say: (*a*) 'I cannot help believing (thinking) that I shall receive news of him to-morrow although the evidence is all against it'; and (*b*) 'I cannot bring myself to believe that he did it although the evidence that he did do it is overwhelming'. It may be objected further that my account rests on a simple confusion between 'believe' and 'ought to believe'. What we indeed cannot properly say, it may be urged, is either: 'I ought to believe that *p* although it is not (in any degree) probable that *p*', or 'It is (in some degree) probable that *p* but I ought not to believe that *p*'. My reply to this objection is as follows. It conflates two different uses of 'believe'. It is true that there is a secondary sense of 'believe' in which we can say (*a*) and (*b*). In this sense, 'I believe' means 'I feel sure' (or 'am convinced, persuaded'). But I am pointing out, with Locke, that there is another sense of 'believe' in which we cannot rightly say (*a*) and (*b*), and moreover that it is this sense that is the primary one. Hume holds that this secondary use is the only use of 'believe', and it is with 'degree of belief' in this sense of 'degree of intensity of feeling of conviction' that he wrongly identifies the meaning of 'degree of probability'. [6.1] After Plato's, Hume's is perhaps the most famous, or notorious, philosophical account of belief, and I imagine that his influence is one cause of the general tendency to take this secondary use of 'believe' for *the* meaning of the word. It is plausibly suggested that another is our natural disposition to suppose that 'I believe' describes some action that I am doing; or rather, some passion that I am undergoing, namely, feeling sure.

I think that there are also other secondary uses of 'believe'. In one of them I say that I believe that *p* when I unclearly and indistinctly perceive or remember that *p*. E.g.: 'I believe that is Jones approaching', 'I believe I did tell him'. The difference between this secondary use and the primary use involves an important point. In this sort of case the proposition believed is not and logically cannot be judged to be probable. For we have probability only when we have evidence; but in cases where the propositions believed are observation- or memory-statements we do not have evidence at all. However, some think otherwise. Locke and Hume write of the 'testimony of our senses' and the 'records of our memory', famous phrases that have passed from philosophical into non-specialist language. [Locke, 326; Hume, E, 26] What they and later phenomenalists mean is something like this. When I make the observation-statement 'Jones is approaching', I have certain visual sensations ('ideas of sensation', 'impressions' or 'sense-data'). These are described by 'sensation-reports', otherwise called 'basic' or 'protocol statements'. And from the evidence of these reports I infer that Jones is approaching; and analogously in the case of memory-statements. Sometimes it is said that the sensation-reports or evidencing-statements are always true or certain whereas the observation-reports or evidenced-statements are never true but only more or less probable; sometimes that the sensation-reports themselves are never true but only more or less probable. But these accounts are not acceptable. For evidencing-statements are generally about common objects, such as fingerprints, not about sensations or memory-images, which are private. I say 'generally' because there are exceptions, e.g. 'The fact that I have an acute pain here is evidence that I have appendicitis'. Moreover, the very notion of a 'sensation-report' involves difficulties, since existing languages are designed in the main for talking about common objects, not about private objects such as sensations.

There is yet another secondary use of 'believe' in which we say of a lunatic 'He believes he is Napoleon' or of a dog 'He thinks he is going to be taken for a walk', when his overt behaviour is of a certain sort; e.g. he harangues his marshals or jumps up and down and wags his tail. This is normally a criterion of 'He (She, etc.) believes that p' rather than of 'I believe that p'; for my reason for saying that I believe that p is not normally my observation, or another's report, of my own overt behaviour; though it may be so in unusual cases.

From Plato on, philosophers have been interested in the resemblances and differences between belief and knowledge, and it will be well briefly to consider this question. What is known, 'the object of knowledge'? Commonly, a proposition. But not always, since there are familiar uses of 'know' that this account will not fit, e.g. 'I know Smith' and 'She knows French'. But given that we are interested only in knowing-that as opposed to knowing-how or simply knowing, we ask next, When is a proposition rightly claimed to be known? Primarily, I submit, when and only when the proposition in question is taken to be true. We can rightly say neither: 'I know that p although it is not true that p'; nor 'It is true that p but I do not know that p'. (On the latter point, cp. the quotation from Locke, 368, above.) Herein lie the essential resemblance and the essential difference between the primary use of 'believe' and the primary use of 'know that'. But, as so often, the distinction is not water-tight. For we sometimes say that we believe that p when we take p to be true, not probable. When a man says that he believes that God exists he usually takes 'God exists' to be true, not probable; though the latter is possible, e.g. when he believes this proposition on what he takes to be inductive evidence, as when he accepts the argument from marks of design in Nature. As with belief, the necessary and sufficient condition of justifiably claiming to know *p* is that *p* should be taken to be true, not that it should be true. Moreover, this is the condition under which I can properly claim to know that *p*, not the condition under which my claim is allowed; for the latter it is necessary that *p* should actually be true. Finally, it is requisite merely that I should hold *p* to be true, not that I should hold it to be necessarily true.

Curiously, Locke and Hume agree with Plato and the high rationalist tradition about the last point. Genuine knowledge, they say, is of what Hume calls 'relations of ideas', i.e. necessary truths, only; Locke indeed allows that we can have 'sensitive knowledge' of 'matters of fact and existence', but maintains that this is an inferior 'degree' of knowledge. [Locke, 265] This mars his answer to the central question of Bk. IV of his *Essay*, which concerns precisely the difference between knowledge and belief or opinion. There is a close parallelism between this Book and Part III of Bk. I of Hume's *Treatise*; it is revealing that, whereas the former is entitled 'Of Knowledge and Opinion', the latter is entitled 'Of Knowledge and Probability'. The correct answer to Locke's question, which he nearly attains, is in my view simply that we rightly say that we believe that *p*, in the primary use of 'believe', when and only when we judge *p* to be probable; whereas we rightly claim that we know that *p*, in the primary use of 'know that', when and only when we hold *p* to be true. Only, from deference to the rationalist tradition, he says that we know that *p* when and only when we hold *p* to be necessarily true. In fact, however, we of course claim to know contingent truths such as 'That cat is black'. And there is one sort of contingent truths that is especially important for the present discussion. A sufficient condition of *p*'s being claimed to be true, and so also known, is when the evidence for it is judged to be, not merely very, very good, but conclusive. In this use of 'true' and 'know', therefore, the difference between truth and probability, knowledge and belief, is one of degree only. I shall revert to this point later. [5.2]

Finally, there are secondary uses of 'know that' that correspond to the secondary uses of 'believe' that I have distinguished. Sometimes I say that I know that *p* when I feel perfectly sure: e.g. 'I know he is innocent although all the evidence is overwhelmingly against him'. The difference between this use of 'know' and the corresponding sense of 'believe' is again one of degree only. And sometimes, when we see the dog behaving as previously described, we say that he knows that he is going to be taken for a walk. But not unless he actually is so. We do not say that the lunatic knows he is Napoleon, because in fact he is not.

To sum up. I agree with Locke that 'believe', in its primary use, is simply the word we use for the manner in which we entertain propositions that we judge to be probable; as 'know', in the primary use of 'know that', is simply the word we use for the manner in which we entertain propositions that we take to be true. Hence, to say that the evaluative meaning of 'It is probable that p' is 'One ought (or, It is reasonable) to believe that p' is to say that the evaluative meaning of 'It is probable that p' is 'One ought to entertain p in the manner in which one entertains propositions that one judges to be probable'. But this is an unsatisfactory, because circular, analysis; for the explaining expression contains the very word the meaning of which is to be explained.

The next view that I wish to consider comes to this: to call p probable is to call it good as a basis for action. After observing that 'probable' as predicated of propositions means 'approvable', Kneale continues: '. . . "approvable" clearly means in the context the same as . . . "such as a rational man would approve as a basis for practical decisions"; for there is no other relevant sense in which a *proposition* can be supposed to be approvable'. [Kneale, 20] Notice that, as Russell explains the evaluative word 'credible' by the evaluative word 'rational' (or 'reasonable'), so Kneale explains the evaluative word 'probable' (or 'approvable') by the same evaluative word. However, it seems to me that the last statement in the passage quoted is untrue, since a proposition can surely be said to be good *qua* assertion. And I think that Kneale's account can be shown to be unacceptable by the following considerations. If he is right, it cannot make sense to say that p is probable unless it can serve someone as a basis for some practical decision. But in fact we sometimes say that propositions are probable when this condition is not fulfilled. Cp. 'It will probably rain this afternoon' with 'It probably rained in London on 13 February 1066'. The former judgement presents no difficulties for Kneale's account, since the proposition that it will rain this afternoon can serve, say, me as a basis for the decision to take my raincoat when I go out. But the latter judgement does present difficulties, since, to put it simply, there is nothing to be done, in any normal sense of 'do', by anybody about its having rained there then; yet it is a perfectly good probability-judgement.

To deny that the evaluative force of '*p* is probable' is '*p* is good as a basis for practical decisions' is not of course to deny that we very often and perhaps usually take our practical decisions on the basis of, among other things, what we judge to be probable and so believe rather than on the basis of what we take to be true and so claim to know. This truth has been amply emphasized, most familiarly by Butler, but also by Locke and by Utilitarians, who stress the importance of judging the probable consequences of alternative courses of action when making up our minds about what we ought to do. This leads to another criticism of Kneale's thesis. To say that the evaluative force of '*p* is probable' is '*p* is good as a basis for action' or 'One ought to act on *p*' is to imply that the degree of probability of *p* is the only consideration to be taken into account when deciding whether and how to act on *p*. But this is plainly false. Suppose that I am deliberating whether and how and how much to bet on the next race, and that I judge that it is virtually certain that Wooden Spoon will win it. I cannot decide on the basis of this judgement alone that I ought to bet £100 on his winning; I have to consider other things, such as whether and how well I can afford to forfeit this stake if he loses. Keynes points this out in criticizing the doctrine that 'the probable is the hypothesis on which it is rational for us to act', and indeed Kneale himself says as much. [Keynes, 307; Kneale, 18 f.] This is true whether my judgement about what I ought to do is ethical or, as in this example, prudential. It is for the same reason that Braithwaite distinguishes between the probability of a statistical hypothesis and its acceptability, or between the superiority of the probability of one statistical hypothesis over that of a rival statistical hypothesis and the preferability of the first hypothesis over the second. He points out that probability, or greater probability, is only one of the considerations that determine respectively the acceptability, or preferability, of such an hypothesis, and contends that another is 'the relative advantages to be obtained by acting on beliefs in the alternative hypotheses, combining these with probabilities . . . to form "mathematical expectations".' [Braithwaite, 253]

In another place, Braithwaite writes: 'The statement that the probability is 1/6 that a particular die will fall five uppermost on the next occasion it is thrown may have several meanings. . . . It may . . . be used to express a rate at which the asserter, or some ideal reasonable man, would be prepared to bet on the die falling five uppermost next time. . . .' [Braithwaite, 121] Let us examine this suggestion. To begin with, this account of the meaning of probability-utterances is incompatible with the view that they are value-judgements. For to make an offer to bet, or any other sort of offer, is not to make any sort of value-judgement, but rather to give what Austin calls a 'performative utterance'. Next, it is necessary to distinguish this view from connected ones. This is a thesis about the meaning of probability-utterances, and should not be confused with the thesis that degrees of probability can be measured by betting-odds. Bentham e.g. maintains the latter thesis, but holds with Hume that 'degree of probability' means 'degree of belief' and that this in turn means 'degree of intensity of feeling of conviction'. [Bentham, 71] His assertion of these equivalences evidently commits him to the position that degrees of belief can be measured by betting-odds. We have already seen that Braithwaite takes this position, as does Ramsey also. [Ramsey, 166 ff.]

The only one of these contentions that concerns us is the first, about the meaning of probability-utterances. It seems to me to be open to the following objections. A probability-judgement can be given as a reason for making an offer to bet. I can properly say 'I offer (to bet any taker at odds of) 5:1 that p because there is a probability of 5/6 that p'. Such an utterance is not (called) tautological. But if the proposed analysis is correct, that is just what it is; it goes 'I offer . . . etc. because I offer . . . etc.' The proposed analysis is therefore incorrect. Again, consider the following objection. If I say 'I offer . . . etc. 5:1 that p' and you say 'I offer . . . etc. 5:1 that $\sim p$', we are not (said to be) disagreeing or contradicting one another. But if I say 'There is a probability of 5/6 that p' and you say 'There is a probability of 5/6 that $\sim p$', we are (said to be) disagreeing or contradicting one another. The former pair of utterances are therefore not respectively equivalent to the latter pair. This illustrates the general truth that, whereas the notions of

37

disagreement and contradiction apply to value-judgements as well as to descriptive statements, they do not apply to performative utterances.

These objections are levelled against the thesis that a probability-utterance expresses the rate at which its actual giver is prepared to bet. But the citation from Braithwaite shows that there is a second form of the thesis, according to which 'There is a probability of $5/6$ that p' means 'One ought (or, It is reasonable) to offer . . . etc. $5:1$ that p'. This form escapes my second objection to the first form of the thesis, since if I say 'One ought to offer . . . etc. $5:1$ that p' and you say 'One ought to offer . . . etc. $5:1$ that $\sim p$', we are (said to be) disagreeing. For now we have, not two performative utterances which logically cannot be opposed, but two value-judgements which logically can be opposed. But it does not escape my first objection to the first form of the thesis, since it is not tautological to say 'One ought to offer . . . etc. $5:1$ that p because there is a probability of $5/6$ that p'. Moreover, it seems to me to put the matter the wrong way round. For, so far from being able to explain 'probability' in terms of a 'reasonable bet', it seems to me that we can only explain the notion of a reasonable bet in terms of, among other things, probability. I say 'among other things' because probability is only one of the things to be taken into account when deciding whether it is sensible to offer, or accept, a given bet.

For the contention implicit in the second form of the thesis under consideration, that the 'ideal reasonable man' always bets on p at a rate which is determined solely by his judgement of the degree of probability of p, is an oversimplification, as the following considerations will show. [Carnap, 165 ff., 262 ff.; Kneale, 7 f.] In Carnap's terminology, this is to say that one ought to offer or accept only 'fair' bets. He defines a 'fair' bet as one in which the 'betting-quotient' has the same value as the estimated probability of p, and defines the 'betting-quotient' in turn as $u_1/(u_1 + u_2)$, where u_1 and u_2 represent the stakes and the ratio $u_1 : u_2$ represents the odds or 'betting-ratio'. Yet one might at least equally well say that the reasonable thing to do is to offer or accept only 'favourable' bets. If I am offering the bet, it will be favourable to me if the betting-quotient is less than the estimated probability of p. But again, it is not always reasonable to offer or accept a favourable bet. Suppose that I am offered a bet on heads being thrown with this penny at 8,000 : 8,001 and that I estimate the probability of this event at 1/2. Then the bet is favourable to me; but it will be anything but reasonable for me to accept it if my fortune is 10,000, since the stake is no less than four-fifths of my fortune. Finally, suppose that I am a bookmaker. It is false that the odds that it is reasonable for me to offer are determined solely by my estimates of probability. The most that can be said is that the latter constitute one of the considerations that ought to contribute to determining the former. The principal consideration will be the correct making of my book, i.e. the adjusting of the odds that I offer in such a way that my clients collectively must lose whatever happens. Hence, the odds that it is reasonable for me to offer them may diverge quite markedly from my estimates of probability. Thus, contrary to what the second form of the thesis claims, there is no simple relationship between one's estimate of the probability of p and the odds at which it is reasonable for one to offer or accept bets on p. And this is only a special case of the general truth which I pointed out when commenting on Kneale's account of the evaluative meaning of probability-judgements, namely, that there is no simple relationship between one's judgement of the probability of p and one's judgement of how one ought to act on p. For offers and acceptances of bets on p are just one sort of actions on p among others.

1.2.2 *The Descriptive Meaning of 'Probable'*

So much for the evaluative meaning of 'probable'; let us now consider its descriptive meaning. Here, the notion of a probabilification-judgement is central. I have discussed so far only probability-judgements, such as 'It is probable that all BU are H'. Consider now the judgement: 'The fact that all observed BU are H and that they are varied and numerous makes it probable that all BU are H'. I call this a categorical probabilification-judgement, and it exemplifies the categorical probabilification-judgement-formula, (2'): $\gamma \mathrm{PF}(fAg, f'Ag \cdot \gamma C_2)$. This formula is a special case of the more general formula, (1'): $\mathrm{PF}(p, q)$, which is read: 'The fact that q makes it (in some unspecified degree) probable that p'. In (1'), q may be called the probabilifying-proposition-formula and p the probabilified-proposition-formula. Formulas (1') and (2') correspond, in a sense to be explained shortly, to evidential-statement-formulas (1) and (2). It is for this reason that I number them (1') and (2'); and so generally in this essay formulas (3'), (4'), etc. correspond to formulas (3), (4), etc. 'PF' is read 'probabilifies', which is not a technical term but a convenient abbreviation for the colloquial 'makes it probable that'. In formula (2') the function of the Greek letters is to indicate degrees. Thus, γPF is read 'makes it probable that', βPF as 'makes it very probable that' and δPF as 'makes it fairly probable that'. C_2 represents the condition that f' are varied and numerous; this too may vary in degree, so that, as γC_2 is read 'f' are varied and numerous', so βC_2 is read 'f' are very varied and numerous'. It is convenient to use a similar notation for probability-judgement-formulas. Thus, βP(p), γP(p) and δP(p) are read respectively 'It is very probable that p', 'It is probable that p' and 'It is fairly probable that p'. I call formula (2') an universal subject-predicate inductive primitive formula. I oppose primitive to derivative probabilification-judgements, meaning by the former judgements the probabilifying-propositions of which do not contain a probability-judgement, and by the latter judgements the probabilifying-propositions of which do contain a probability-judgement.

What makes it probable that what? That which is probabilified is a proposition; this follows from the conclusion already reached, that that which is probable is a proposition. And that which probabilifies is what is taken to be a fact or true statement. To make a categorical probabilification-judgement correctly, one must take the probabilifying-proposition to be true. And one ground on which such a judgement may be opposed is that the alleged probabilifying fact is actually false or no fact. Practically, this is an important point; but it presents no epistemological problem. Categorical probabilification-judgements must be distinguished accordingly from hypothetical. The latter are of the form: 'If q, that makes it probable that p'. The difference is precisely that in these the probabilifying-proposition is not asserted as true, so that they cannot be opposed on the ground that it is actually false. Similar remarks apply to evidential-statements. That which evidences is a putative fact, and that which is evidenced is a proposition. The categorical formula 'The fact that q is evidence that p' must be distinguished from the hypothetical formula 'If q, that is evidence that p'. The former, but not the latter, may be opposed on the ground that q is actually false.

Finally, categorical and hypothetical probabilification-judgements may be expressed respectively in the equivalent forms: 'Since q it is probable that p' or 'q, therefore it is probable that p', and 'If q, it is probable that p' or 'q would make it probable that p'. Similarly, *mutatis mutandis*, with categorical and hypothetical evidential-statements.

Consider next the relation of probability-judgements to probabilification-judgements. Obviously, the probabilification-judgement-formula (2') entails the corresponding probability-judgement-formula: $\gamma P(fAg)$. Equally obviously, the latter formula does not entail formula (2'). Yet it implies it in a familiar sense of 'implies' that is not equivalent to 'entails'. For when I make a probability-judgement, say 'It is probable that all BU are H', I am understood and expected to have some reason for doing so, namely to (think that I) know (what I take to be) a fact that I judge to make this proposition probable. To make such a probability-judgement without a reason in this sense is certainly wrong. Then, the descriptive meaning of this probability-judgement is revealed by the corresponding probabilification-judgement that it 'implies', say 'The fact that all observed BU are H and that they are varied and numerous makes it probable that all BU are H'. Analogously, we may say that the descriptive meaning of the judgement 'This is a good watch' is revealed by the good-making-judgement that it 'implies', say 'The fact that it is accurate makes this a good watch'. But this is true of all probability-judgements. So that to explain the descriptive meaning of probability-judgements generally, or of 'probable', is to specify the conditions or criteria that make propositions probable, to formulate what Locke calls the 'grounds' of probability. [Locke, 335 ff.] So that discriminating the several types of probabilification-judgements and explaining the descriptive meaning of 'probable' are one and the same activity. It is also answering the second main question of the Philosophy of Probability, namely, When is a proposition (rightly called) more or less probable?

These considerations shed some light on the oracular principle 'Probability is relative to evidence'. If this means that a probability-judgement 'implies' a corresponding probabilification-judgement, it is true, as has just been shown. Or again, if it means that the same proposition is commonly, though not always, probabilified in a different degree by different pieces of evidence, it is true, not to say truistic. But if it means that 'It is probable that p' is an ill-formed expression in the way that 'Edinburgh is north of' is ill-formed, it is false; though it is of course true that 'Makes it probable that p' is ill-formed in this sense. All three ideas are present in Keynes' remarks on this topic. [Keynes, 6 f., 90 f.] The doctrine that probability is in some sense relative to evidence must naturally be distinguished from the doctrine that it is in some sense relative to the speaker or subjective. We have already seen that the latter is false, and have objected to the betting analysis of probability-judgements on this ground among others; we shall also see that the analyses of Hume and Toulmin are objectionable on the same score. [6.1]

It is desirable to introduce here the conception of an evidential-evaluation. By a categorical evidential-evaluation I mean a judgement exemplifying the formula: 'The fact that q is good evidence that p'. It is generally thought that this formula means the same thing as the formula $\gamma PF(p, q)$. [Hare, 60] The thought is right, but there is a fairly obvious *prima facie* difficulty about it that needs to be resolved. For it may be objected that the evaluative force or meaning of the two formulas is plainly different, that of the latter being to commend p as an assertion, but that of the former being to commend q as evidence for p. The solution, I believe, is this: both formulas are ellipses of the same doubly evaluative formula, namely: 'The fact that q is (very, fairly, etc.) good evidence that p makes it (very, fairly, etc.) probable that p'. When I say 'The fact that q makes it probable that p', it is understood that I am also saying that the fact that q is good evidence that p; and when I say 'The fact that q is good evidence that p', it is understood that I am also saying that the fact that q makes it probable that p.

We often speak of evidence, not as more or less good, but as more or less strong or weighty. But these locutions are apt to conceal the essential point that what we do is evaluate or appraise evidence. 'Weighty' and 'strong' are normally descriptive words; and if we take literally such metaphorical expressions as 'weighing the evidence' and 'measuring the probative force of the evidence', we are likely to go quite astray.

We must now consider the relation of evidential-evaluations or probabilification-judgements to evidential-statements. Plainly, they do not mean the same thing. To say 'The fact that q is evidence that p' is by no means to say 'The fact that q is good (very good, rather poor, etc.) evidence that p'. The former is a descriptive statement, but the latter, as I have just explained, is a double value-judgement. But equally plainly, they are closely related. The relation is this: any evidential-evaluation or probabilification-judgement presupposes its corresponding evidential-statement. By this I mean that the truth of 'The fact that q is evidence that p' is a necessary condition not merely of the truth but also of the falsity of 'The fact that q is good (fair, poor, etc.) evidence that p'.

Despite their non-equivalence, evidential-statements and evidential-evaluations or probabilification-judgements are sometimes confused. Reid e.g. writes: 'Every degree of evidence perceived by the mind produces a proportional degree of assent or belief'. [Reid, 434] But 'degree of evidence' is an illogical expression; it makes no sense to say 'The fact that q is very (fairly, etc.) evidence that p'. A fact either is evidence for or against a proposition or it is not; there is no more or less about it. On the other hand, 'The fact that q is very (fairly, etc.) good evidence that p' makes perfectly good sense; Reid manifestly conflates the two.

It seems to me that the same confusion is to be found in what some contemporary philosophers say about 'degree of confirmation'. Carnap e.g. writes as follows. He tells us that the chief aim of his book is to explain one of the two meanings of 'probability', which he distinguishes as 'probability$_1$'. And he writes: 'To say that the probability$_1$ of h on e is high means that . . . h is highly confirmed by e . . . this explanation may be said to outline the primary and simplest meaning of probability$_1$. . . .' But earlier he equates 'h is confirmed by e' with 'e gives some (positive) evidence for h'. [Carnap, 164, 21] But if 'e confirms h' means 'The fact that e is evidence that h', the expressions 'highly confirms' and 'degree of confirmation' generally are illogical and cannot explain the meaning of anything. He too, I think, conflates 'is evidence that' with 'is good (very good, poor, etc.) evidence that'. What he really intends is that, in one sense of 'probabilification' (not, incidentally, of 'probability'), 'degree of probabilification' means 'degree of goodness (or strength, etc.) of confirmation'. For the terms 'confirms' and 'supports', as ordinarily used, mean 'is evidence that', not 'is good evidence that' or 'makes it probable that'. For if the latter were true 'strongly confirms' and 'supports well' would be pleonastic, would mean 'strongly strongly confirms' and 'supports well well'; which however they plainly are not. The same confusion is found in Hempel's discussion; he too says first that 'confirms' means 'evidences' and then that 'degree of confirmation' means 'degree of probability' (meaning rather 'degree of probabilification'). [Hempel, I, 2, 5] Similarly Popper uses the expression 'degree of confirmation' notwithstanding that he admits that 'we habitually characterize theories as better and less well confirmed'. [Popper, 198]

The consequences of this confusion for Carnap's philosophy of probability are grave. For, through conflating probabilification-judgements or evidential-evaluations with evidential-statements, he is led to think that the relation between the probabilifying-proposition and the probabilified-proposition in a probabilification-judgement is essentially similar to that between the evidencing-statement and the evidenced-statement in an evidential-statement. In particular, he is led to overlook the fundamental difference that the former relation is, as the latter relation is not, of the peculiar type that holds between a value-judgement and the factual statement that is given as a reason for making it. I shall return to this point shortly.

Of the two aspects of the meaning of 'probable', the descriptive is primary. For to say that part of the meaning of $\gamma P(p)$ is to commend the assertion of p is not, after all, to say very much. The serious business of the Philosophy of Probability consists in elucidating the descriptive meaning or criteria of 'probable'. Nevertheless, the recognition that 'probable' is an evaluative and not a descriptive word, and that its logic is like that of other evaluative words such as 'good', enables us to deal with certain questions that are regarded by many as crucial. I will give some illustrations of this.

1.2.3 *Solution of Some Crucial Questions in the Philosophy of Probability*

Many philosophers hold that the central task of the Philosophy of Probability is to provide a definition of the meaning of 'probable'. Thus, some say that 'degree of probability' means or is 'degree of relative frequency'. The defining expression is descriptive. Hence, these theorists may be confronted with the following dilemma. Either they recognize that 'probable' is an evaluative word or they do not. If they do not, they commit what Austin calls the descriptive fallacy. If they do, they commit what Moore calls the naturalistic fallacy, i.e. the fallacy of supposing that the meaning of an evaluative word can be defined or explained in terms of descriptive ones. Other definitions also are open to this objection; e.g. the doctrines that 'degree of probability' means 'degree of conviction', or 'ratio of ranges of possibilities', or 'degree of confirmation'. For these defining expressions are all descriptive; that this is so in the case of the last I have just tried to make plain. Actually, the error into which theorists fall is usually the former one.

Of course, this objection holds only against those who offer descriptive expressions as definitions of 'probable', not against those who offer them as criteria thereof. The distinction can be illustrated by reference to relative frequency theories of probability. Braithwaite calls his theory of the meaning of probability in (not of) statistical hypotheses and in games of chance a frequency theory of probability, because he holds that '. . . the criteria for the meaning of [this sort of] probability statements are to be found in their being rejected or failing to be rejected on the basis of the frequencies (i.e. class-ratios) in observed sets'. [Braithwaite, 191] Most so-called (relative) frequency theorists, on the other hand, offer definitions of 'probability' in terms of 'relative frequency'. [Venn, L, 162 ff.; Mises, 37 f.] The two senses of the name 'relative frequency theory of probability' need accordingly to be kept distinct. The name is also used for two different types of definition of 'probable'. The first is the one which I have criticized above, and which is called by Russell 'the finite-frequency theory'. [Russell, H, 368 ff.] According to it, 'There is a probability of m/n that x is g' means 'm/n f are g and x is an f and x has been selected at random from among the fs'. The second is the one, versions of which are advanced by Venn, Mises, Reichenbach and Popper, according to whom the meaning of 'There is a probability of m/n that x is g' is to be defined in terms of the limiting value of the relative frequency of gs among fs, as opposed to in terms of the (observed) value of the relative frequency of gs among fs. I shall say something more about relative frequency theories of probability in 2.2. and 4.3.

In some cases, one can imagine pretty readily how those who fall into the descriptive fallacy reached their conclusions about the meaning of 'probable'. Hume presumably reasoned somewhat as follows. When someone says 'Rain is probable to-day', the adjective 'probable' must describe something. But what? Not rain, since the statement does not describe this as 'Rain is wet' does. So that the statement is not really about rain at all, though it seems to be so; it is really about the feelings of the speaker who makes it. The use of the expressions '(very, fairly, etc.) probable' is to describe the degree of belief in the mind of the speaker, 'degree of belief' meaning in turn according to Hume 'degree of intensity of feeling of conviction'. There is therefore a suggestive analogy between his accounts of probability-judgements and of ethical value-judgements; as the former describe the speaker's feelings of belief and disbelief, so the latter describe his feelings of approval and disapproval.

Other philosophers say that the central task of the Philosophy of Probability is the elucidation of the probability-relation (or relations). They mean rather 'the probabilification-relation' (or relations), for what they have in mind is the relation between the probabilifying-proposition and the probabilified-proposition in a probabilification-judgement. Consider Carnap's remarks on this. We have seen that what he really intends by 'degree of confirmation' is 'degree of goodness of confirmation', i.e. of probabilification. One of his basic theses is that 'inductive statements', i.e. inductive probabilification-judgements, are, if true, 'logically true' or analytic, and, if false, 'logically false' or self-contradictory. Thus he tells us that the categorical probabilification-judgement 'On the basis of the available evidence it is very probable that the degree of uniformity in the world is high' is logically true. [Carnap, 180 f.] On his view, therefore, as the formula $p \supset p$ is analytic, so e.g. the hypothetical inductive probabilification-judgement-formula $f'Ag \cdot \gamma C_2 \supset \gamma P(fAg)$ is analytic. But this again reveals the naturalistic fallacy, for a conjunction of descriptive statements cannot entail a value-judgement.

Again, consider Keynes' views on this matter. [Keynes, 3 ff.] We have seen that he rightly says that that which is probable is a proposition. He holds further that to say 'p is probable' is to describe p, that probability is a property of propositions. But it is a relational property; in this respect the statement resembles 'Edinburgh is north of', and like this it is ill-formed. As the latter is an ellipsis of the properly-formed 'Edinburgh is north of London', so the former is an ellipsis of the properly-formed 'p is probable on q'. I have already discussed this last point and observed that, while it is false that probability-judgements are ill-formed, it is true that they 'imply' corresponding probabilification-judgements. The point of present importance is that Keynes too falls into the descriptive fallacy in assimilating 'probable' to relational property-words like 'distant'; for these are no less descriptive than simple property-words like 'red'.

Take now the formula 'If q it is probable that p'. This involves what Keynes calls 'the probability-relation' (or relations); he means rather 'the probabilification-relation'. About this, he says that we perceive it, that it is indefinable, and that it is a relation of 'partial implication', meaning I think 'partial logical implication' (or 'partial entailment'). The first objection is that we do not in fact perceive it or them. Second, his contention that the relation is indefinable is inconsistent with his further statement that it means 'partial implication'. But the point of present interest is that in saying that 'probabilifies' means 'partially entails' he falls into the naturalistic fallacy. For partial entailment evidently differs from entailment only in degree, not in kind; so that in saying that probabilification is a relation of this kind he is open to the same objection as I have just brought against Carnap.

I imagine that he reached his position in this sort of way. He interprets 'If q then probably p' as 'If q probably-then p', and takes the problem to be that of explaining the meaning of the logical relation 'if . . . probably-then'. Consequently, he also thinks that the terms between which the relation holds are two descriptive statements. E.g., he interprets 'If all observed BU are H and they are varied and numerous, then probably all BU are H' as 'If (All observed BU are H, etc.), probably-then (All BU are H)'. On this interpretation, what we have is two descriptive statements (in brackets) related by 'if . . . probably-then' (the probabilification-relation). But in fact the judgement means 'If (All observed BU are H, etc.), then (Probably all BU are H)'. And on this interpretation, what we have is a descriptive statement and a value-judgement (both in brackets) related by 'if . . . then'. Thus Keynes was misled, both into believing in the existence of a mysterious logical relation 'if . . . probably-then', whereas actually only 'if . . . then' is involved; and also into overlooking the vital point that the apodosis is a value-judgement and not a descriptive statement.

Finally, if by 'partial implication' Keynes means, as I think he does, 'partial entailment', his definition of 'probabilification' is in any case meaningless. For entailment logically cannot have degrees; either q entails p or it does not; there can be no more or less about it. But if by 'partial implication' he means, as he may, 'partial material implication', it is possible to make sense of his definition of 'probabilification'. For, as we may say that q fully materially implies p if and only if p is always true whenever q is true, so we may say that q partially materially implies p if and only if p is generally true whenever q is true. But to say this is to embrace the relative frequency theory of probability, specifically, that form of it which can conveniently be distinguished as the relative truth-frequency theory of probability and which is associated with the name of Peirce in particular. [4.3] But Keynes rejects the relative frequency theory. [Keynes, 92 ff.] Therefore, his definition of 'the probability-relation' is either on his own showing false, or meaningless; for I think that the notion of partial implication can only be made sense of in terms of relative truth-frequency.

Yet other philosophers take the central problem of Inductive Philosophy to be the justification of induction. About this problem generally, I agree with the following remark of v. Wright's: 'The justification of Induction constitutes, it would seem, a "philosophical" problem in a peculiar sense. What is meant by this can be imperfectly explained by saying that it is a problem, the essential issue of which is to make clear wherein the problem itself consists.' [Wright, T, 21; Black, J, 63 ff.; Lalande, 15 ff.] I would add that whether it is a genuine problem or not naturally depends on what one takes it to be. On some interpretations it is doubtless, as the logical empiricists say, a pseudo-problem. [Ayer, 49 f.; Weinberg, 136 ff.] But not on all. I interpret the question 'What is the justification of induction?' as 'Given that (at least) some inductions are (said to be) just (or good, or sound, or probable, etc.), what makes them so (or, when, under what conditions, are they so)?' Of the three different senses of 'the problem of the justification of induction' that he distinguishes, Lalande also maintains that this is the primary one. On my interpretation of it, the philosophical problem of the justification of induction is therefore identical with the philosophical problem of inductive probability; for 'just', as predicated of inductions, is simply one more synonym for 'probable', as is 'justified' for 'probabilified'. And what I take the philosophical problem of inductive probability to be will by now be fairly clear. On this interpretation, the problem of inductive justification or probabilification seems to me not only a genuine problem but in truth, as these philosophers claim, the central problem of Inductive Philosophy.

I wish next to show how the recognition that 'probable' is an evaluative and not a descriptive word enables us to assess one very simple proposed solution of the problem of the justification of induction. Lewy formulates the problem as, What justifies us in passing from a premiss of the form $f'Ag$ to a conclusion of the form $\gamma P(fAg)$? His solution is that we are justified in so doing because the former formula entails the latter formula; i.e. because the formula $f'Ag \supset \gamma P(fAg)$ is analytic, or the formula $f'Ag \,.$ $\sim(\gamma P(fAg))$ is self-contradictory. [Lewy] The constituent formula $\sim(\gamma P(fAg))$ is to be read 'It is not the case that it is probable that all f are g'. (Incidentally, 'It is not (the case that it is) probable that p', symbolized $\sim(\gamma P(p))$, is not equivalent to 'It is improbable that p', which is equivalent to 'It is probable that not-p' and is accordingly symbolized $\gamma P(\sim p)$.) But this solution involves the naturalistic fallacy, since Lewy alleges that descriptive statements of the form $f'Ag$ entail value-judgements of the form $\gamma P(fAg)$. We have already detected the same error in Keynes and Carnap.

As final illustration, let us consider a question that has been much debated of late, namely, Is the word 'probable' univocal or equivocal? Until fairly recently, it was taken for granted that it is univocal. Hume, indeed, distinguishes different 'kinds' of probability; namely, the probability of chances, of causes, of analogy, and unphilosophical probability. [Hume, T, 124 ff.] But this is not a distinction between different meanings of 'probable'; Hume holds that 'degree of probability' always means 'degree of belief', which in turn means 'degree of intensity of feeling of conviction (or expectation)'. It is rather a distinction between different conditions or criteria, the different ways in which propositions are made probable in different degrees. But in consequence of his psychological approach, this distinction tends to become identified with the distinction between the different ways in which the feeling of conviction or expectation (the 'idea') in its different degrees originates. Latterly, however, many have contended that there are different kinds or concepts of probability, or different meanings or senses or uses of 'probable', and that this fact furnishes the solution to some of the chief philosophical problems of probability. [Apelt, 34 ff.; Braithwaite, 118 ff.; Carnap, 182 ff.; Johnson, I, xl; Kneale, 22; Nisbet, 9 f.; Popper, 73, 94 f.; Ramsey, 157; Reichenbach, 297 ff.; Russell, H, 356 ff.; Ryle, I, 43 ff.; Urmson; Waismann, 228; Wright, T, 296] I submit that neither party to this dispute is wholly wrong or wholly right, since the true account of the matter is that the evaluative meaning of 'probable' is univocal but its descriptive meaning equivocal. This needs clarification.

Consider the probability-judgement 'It is probable that this BU is H', which exemplifies the formula: $\gamma P(gx)$. Its evaluative force is always to commend both the assertion of the proposition 'This BU is H' and the evidence for this proposition. But the descriptive meaning of the judgement varies according to the way in which this proposition is made probable. Compare the following categorical probabilification-judgements: (*a*) 'The fact that most BU are H and that this is a BU taken at random makes it probable that this is H'. This exemplifies the formula, (6'): $\gamma PF(gx, fMg . fx . C_1)$. C_1 represents the condition that x has been selected at random from among f. I call this a non-numerical *casual* primitive formula. The meaning of 'primitive' has been explained in connexion with formula (2'). I call it non-numerical to distinguish it from the corresponding numerical formulas, e.g.: $m/n PF(gx, f m/n g . fx . C_1)$, which is read: 'The fact that m-$n$ths f are g and that x is an f and that x has been selected at random from f, makes it probable in the degree m-$n$ths that x is g'. (*b*) 'The fact that all BU are probably H and that this is a BU makes it probable that this is H.' This exemplifies the formula, (3'): $\gamma PF(gx, \gamma P(fAg) . fx)$. I call this a singular subject-predicate *inductive* derivative formula, it being understood that the constituent formula $\gamma P(fAg)$ of the probabilifying-proposition-formula is a probable inductionformula. (*c*) 'The fact that, if this is an H ball it is a BU, and that this is a BU and that being a BU is very selective of being H, makes it probable that this is H.' This exemplifies the formula: $\gamma PF(gx, (gx \supset fx) . fx . \beta C_4)$. C_4 represents the condition that being f is in an unspecified degree selective of being g, and the Greek letters specify the degree in which it is so. I call this an *hypothetic* primitive formula. The meanings of the expressions 'degree of selectivity' and 'hypothetic' will be explained shortly.

The important point is this. In (*a*), (*b*) and (*c*) the same probability-judgement, 'It is probable that this BU is H', 'implies' and is entailed by three different probabilification-judgements. In it, 'probable' therefore has three different descriptive meanings according as it 'implies' (*a*), (*b*) or (*c*); its descriptive meaning being in (*a*) casual, in (*b*) inductive and in (*c*) hypothetic. It is indeed precisely in this way that the different (descriptive) meanings (or concepts) of 'probable' must be discriminated; for, to repeat it, distinguishing the different types of probabilification-judgements and distinguishing the different descriptive meanings of 'probable' are one and the same activity. Consider the following rough analogy. A, B and C all say 'This is a good painting'. The evaluative meaning of this judgement is the same in all three cases. But A holds that the sufficient condition of a painting's being good is that it is brown, whereas B holds that the sufficient condition is that it has significant form (whatever that may be), and C holds that the sufficient condition is that its cash-value will very probably appreciate with the passage of time. The descriptive meanings of this same form of words in their several mouths will accordingly be quite different.

My topic in this essay is, not probability, but inductive probability. Casual and hypothetic probability therefore fall outside its scope. But it is necessary to say something about them in order to fix their relations to inductive probability, especially since there are in the Philosophy of Probability radical confusions both between inductive and casual evidential-statements, inferences and probabilification-judgements, and also between inductive and hypothetic evidential-statements, inferences and probabilification-judgements. The natural place to discuss casual probability, or 'the probability of chances' as Hume calls it, will be 2.2; but this will be a convenient point at which to say what I have to say about hypothetic probability.

Before doing so, however, I wish to point out one important difference between casual probability on the one hand and inductive and hypothetic probability on the other. The distinction turns on the different senses in which the three sorts of probability are measurable. [Keynes, 20 ff.; Kneale, 214, 243 f.] Inductive probability is always, and hypothetic probability is generally, measurable only in the following sense. Inductively or hypothetically probable propositions can be ranked or ordered by means of the transitive asymmetrical relation 'more probable than'. I call this the weak sense of measuring probability: it is in this sense that hardness e.g. is measurable. The several degrees of inductive and hypothetic probability are correctly expressed by words: we call some inductions and hypotheses 'probable', others 'very probable', and others 'fairly probable'. Casual probability, on the other hand, like temperature e.g., is measurable on an interval scale, where the zero and unit are both conventional, but there is a criterion for equating intervals. I call this the strong or strict sense of measuring probability. The minimum and maximum are expressed by 'o' and '1' respectively, and the intermediate degrees by fractions such as '4/5' or '2/3'.

1.2.4 *Hypothetic Inference and Hypothetic Probability*

Hypothetic evidential-statements, inferences and probabilification-judgements are commonly discussed in the literature under such names as 'the hypothetico-deductive method', 'the method of hypothesis and verification' and 'the confirmation of hypotheses'. I take the name 'hypothetic inference' from Peirce, who employs 'abduction' and 'retroduction' as synonyms. [Peirce, 150 ff., 379] It will be convenient to begin with his account of it.

According to Peirce, the form of hypothetic inference is: 'The surprising fact, C, is observed; But if A were true, C would be a matter of course; Hence, there is reason to suspect that A is true'. [Peirce, 151] This formulation can be improved upon. It is not necessary that C should be surprising. And, much more important, the psychological term 'suspicion' should be replaced by the epistemological term 'evidence'. These amendments made, Peirce may be represented as saying that the categorical hypothetic evidential-statement-formula, in accordance with which we make hypothetic inferences, is: $E(p, (p \supset q) . q)$. There are also, incidentally, hypothetical hypothetic evidential-statements, e.g.: 'Since if this is sugar this is sweet, if this is sweet that is evidence that this is sugar'.

Of course, the existence of inferences in accordance with this formula was recognized long before Peirce, as he himself points out. Aristotle e.g. recognizes it in the course of a well-known discussion of signs. His example may be rendered: 'The fact that if a woman is pregnant she is sallow, and that this woman is sallow, is evidence that she is pregnant'. And he distinguishes this from what I call primitive inductive evidential-statements, his example of which may be rendered: 'The fact that Pittacus is both a wise and a good man is evidence that all wise men are good'. [Aristotle, 524 ff.] This exemplifies the formula: $E(fAg, gfx)$, which is a special case of the formula, (2): $E(fAg, f'Ag)$, and which illustrates generalization from a single observed instance. In speaking in this connexion of the differences between sorts of 'signs', Aristotle seems to me to be recognizing differences of type between evidential-statements.

Consider now hypothetic probabilification-judgements. It will be convenient to divide these according as their probabilified-propositions, i.e. the hypotheses, are (a) empirical universal or singular, (b) non-empirical universal or singular, (c) empirical proportional and (d) non-empirical proportional. I shall discuss them in this order. Non-empirical hypotheses are called by Kneale 'transcendent'. [Kneale, 92 ff.] Proportional hypotheses are sometimes called 'statistical' or 'indeterministic', and universal ones 'causal' or 'deterministic'.

(a) *Example* (i). In the formula given above, $\gamma PF(gx, (gx \supset fx) . fx . \beta C_4)$, the probabilified-proposition logically must be an empirical hypothesis for reasons that will be given below in connexion with Example (iv). I borrow the following exemplification from Peirce: 'The fact that if this man is a Roman Catholic priest then he understands Latin pronounced in the Italian manner, and that he does understand Latin so pronounced, and that this property is very selective of being a R.C. priest, makes it probable that he is a R.C. priest'. [Peirce, 152 f.] In this type of judgement, then, the degree of probabilification is determined by the degree of the selectivity of the consequence; accordingly, the next task is to explain the meaning of 'degree of selectivity'. Suppose that I make a judgement of the same type to the effect that there is a very slight probability that the man is a R.C. priest because he always wears dark clothes. Why do I judge that the man's possession of the former property probabilifies my hypothesis in a higher degree than does his possession of the latter property? I think, simply because I can generalize that the proportion of R.C. priests among men who understand Latin pronounced in the Italian manner is greater than the proportion of R.C. priests among men who always wear dark clothes. And I express this by saying that the former characteristic or consequence is more selective of my hypothesis than is the latter. Of course, my generalization about the degree of selectivity of the consequence may itself be only in some degree probable, in which case we have a derivative and heterogeneous, because both inductive and hypothetic, formula such as: $\delta PF(gx,$ $(gx \supset fx) . fx . \alpha P(C_4))$. There is therefore an important resemblance between this type of hypothetic probability and casual probability, in that the descriptive meaning of both turns on the notion of proportion. [2.2] If, however, I know that the proportion of R.C. priests among men who understand Latin pronounced in the Italian manner is greater than half, then my probabilification-judgement logically cannot be hypothetic. For then it goes: 'The fact that most men who understand Latin so pronounced are R.C. priests, and that this man understands Latin so pronounced, and that he may be regarded as having been selected at random from among the men who understand Latin so pronounced, makes it probable that he is a R.C. priest'; which exemplifies the casual judgement-formula, (6′).

Example (ii). Consider the formula: $\gamma PF(fAg, (fAg \supset f'Ag) .$ $f'Ag . \beta C_4)$, an exemplification of which is: 'The fact that if all BU are H then all observed BU are H, and that all observed BU are H, and that this consequence is very selective of that hypothesis, makes it probable that all BU are H'. Here, the hypothesis is empirical universal. To say in this case that this consequence is very selective of that hypothesis is to generalize that the proportion of cases of the truth of exemplifications of fAg among cases of the truth of exemplifications of $f'Ag$ is fairly near to though less than half. It is of course possible for an instance of $f'Ag$ to be true when an instance of fAg is false, though not conversely. But in fact I do not think that we ever reason in this way in this sort of case, precisely because we are in no position to make any such generalization, still less judge such a generalization to be in any degree probable. The appropriate type of reasoning to employ in this sort of case, in which we are attempting to determine the composition of a population, and moreover the one that we actually do employ, is not hypothetic at all but inductive. (Cp. Example (v), below.)

Example (iii). Consider the formula: $\epsilon PF(gx, \beta P(gx \supset fx) .$ $fx . \beta C_4)$. Whereas Example (i) is a primitive formula, this is a derivative one. This sort of case frequently occurs, and Aristotle's example provides an illustration. His evidential-statement contains the constituent statement 'If this woman is pregnant then she is sallow'. This may be called a hypothetical derivative induction, being a deduction from the generalization 'All pregnant women are sallow'. But this generalization may be judged to be very probable, in which case the hypothetical derivative induction will be judged to be so also. Then, if the latter is included as constituent in a hypothetic probabilification-judgement, we have the type of judgement illustrated by Example (iii). The type is accordingly heterogeneous, being both inductive and hypothetic. In this sort of case, the degree of probability of the conclusion is determined not only by the degree of selectivity of the consequence, but also by the degree of probability of the relevant constituent of the probabilifying-proposition. We shall see that this last point is true of derivative probabilification-judgements generally. [2.2, 3.2]

In discussing hypothetic probabilification-judgements, Lewis justly observes that a single piece of hypothetic evidence probabi-lifies an hypothesis only in a low degree at best. Hence, if we are restricted to this type of evidence, we can only establish our hypothesis with a respectable degree of probability by adducing a number of pieces of favourable independent evidence and 'adding' the degrees of probability that they severally confer on it. [Lewis, 343 ff.] The fact that the man understands Latin pronounced in the Italian manner probabilifies only in a low degree our supposition that he is a R.C. priest; but if we also know that if he is one then he always wears dark clothes, possesses a missal and is knowledgeable about plainsong, and that he does in fact possess these properties too; then this, as we say, 'all adds up'.

These considerations introduce an important type of probabilification-judgement, which I call the compositive type. There are two sub types, which I call additive and subtractive respectively, and which I shall next discuss in outline. Epistemologically speaking, the main division of probabilification-judgements seems to me to be that into primitive and derivative. The former subdivides into casual, inductive and hypothetic. And two important subdivisions of the latter are into heterogeneous (as opposed to homogeneous) judgements and compositive judgements. Casual and inductive derivative judgements logically must be homogeneous, and heterogeneous judgements logically must be derivative.

The additive sub type may be illustrated by the formula:

γPF(gx, δP(gx) . δP(gx) . C$_5$). C$_5$ is the independent evidence condition, and is to be understood as follows. In this formula, the constituent probability-judgement-formulas of the probabilifying-judgement-formula 'imply' corresponding probabilification-judgement-formulas. C$_5$ states that the pieces or lots of evidence that make these constituent probability-judgement formulas probable are independent. Notice that C$_5$ differs from C$_2$ and C$_4$ in these respects. It logically cannot vary in degree; pieces or lots of evidence logically cannot be more or less independent. Nor consequently do its variations in degree determine the degree of probability of the conclusion.

What then does '(in)dependent' mean when predicated of evidence? Evidences may be either logically or physically (causally) (in)dependent. The evidence that the man understands Latin prayers pronounced in the Italian manner is not logically independent of the evidence that he understands Latin pronounced in the Italian manner. Physical (in)dependence is more important. Both B and C say that A stole the money. Then, the evidence of C's statement is not (called) independent of the evidence of B's statement when C's statement is a hearsay of B's. For the existence of the one piece of evidence depends on that of the other; if B's statement had not been made, neither would C's have been made. It makes sense to speak of evidences as (in)dependent only when they are evidence for (or against) the same conclusion. Given that E(p, r) and E(p, s) we can ask whether r and s are independent; but not given that E(p, r) and E(q, s)—unless indeed either q is deducible from p or conversely, or q is evidence for p or conversely, where $\sim p$ and $\sim q$ are special cases of p and q respectively. It is perhaps tempting to define '(in)dependent evidence' in terms of 'degree of probabilification', thus: The evidence, r, for (or against) p is not independent of the evidence, q, for (or against) p if the conjunction q . r probabilifies p (or $\sim p$) in the same degree as does q alone. But this definition will not do. For, if it is correct, the statement 'If r is dependent on q then q . r probabilifies p in the same degree as does q' is analytic. But in fact, though doubtless truistic, it is synthetic. Therefore, this definition is incorrect.

The subtractive sub type of compositive judgements may be illustrated by the formula: γPF(gx, βP(gx) . ϵP($\bar{g}x$) . C$_5$). The presence of C$_5$ in this formula needs explaining. For it may be thought that, since gx and $\bar{g}x$ are contradictories, the evidence for each must be independent. But this is true only of logical (in)dependence. If r is logically dependent on, i.e. entailed by, q, and q probabilifies p, then it is logically impossible that r should probabilify $\sim p$. But q and r may nevertheless be physically (or causally) dependent. For suppose that C's statement that A did it is a mishearsay of B's statement that A did not do it. Then one piece of testimonial evidence, r, namely C's statement that A did it, will be evidence for p, and another piece of testimonial evidence, q, namely B's statement that A did not do it, will be evidence for $\sim p$; yet r will be physically dependent on q.

The most interesting kind of situation involving compositive judgements, and the one most commonly encountered in practice, is that in which we have to estimate what may be called the net probative weight of a large body of evidence relevant to p, some of the items of which are for p and other items of which are against p (i.e. for $\sim p$). We describe our procedure in such situations as 'weighing' the evidence or 'balancing' the *pros* and *cons*. As Locke puts it: 'The mind, if it will proceed rationally, ought to examine all the grounds of probability, and see how they make more or less for or against any proposition, before it assents to or dissents from it; and upon a due balancing of the whole, reject or receive it with a more or less firm assent proportionably to the preponderancy of the greater grounds of probability on one side or the other. . . . The difficulty is, when testimonies contradict common experience, and the reports of history and witnesses clash with the ordinary course of nature, or with one another.' [Locke, 336, 339] What we do is 'add' the degrees of probability conferred on p by each of the favourable pieces of evidence, also the degrees of probability conferred on $\sim p$ by each of the unfavourable pieces of evidence, 'subtract' the smaller from the larger 'sum', and judge p (or $\sim p$) to be probable in the degree that is the 'remainder'. But although it is natural to use the terminology of addition and subtraction to describe these procedures, it is necessary to remember that the words do not carry their literal mathematical senses in this context.

The sort of situation that I am speaking of is best illustrated by cases at law. In these, the compositive judgements involved are usually heterogeneous; i.e. we add and subtract degrees of casual, inductive and hypothetic primitive probability, of derivative probability, etc. [Wigmore, 46 ff., 659 ff.] Consider the following highly simplified illustration. A juror has to estimate the degree of (im)probability that Tom Jones is the murderer of Bob Smith (gx) on the following three pieces of independent evidence: (i) Most of the Jones family are non-murderers; (ii) Dick Brown testifies that he saw Tom Jones do it; and (iii) Tom Jones' fingerprints are on the knife with which Smith was stabbed. The three pertinent probabilification-judgements exemplify respectively the formulas: (i) $\gamma\mathrm{PF}(\bar{g}x, f\bar{M}g . fx . C_1)$, which is a casual primitive formula; (ii) $\delta\mathrm{PF}(gx, \alpha\mathrm{P}(fMg) . fx . C_1)$, which is a casual and inductive heterogeneous formula. The judgement to be substituted upon the constituent probable generalization-formula is: 'It is very, very probable that most persons testifying on oath speak the truth'. (iii) $\gamma\mathrm{PF}(gx, (gx \supset fx) . fx . \beta C_4)$, which is an hypothetic primitive formula. This is actually an over-simplification. For it is not from the main hypothesis alone, namely, 'Tom Jones stabbed Smith with this knife' (gx), that we draw consequences such as 'Tom Jones' fingerprints are on this knife' (fx). It is from the main hypothesis conjoined with an indefinite number of auxiliary assumptions, such as 'Tom Jones was not wearing gloves, did not remove his fingerprints, etc.'. The next step is to add the degrees of probability conferred on gx by the pieces of evidence (ii) and (iii); this exemplifies the additive formula: $\beta\mathrm{PF}(gx, \delta\mathrm{P}(gx) . \gamma\mathrm{P}(gx) . C_5)$. And the final step is to subtract from this sum the degree of probability conferred on $\bar{g}x$ by the piece of evidence (i); this exemplifies the subtractive formula: $\delta\mathrm{PF}(gx, \beta\mathrm{P}(gx) . \gamma\mathrm{P}(\bar{g}x) . C_5)$. The conclusion is that the lot of evidence comprising pieces (i), (ii) and (iii) makes it fairly probable that Tom Jones is guilty.

The respect in which this illustration is over-simplified is of course the supposition that only three pieces of evidence are adduced. For into an actual trial there may be admitted very many pieces of evidence. I think that it is chiefly this sheer bulk of the evidence to be evaluated that makes the juror's task difficult. The operations he must perform are essentially as just outlined, and generally not difficult; though of course it is sometimes hard to know what weight to attach to a given item of evidence. What complicates the task is the number of evidential facts to be taken into account; it may be exceedingly difficult even to remember them all. It is partly on one's view of the capacity of the ordinary man to perform these tasks, even with the powerful assistance of the judge's summing-up, that one will decide on the desirability or undesirability of trial by jury. But one will also do well to consider whether trial by experts in making this sort of probabilification-judgement would not be likely to possess disadvantages of a different kind at least as great as those attendant upon trial by jury.

(*b*) *Example* (iv). Consider the evidential-statement: 'The fact that if all light travels in straight lines (and the angle of elevation of the Sun is 30° and the height of this wall is 6′) then the depth of this shadow cast by this wall is 10′ 6″, and that the depth of this shadow cast by this wall is 10′ 6″ (and the angle of elevation of the Sun is . . . etc.), is evidence that all light travels in straight lines'. Here, the evidenced-statement is a non-empirical universal hypothesis called the principle of the rectilinear propagation of light. [Toulmin, Ph, 17 ff.] In this type of case, unlike Example (i), the circumstance that one single consequence of the hypothesis (and of its conjoined auxiliary hypotheses) is observed to be true, constitutes evidence, but worthless evidence, for the hypothesis; i.e. evidences it but does not in any degree probabilify it. We say that the observed depth of this single shadow coinciding (nearly enough) with the theoretically expected depth is evidence, but worthless evidence, for the principle. Compare the evidence of a single confirmatory instance for a universal generalization; we say that gfx is evidence, but worthless evidence, for I(fAg). I think that the reason why a single consequence cannot probabilify the hypothesis in Example (iv), whereas it can in Example (i), is that such a consequence can only probabilify an hypothesis in some degree if it is in some degree selective of that hypothesis. But in the sort of case illustrated by Example (iv), a single consequence logically cannot be selective of the hypothesis because the latter is non-empirical. For to determine the degree of selectivity of this consequence for that hypothesis, one would have to be able to generalize that a certain proportion less than half of cases of 'This shadow is 10′ 6″ deep (and the angle of elevation of the Sun is 30° . . . etc.)' being true are cases of 'All light travels in straight lines' being true. But to make this generalization one would have to establish that this proposition held true in observed cases. But this is impossible, since we cannot observe light travelling in straight lines; for we have previously noticed that 'light' in this context is a theoretical term that refers to an unobservable entity.

How then is such a theory probabilified or well-evidenced as opposed to merely evidenced? It is not made in any degree probable by its explaining the observed depth of this single shadow; but it is made in some degree probable by its explaining different observed depths of a number of shadows at different heights of wall and of other types of screen, and at different angles of elevation of the Sun and of other sources of light. But it is made much more probable by its explaining quite different kinds of optical phenomena; not merely a variety of observed facts about shadow-casting, but also, when it has been appropriately modified, a variety of observed facts about, say, refraction. Consider e.g. how Newton's law of gravitation (conjoined with additional premisses, including his laws of motion) entails and explains both Galileo's law of falling bodies and Kepler's laws of planetary motion. It is necessary to remember that what is meant by the 'facts' which theories of this sort explain is commonly, not individual descriptions of e.g. the depth of this shadow, but true generalizations, some of which are what I call inductive laws. But cases in which generalizations so explained by a theory are rightly claimed to be true are limiting cases of cases in which such generalizations are rightly claimed to be probable; namely, cases in which the evidence for them is judged to be conclusive. So that the degree of probability of a principle of this type is determined, first, by the variety and number, i.e. the number from different domains, of the empirical generalizations that it entails and explains; and second, by the degree of inductive probability of these.

When a non-empirical hypothesis thus explains a number of probable generalizations, an important consequence is that each of the latter indirectly evidences and probabilifies every other, so that each is probabilified in a higher degree than it is simply by the direct evidence for it. This relates to what Whewell calls 'the consilience of inductions'; more precisely, to that special case of it in which a number of probable generalizations are deduced from and explained by a non-empirical hypothesis. I shall have something to say later about the similar sort of case in which a number of probable generalizations are deduced from and explained by another generalization, so that each of the former indirectly evidences and probabilifies every other. [2.2; Kneale, 106 ff.; Whewell, 77 ff.] There are consequently two notable differences between the probabilification of a universal non-empirical hypothesis, e.g. Example (iv), and that of a universal empirical hypothesis, e.g. Example (ii). The selectivity criterion applies to neither, but for different reasons. It is physically inapplicable to the latter, but logically inapplicable to the former. Again, I suggested that the appropriate way to establish a proposition of the latter type was by inductive, not hypothetic, inference. But this is not true of propositions of the former type. Such a proposition can only be probabilified by an hypothetic probabilification-judgement, since it logically cannot be so by an inductive probabilification-judgement. For to generalize that 'All light travels in straight lines' one would have to establish that all observed light does so; but this is logically impossible, since 'light' here denotes an unobservable entity. Such a statement therefore logically cannot be a generalization, though one might be misled into thinking that it is by its superficial resemblance to genuine generalizations such as 'All migrating swallows travel along great circles'. Inductions logically must be about the unobserved, but logically cannot be about the unobservable. Hence, and this is the important point for our purposes, the criteria of the probability of the two types of hypothesis are different.

It is on this logical impossibility of inductive inferences about the unobservable that turn some classic objections by Hume and Reid to certain doctrines concerning our knowledge of the existence and attributes of God, of the external world and of other minds. I will review them briefly.

These authors represent the argument from design as the contention that we are to infer inductively that the world was probably made by God because it bears such-and-such marks. This judgement exemplifies the formula, $(3')$: $\gamma PF(gx, \gamma P(fAg) \cdot fx)$, where the judgement to be substituted upon the constituent probability-judgement-formula is 'It is probable that all worlds bearing such-and-such marks are made by gods'. But Hume and Reid point out that this probable generalization logically cannot be made. For to make it we must establish that $f'Ag$, that all observed worlds bearing such-and-such marks are made by gods. But this is impossible since, according to the patrons of this argument, gods and their operations are unobservable. To which Hume adds that it is impossible to establish this proposition for the further reason that, according to these theorists, there is but one God and one World. [Hume, E, 147 f.; *Dialogues concerning Natural Religion*; Reid, 402 ff.]

Hume's theory of the external world is a theory of the cause of our belief that common objects exist when unperceived. He claims that the cause is the 'constancy' and 'coherence' of certain of our sensations or 'impressions'. He adds that inferences from constant or coherent impressions to continuously existing objects are not inductions, or 'reasonings concerning causes and effects' as he calls them, though they may seem to be so on account of their superficial resemblance to inferences which really are inductive. For consider the constancy, i.e. the qualitative sameness, of the numerically different visual sensations that I have when I repeatedly look at my desk and look away from it. The fact that these sensations possess this property logically cannot be inductive evidence for the unperceived existence of the desk. It could only be this if we could experience both the constancy of our impressions and the continued existence of the desk when unobserved; but it is of course logically impossible to observe that the desk exists when it is unobserved. Hence, '. . . this inference arises from the understanding and from custom, in an indirect and oblique manner'. [Hume, T, 197]

Reid brings against the contention that we know others' states of mind by analogical, or better, inductive inference an objection similar to that which he and Hume bring against the argument from design. [Reid, 386 ff., 407 f.; J. L. Austin, 'Other Minds', *Aristotelian Society Supplementary Vol.* XX, 1946; C. D. Broad, *The Mind and its Place in Nature*, London, 1925, pp. 317 ff.; Hampshire; Thomson] Suppose that I judge that Tom probably feels angry because he is frowning. This judgement too exemplifies formula (3'); in this case the judgement to be substituted upon the constituent probability-judgement-formula is 'It is probable that all cases of Tom's frowning are cases of his feeling angry'. But Reid objects that this judgement cannot logically be made. For to make it we must establish that $f'Ag$, that all observed cases of Tom's frowning are cases of his feeling angry. But this is impossible because feelings are private and cannot be 'observed', or rather experienced, by anyone but the patient himself. 'When we see the sign, and see the thing signified always conjoined with it, experience may be the instructor and teach us how that sign is to be interpreted. But how shall experience instruct us when we see the sign only, when the thing signified is invisible? Now, this is the case here: the thoughts and passions of the mind, as well as the mind itself, are invisible, and therefore their connection with any sensible sign cannot be first discovered by experience; there must be some earlier source of this knowledge. Nature seems to have given to men a faculty or sense by which this connection is perceived.' [Reid, 387 f.] We see from the conclusion of this passage that Reid's positive account of the way in which we know that frowns signify anger, that tears mean grief and that winces evidence pain is, not by experience of their conjunctions, but by a special and original intellectual power.

It is not my affair to solve the problem of our knowledge of other minds, which is a major philosophical problem in its own right and which moreover involves questions of the meaning of mental concepts as well as of evidence, probability and truth. But it is closely enough connected with my present inquiry to justify and indeed require probing into it a little more deeply.

Obviously, one way in which we can know that Tom feels angry is because he tells us so. Is inductive probability or truth involved in this case? It is at least arguable that it is, on the ground that what we here do, or ought to do, is apply to Tom the true preponderant generalization 'Most men tell the truth about their inward states'.

Equally obviously, this is not the only way in which we can know this fact. According to the commonest presentation of the argument from analogy, we know it by inductive inference in the following way. I observe a conjunction between my frowning and my feeling angry, make a more or less probable generalization accordingly, and apply it to the case of Tom's frowning. Reid's objection naturally does not touch this thesis, since it is not denied that my feeling angry can be 'observed' by me. There is an important disparity in this regard between the analogical argument about other minds and the argument from design about God: Tom's anger is not unobservable by any man, whereas God's skill is. However, there are other objections which do touch this thesis. The most familiar is on the point of fact; in reality I do not observe a conjunction between my frowns and feelings of anger, or tears and feelings of sadness, since I do not use a looking-glass that much.

But there seems to me to be another and more fundamental objection. Even if I do observe a conjunction between my frowns and feelings of anger, the only generalization that I can make from this evidence with any degree of probability is 'All (or Most) cases of my frowning are probably cases of my feeling angry'. But this judgement cannot be applied to Tom's frowning. Its conjunction with the additional premiss 'This is a case of Tom's frowning' yields no conclusion. It may be replied that the judgement that we actually make is 'All (or Most) cases of anyone's frowning are probably cases of his feeling angry', and that the case of Tom's frowning can of course be subsumed under this. But I counterobject that, if I have observed a conjunction only between my frowns and my feelings of anger, I cannot with any degree of probability make this generalization about anyone's frowns and anger, since the evidence for it is insufficiently varied. The main objection to the stock version of the argument from analogy lies precisely in the weakness of the alleged 'analogy'. Cases of Tom's frowning are a different thing from cases of my frowning, so that a case of the former cannot properly be subsumed under a probability-judgement about the latter. For how do I know that it is not my individual peculiarity to feel angry when I frown? Perhaps because others have *told* me that they were feeling angry when I observed that they were frowning; and perhaps it is in some such way as this that we get a probable generalization of the requisite scope to apply to Tom's case, namely, 'All (or Most) cases of anyone's frowning . . . etc.'. But this goes beyond the simple account offered in the stock version of the argument from analogy, since it introduces into the account of how we know, the testimonial evidence of others' statements and the circumstantial evidence of their behaviour in addition to the simply circumstantial evidence of just my feelings and my behaviour. I discuss the relation between induction and analogy below. [4.1] Notice further that such 'natural signs or expressions' as frowns, tears and winces are not the only sort of circumstantial evidence from which we judge of others' states of mind or heart. As Thomson reminds us, we judge that Tom is probably in pain not merely from what he is doing, namely wincing, but also from what is being done to him, namely having a tooth drilled.

Notwithstanding the preceding objections, I am satisfied that the only ways in which we know others' inward states are by inductive inference from circumstantial and/or testimonial evidence, and perhaps sometimes by hypothetic inference too. The simplest way to show this is by an eliminative argument. For what are the alternative solutions? The most radical is the behaviourist solution; it may be said that people have no inner lives, so that the question how we know about other people's inner lives does not arise. But this thesis cannot be taken seriously. Scarcely less radical and ridiculous is the sceptical solution; we can never know what is going on in another's mind. In fact, we of course sometimes, but not always, know more or less, but not perfectly, well what Tom is feeling. The two remaining solutions allege the existence of special mental powers, itself always a suspect move in philosophical argument. It may be contended that we 'see' what is going on in Tom's mind by 'extraspection'. But certainly I, and apparently the vast majority of other people, possess no such faculty. Or finally there is Reid's solution, already noticed: we know that Tom's frowning is evidence of his anger, not from past experience, but from 'the constitution of our nature'; tears and winces have for us 'an unacquired meaning', as Broad puts it. This account is at least specious; but I do not think it really holds water. It runs counter to a point on which Hume repeatedly insists, surely with justice, that the only way in which we can learn that the presence of an A is inductive evidence for the presence of a B is from experience, from observation of the constant or 'frequent' (i.e. preponderant) conjunction of Bs with As. Moreover, the account fits with any colour of plausibility only such 'natural signs' as frowns and tears. Will it be contended that the whirr of a dentist's drill has for us the 'unacquired meaning' of pain?

Of course, to set down thus baldly this general conclusion about how we know others' inward states is by no means to solve the problem of other minds. For doing this would consist precisely, I think, in describing in detail just how, i.e. by what inductive and/or hypothetic inferences from what evidence and making use of what previous inductive and/or hypothetic inferences from what evidence, we reach these conclusions. This is not the place to undertake that task. I will only observe in conclusion that, as I hinted above, the full account is bound to be much more complicated and subtle than that offered in the stock version of the analogical argument.

Examination of Example (iv) has shown that the degree of probability of at least one type of hypothesis is determined by the variety and number of its logical consequences that are verified, observed to correspond with the facts. I think that some philosophers confuse 'variety and number of facts explained by an hypothesis' with 'variety and number of confirmatory instances of a generalization', and that this confusion of two apparently similar but really different criteria leads them to misassimilate hypothetic to inductive inference or conversely.

Peirce e.g. takes the former course and equates hypothetic (or 'abductory' or 'retroductive') *inference* with hypothetic (or 'abductory' or 'retroductive') *induction*; cp. Russell on 'hypothetical induction'. [Peirce, 152 f., 195 ff.; Russell, H, 435] The idea is this. As in plain inductive probabilification-judgements we establish the generalization, say, that all ravens are probably black by observing a variety and number of ravens and finding them all to be black, so in hypothetic inductive probabilification-judgements we establish the hypothesis, say, that all light probably travels in straight lines by observing a variety and number of its logical consequences and finding them all to be true. The application of the term 'inductive' to both types of judgement is held to be justified by the fact that the 'sampling of consequences' of an hypothesis is essentially similar to the sampling of instances of a generalization. The following passage by Williams on the probabilification of singular hypotheses, e.g. that Tom did it, expresses the thought clearly enough: 'This kind of inference . . . may be construed as carried by the principles that if and only if all the consequents of an hypothesis are true, the hypothesis is true, while if all its tested consequents have been proved true, then probably all its consequents are true, and so accordingly is the hypothesis. Hypothesis thus understood as a universal generalization concerning all the properties which belong to a given individual is logically the counterpart of ordinary induction, which is a universal generalization concerning all the individuals which have a certain property.' [Williams, G, 112 f.; cp. Example (i), above] Notice that this account presupposes another questionable doctrine of Peirce's, that the meaning of an hypothesis 'is' the conjunction of all its observable consequences. [W. B. Gallie,

Peirce and Pragmatism, London, 1952, pp. 165 ff.] Apelt too distinguishes the 'hypothetical' from the 'categorical form of induction', and gives the following formula for the former: 'If all the effects [consequences] of a cause [hypothesis] occur [are true], the latter itself occurs [is true]; but if even one of the former does not occur [is false], the latter too does not occur [is false]'. [Apelt, 17, 88, 103, 189 f.]

Conversely, some philosophers take the latter course and contend that inductive inference is 'really' hypothetic inference. We have already noticed this point when commenting on the 'no induction' thesis advanced by Whewell and other hypothetists. [1.1] The idea, it will be remembered, is this. A (primitive) induction is usually typified as the conclusion of an inference from $f'Ag$, or more specifically from the conjunction $gfx . gfy . gfz \ldots$ etc., to fAg, and its degree of probability is said to depend on the variety and number of these observed confirmatory instances of it. But this, the hypothetists argue, is wrong. What we really do in such a case, they say, is form the hypothesis that fAg, deduce from it the consequence that $f'Ag$, or more specifically the conjunction $gfx . gfy . gfz \ldots$ etc., and see whether these consequences fit the facts. And its degree of probability depends on the variety and number of these true consequences of it. I have already said [1.1] that I disagree with this proposed reduction of inductive inference and probabilification to hypothetic inference and probabilification, and have given some reasons for doing so. Additional reasons for rejecting it are these.

The evidence for primitive inductions or generalizations is always instantial evidence, whereas the evidence for hypotheses is always consequential evidence. In the example just considered it so happens that the instantial evidence for the generalization fAg and the consequential evidence for the corresponding hypothesis fAg are the same, namely, the observation-statement $gfx . gfy . gfz \ldots$ etc. But this is by no means generally true; on the contrary. The facts that Tom's fingerprints are on the knife and that the depth of this shadow is so-and-so are consequential but not instantial evidence for the respective hypotheses that Tom did it and that light travels in straight lines. 'This is a raven and black' is (rightly called) an 'instance' or 'case' of 'All ravens are black', but 'Tom's fingerprints are on this knife' is not (rightly called) an 'instance' or 'case' of 'Tom stabbed Bill with this knife'.

There is another and connected respect in which what is true of the preceding example is not true generally. The reason why, in that example, the instantial evidence for the generalization happens to be the same as the consequential evidence for the corresponding hypothesis is that $f'Ag$ is a logical consequence of fAg. But this again is not generally true. For consider proportional generalizations, e.g. a statement substituted upon the evidenced-statement-formula of the formula, (10): $E(fMg, f'Mg)$. Here, $f'Mg$ is instantial evidence for the generalization fMg, but it logically cannot be consequential evidence for the corresponding hypothesis fMg because $f'Mg$ is not a logical consequence of, is not entailed by, fMg. The hypothetist's proposed reduction of inductive inferences and probabilification-judgements to hypothetic inferences and probabilification-judgements cannot therefore be applied to inductions generally. For whereas generalizations are probabilified when there is good instantial evidence for them, hypotheses are probabilified when there is good consequential evidence for them; and instantial evidence is generally different from consequential evidence.

I shall revert to this topic later. [5.2] At present, I simply record my opinion that both proposed reductions are unacceptable. Inductive and hypothetic inference are independent and mutually irreducible modes of ampliative or synthetic inference; and inductive and hypothetic probability have different descriptive meanings, since a proposition which has hypothetic probability is made probable in a fundamentally different way from that in which a proposition which has inductive probability is made probable.

I suspect that what underlie both types of attempted reduction are certain dogmas about the possible kinds of reasoning. It seems likely that the ground for representing hypothetic inference as a sort of inductive inference, namely abductory induction or induction of logical consequences, is the influential but false dogma that all reasoning is either deductive or inductive. For if there is no third alternative, and hypothetic inference is not deductive inference, then it must 'really' be inductive inference. The dogma underlying the converse reduction is more difficult to detect. I offer the following diagnosis. Hypothetists tend to direct their attention to only one aspect of hypothetic inference, namely, the deductive working out of the hypothesis. In the formula $E(p, (p \supset q) . q)$, they are interested only in the constituent

HYPOTHETIC PROBABILITY

formula $p \supset q$; so that they slide insensibly into the view that there is nothing to hypothetic inference but deductive inference. Hence, in reducing inductive to hypothetic inference they reckon in effect to be reducing it to deductive inference. And I imagine that their reason for setting themselves this task is another influential but false dogma, namely, that all reasoning is deductive reasoning, about which I shall have more to say later. [6.1]

My suggestion that hypothetists see nothing in hypothetic inference but deductive inference is borne out by the following considerations. They tend to say such things as: 'All inductive arguments in the last resort reduce themselves to the following form: "If this is true, that is true: now that is true, therefore this is true." This argument is, of course, formally fallacious.' [B. Russell, *The Scientific Outlook*, London, 1931, p. 77] There are two points to notice in this passage. The thesis that inductive arguments are reducible to hypothetic arguments is advanced very explicitly. But the immediately relevant point is that hypothetic inference is represented as fallacious deductive inference. Similarly, Broad states that 'the hypothetical method . . . commits the formal fallacy of asserting the consequent in a hypothetical syllogism'. [Broad, R, I, 389 ff.] But this violent paradox is unjustified. These authors confuse inferences in accordance with the formula $E(p, (p \supset q) . q)$ with inferences in accordance with the formula $((p \supset q) . q) \supset p$. Hypothetic inferences are actually of course of the former type; but those who represent them as being of the latter type show very clearly that they see them, not as what they really are, an independent mode of synthetic inference, but as a mode of invalid or pseudo-deduction.

In the same place, Broad makes a charge against inductive inference similar to that which he levels against hypothetic inference. Incidentally, he too represents ordinary inductive inference and hypothetic inference as two kinds of inductive inference. He argues that the type of the former is $f'Ag \therefore fAg$; but that since we generally know or believe that we have not observed all f, it may be represented as $fIg \therefore fAg$, which of course commits an illicit process of f. I have the following remarks to offer on this argument. It is misleading to represent the type of generalization as $fIg \therefore fAg$. For what we do in generalization is assert exactly the same thing about f or a as we observe to be true of f' or a'; but if we change the quantity of our assertion from I to A this rule is

69

broken. To put the same point another way: to every generalization there logically must be a corresponding description, and to every description there is a corresponding possible generalization; indeed, that which is generalized is precisely a description, e.g. predicative, associative, functional or correlative.

Again, what is to be said on this view of proportional, e.g. preponderant, as opposed to universal generalizations? Presumably they too must be represented as of the pattern $fIg \therefore fMg$. But to give the inference-patterns of universal and preponderant generalizations respectively as $fIg \therefore fAg$ and $fIg \therefore fMg$ is to leave the reader quite in the dark as to why, when the respective premisses are the same in quantity, the respective conclusions should nevertheless differ in quantity. Moreover, and more immediately relevant to the present discussion, it seems to me also wrong to say that the type of primitive inductive inference is $f'Ag \therefore fAg$, or that it typically proceeds in accordance with the principle-formula $f'Ag \supset fAg$. Rather, I have already suggested that 'a generalization' is to be typified as a statement substituted on the evidenced-statement-formula in an inference drawn in accordance with the principle-formula $E(fAg, f'Ag)$. [1.1, beginning]

This objection to Broad's account of primitive inductive inference corresponds to my preceding objection to Russell's account of hypothetic inference. The root of the matter is, I believe, this. We are prone to think that the only sort of principles in accordance with which inferences are drawn is 'If q then p', and to overlook the fact that they are also drawn in accordance with the principle 'If q, that is evidence that p'. Yet this way of drawing the distinction is unsatisfactory because 'if . . . then' sometimes, but not of course always, means precisely 'if . . . that is evidence that'. 'If Paul has a temperature and a dry cough he has measles' means 'If Paul has a temperature etc. that is evidence that he has measles'. We must say rather that the root error is taking it for granted that the only sort of principles in accordance with which inferences are drawn is 'If q then p' in that use of 'if . . . then' in which it expresses the fact that the protasis entails the apodosis. But this is only another way of saying that we are all liable to take for granted the truth of the false dogma just exposed, that all reasoning is deductive reasoning, to commit what may be called the deductivist fallacy. But in truth the propositional relation of evidencing or signification is epistemologically at least as important as the propositional relation of entailment; perhaps indeed more so, since there is some truth in the old and rather unfortunately expressed charge that explicative or analytic reasonings tell us nothing that we do not know already, whereas ampliative or synthetic reasonings do.

Finally on this topic, I suspect that the deductivist fallacy lies at the bottom of an important error about 'probable reasoning (or inference)', an expression which I have already discussed in connexion with the question, What is (judged) probable? One thing that is meant by 'a probable inference' is 'an inference the conclusion of which is a probability-judgement'. Now we have seen that Jevons, following Laplace, contends that inductive reasoning is 'probable deductive reasoning'; or strictly, I think, that probable inductive reasoning is probable deductive reasoning. [1.1] By 'probable deductive reasoning' he means making casual derivative probabilification-judgements. The general nature of such judgements may be illustrated by the formula: $1\mathrm{PF}(fx \lor gx, 1/2\mathrm{P}(fx)$. $1/2\mathrm{P}(gx))$, where $\lor$ is to be read 'or' and where being f and being g are mutually exclusive as well as jointly exhaustive equally probable alternatives. An exemplification of this formula is: 'The fact that it is probable in the degree $1/2$ that this penny will fall heads upwards and that it is probable in the degree $1/2$ that it will fall tails upwards, makes it probable in the degree 1 that it will fall either heads upwards or tails upwards'. This result is obtained simply by applying to this case the disjunctive theorem of the Calculus of Probabilities. I suggest that the following is the underlying reason for what Kneale calls such 'attempts to justify induction within the theory of chances'. [Kneale, 211] Making inductive probabilification-judgements may be called 'probable reasoning' in the sense explained. But I suspect that Jevons and other philosophers of like mind take it for granted that all probable reasoning is probable deductive reasoning as a consequence of taking for granted the wider fallacious dogma that all reasoning is deductive reasoning; and that this is what, or one of the things that, leads them to represent probable inductive reasonings as probable deductive reasoning.

(c) We have next to examine the probability of proportional or statistical hypotheses. [Braithwaite, 115 ff.] *Example* (v). Let us consider first the probabilification of empirical proportional hypotheses, say '$1/2$ BU are H', exemplifying the formula $f1/2g$.

This example should be compared with Example (ii), where we considered the probabilification of the corresponding universal hypothesis 'All BU are H', exemplifying the formula fAg. Notice first a vital difference in the consequences of the two hypotheses. From fAg we can immediately deduce that $f'Ag$, but from $f\text{I}/2g$ we cannot deduce that $f'\text{I}/2g$. For, though $fAg . \sim(f'Ag)$ is logically impossible, $f\text{I}/2g . \sim(f'\text{I}/2g)$ is not. However, we can deduce from $f\text{I}/2g$ that is casually probable in a therefore numerical degree that approximately $f'\text{I}/2g$, provided that we know that f' are numerous, i.e. that our sample is large, and that every possible sample of the size of this one that we have selected had an equal chance of being selected, i.e. that our sample is random. This last provision is the condition C_1, previously introduced in connexion with formula (6'). Again, whereas the deductive elaboration of the hypothesis fAg involves no mathematics, that of the hypothesis $f\text{I}/2g$ does. This is a feature that Example (v) shares with Example (iv). As in the latter one sort of mathematics, namely Trigonometry, is used to work out what follows respecting the depth of this shadow cast by this wall from the hypothesis that light travels in straight lines and the facts that the angle of elevation of the Sun is 30° and the height of this wall is 6'; so in the former another sort of mathematics, namely Combinatorial Analysis, is used to work out what follows respecting the degree of probability that approximately $f'\text{I}/2g$ from the hypothesis that $f\text{I}/2g$ and the facts that f' are numerous and C_1 is satisfied.

The crucial question then is, Given that it is the case that $f'\text{I}/2g$, what may be concluded concerning the probability of the hypothesis $f\text{I}/2g$? We have already seen that two different answers are returned to this question: in 5.1 I shall expound and criticize a third account which bears some resemblance to these two, yet which actually differs essentially from them. According to the older school of thought, we use the principle of inverse probability to compute the degree of inverse casual probability of the hypothesis. But there is a practical objection to this line of procedure that is generally decisive, namely, that to apply the principle we must have previous knowledge of the antecedent probabilities of the different possible compositions of the population, whereas we usually do not possess this knowledge. The modern school of thought in effect simply equates the degree in which $f'1/2g$ etc. makes it probable that $f1/2g$ with the degree in which $f1/2g$ etc. would make it probable that approximately $f'1/2g$, i.e. uses a direct instead of an inverse casual probability. This is also the answer given by Williams. It should be noticed that the two schools of thought return different answers to our question, since the value of the inverse probability generally differs from that of the direct probability. Hence an objection which, despite or because of its obviousness, seems to have been overlooked; namely, that at least one of these schools of thought must be wrong. The objection to the second line of procedure, to judging of the probability of the hypothesis in the manner sketched by Williams, seems to me to be again a practical one. For the direct probability too can only be computed if the sample is large and random or fair; but in practice we usually do not know that the latter condition, C_1, is certainly, as opposed to probably, satisfied. Williams burkes the practical problem involved here because he incorrectly holds that 'if the sample is not known to be unfair . . . it is fair'. [Williams, G, 141] This objection evidently applies also to the inverse probability solution, since it too requires that C_1 be satisfied.

My general conclusion is then this. Since there are normally practical objections to making an hypothetic probabilification-judgement about e.g. '1/2 BU are H' by either the inverse or the direct probability procedure, our best course is generally to establish such proportional propositions by inductive and not by hypothetic inference. [Kneale, 216 f.] This conclusion should be compared with that reached about Example (ii), where I concluded for a different reason that it is also impracticable to make an hypothetic probabilification-judgement about e.g. 'All BU are H', and that the appropriate way to establish such universal propositions too is by inductive and not by hypothetic inference; also with the opposed conclusion reached about Example (vi), below. These points are developed and clarified later. The objection to inverse or direct probabilification-judgements on the score of the practical difficulty of satisfying C_1, and the connected point about the preferability of inductive probabilification-judgements where these can be made, is considered in 4.1, end. And the objection to Williams' theory on the score of the unacceptability of his criterion of the randomness of a sample is elaborated in 4.2.

(d) *Example* (vi). I shall consider finally the probabilification of the non-empirical proportional hypothesis: '51% of cases of a gamete (sperm) fusing with another gamete (ovum) are cases of a Y gamete (i.e. a gamete carrying a Y sex-chromosome) fusing with an X gamete (i.e. a gamete carrying an X sex-chromosome)'. Like Example (iv), this is a non-empirical hypothesis. For it involves the concept of chromosomes carrying sex-determining genes; and genes, like light in the context of Example (iv), are unobservable. This fact is apt to be obscured by talk about their 'existence', and in particular by talk about their 'location along' the chromosomes; but these are familiar obstacles to the comprehension of non-empirical hypotheses. The latter sort of locution is especially significant. For I think that it is the attribution to theoretical entities of properties that belong to physical objects like tables, such as being in a certain spatial relation to another physical object, which makes us want to say that they exist in the same sense of 'exist' as do tables and the like.

This hypothesis is formulated in the language of abstract theory; it forms part of the explanation of the inheritance of sex by the chromosome theory. But it may also be expressed in everyday language as '51% of births are male'. For in the chromosome theory a male birth is 'interpreted' as the result of the fusion of a Y gamete with an X gamete, and it is because the theoretical statement is thus 'translatable' into physical object language that it is connected with observable fact. As is familiar, the theory similarly interprets a female birth as the result of the fusion of an X gamete with an X gamete. It is also supposed that X and Y sperms are produced on meiosis in equal numbers, but that the proportion of cases of Y gametes fusing with X gametes is slightly greater than that of X gametes fusing with X gametes on account of the greater motility of the Y gametes; hence the ratio 51% as opposed to 50%. The hypothesis so expressed in ordinary language is usually represented by the model of an urn containing infinitely many balls (corresponding to births) of colour-composition 51% black (corresponding to male) and 49% white (corresponding to female), and the observation of the sex-ratio in a set of actual births is assimilated to the drawing of a sample of balls from the urn and noting its colour-composition.

How then is an hypothesis of this type probabilified? It can be deductively elaborated in the same way as Example (v); i.e. it is deducible that it is (casually) probable that approximately 51% of an observed sample of births will be male provided that it is large and random. Suppose then that it is the case that 51% of a large and random sample of observed births are male; what follows respecting the probability of the hypothesis? It may be said that, on this supposition, we can attribute to the hypothesis a degree of direct casual probability using the type of probabilification-judgement advocated by Williams. I think, however, that the hypothesis is rather probabilified in the following manner.

We consider the evidence, not of one, but of a number of large random samples. If the hypothesis is true and the samples are large and random, we can deduce and represent graphically what the statisticians call the theoretical sampling distribution of the ratio. I.e., the possible samples of the size of the ones we have observed can be arranged in a frequency distribution. This will show, to put it crudely, that the majority of the possible samples will be approximately 51% male, that a fairly small proportion of them will be approximately 25% male, and that a very, very small proportion of them will be approximately all male . . . etc. I.e., the theoretical distribution will take the form of a bell-shaped curve, the apex of which represents the number of possible samples of composition about 51% male. (Incidentally, it is this fact that the majority of the possible samples are approximately 51% male which constitutes the descriptive meaning of the judgement that it is (casually) probable that any large random sample has approximately the same composition as its population.) If we now take a number of actual large random samples and note their compositions, we can arrange these too in a frequency distribution, and see how closely this actual sampling distribution of the ratio fits to the theoretical distribution thereof. Then, the hypothesis is judged to be more probable, first, according as the fit of the actual to the theoretical distribution is closer.

But I believe that there is also a second determinant, namely, the variety of the observed samples. We consider the evidence of the observed sex-ratio not only, say, in Liverpool between 1850 and 1860, but also that in, say, some rural district of Japan between 1920 and 1930, etc. We shall re-encounter this conception of a symmetrical distribution of samples or subsamples later in discussing the notion of 'stability'. [2.1] Hence, the probabilification of Example (vi) resembles that of Example (iv) in that mathematics is used in the deductive elaboration of the hypothesis, and resembles that of Example (v) in that the sort of mathematics employed is Combinatorial Analysis. It also resembles that of Example (iv) in that one test of the probability of the hypothesis is the variety of the facts it explains, the facts here taking the special form of observed ratios in samples. Finally, Example (vi) involves the same practical difficulty about satisfying the condition that the samples be random as we noticed in discussing Example (v). But we cannot evade the difficulty in the former case, as we can in the latter, by employing inductive as opposed to hypothetic inference. For Example (vi), like Example (iv), logically cannot be established by inductive inference since it is a non-empirical proposition; it can only be established by hypothetic inference. Consequently, we have to surmount as best we can the practical difficulty of ensuring that our samples from the 'hypothetical infinite population' of births are probably random. But this probability too varies in degree; so that the third determinant of the degree of probability of an hypothesis of this type is the degree of inductive probability of the proposition that the samples are random, otherwise the degree of reliability of the method of random sampling employed. The intimate connexion between the inductive probability of propositions and the reliability of methods will be explained later. [4.1; Yule, 333, 346]

I shall conclude this excursion into hypothetic probability with a few necessary additional elucidations. It is obviously implicit in all this discussion that I take the expression 'the probability of an hypothesis' to have a meaning: there would be no sense in trying to explain it otherwise. However, some think differently. Toulmin e.g. writes: '. . . theories are not spoken of in practice as . . . probable, nor is it clear what one could be expected to understand by the statement, "The probability of the kinetic theory of gases is 17/18". . . .' [Toulmin, Ph, 112] And Popper asserts that there is really no such thing as 'degree of probability of an hypothesis', only 'degree (or value) of confirmation of an hypothesis'; belief to the contrary is due, he suggests, to confusing the genuine notion of 'an hypothesis of probability' (*Wahrscheinlichkeitshypothese*: i.e. a proportional hypothesis) with the spurious one of 'probability of an hypothesis' (*Hypothesenwahrscheinlichkeit*: i.e. hypothetic probability). [Popper, 186, 194; Wisdom, 203 f.] But I consider it beyond doubt that both plain men and specialists, such as physicists and historians, do call suppositions of all the types that I have reviewed 'probable'; and most philosophers who have considered the question are of the same opinion. [Braithwaite, 120; Kneale, 2, 150; Nagel, 62 ff.]

To be sure, Toulmin is right in saying that the judgement 'The probability of the kinetic theory of gases is 17/18' makes no sense. For this theory is a non-empirical proportional hypothesis like Example (vi). And I have just argued that the degree of probability of the latter depends on the degree of closeness of fit of its consequences to the observed facts, the variety of the latter and the degree of probability that the samples are random; there is consequently no question of the degree of probability of this type of hypothesis being measurable in the strong sense. But this is not to say that it makes no sense to make non-numerical probability-judgements about such hypotheses, to call them very, fairly, etc., probable. One might as well argue that inductions are not spoken of as probable because it makes no sense to say 'The probability (of the generalization) that all BU are H is 17/18'. It seems to me to be no more open to doubt that hypotheses are called probable than that inductions are. Nor, by the way, is it true that there logically cannot be any numerical hypothetic probabilification-judgements. For there do exist cases, namely, those in which the conditions approximate to those obtaining in games of chance, where the requisite conditions for making inverse or direct casual, and therefore numerical, probabilification-judgements about hypotheses are known to be satisfied; the objection to these methods of inference is the practical one that in most investigations these conditions are not known to be satisfied. [Kneale, 214 ff.; Wright, T, 290 ff.] This puts an important difference between casual and hypothetic probability on the one hand and inductive probability on the other, for degrees of inductive probability logically cannot be measured in the strict sense at all.

Not only does the descriptive, but not the evaluative, meaning of hypothetic probability differ from that of casual and inductive probability, but it is itself equivocal, since different types of hypothesis are made probable in different ways. E.g., the selectivity criterion, C_4, is applicable to Example (i), an empirical singular hypothesis, but is practically inapplicable to Example (ii), an empirical universal hypothesis, and logically inapplicable to

Examples (iv) and (vi), which are non-empirical hypotheses. And the probabilification of proportional hypotheses (Examples (v) and (vi)) involves Combinatorial Analysis, whereas the probabilification of universal hypotheses (Examples (ii) and (iv)) does not. And so on. This holds true of casual and inductive probability-judgements as well; for the probabilified-proposition of a casual or inductive derivative probabilification-judgement is made probable in a different way from that in which the probabilified-proposition of a casual or inductive primitive probabilification-judgement is made probable.

I believe that the two mutually associable divisions of hypotheses into empirical and non-empirical on the one hand and into universal and proportional on the other, are the most important ones for explaining the meaning of 'hypothetic probability'; and that other familiar distinctions are subordinate to these. Such are the distinction between general and singular hypotheses, of which the former are primarily of interest to the scientist and the latter to the historian and detective (cp. Examples (i) and (ii)); and the distinction between descriptive and existential hypotheses, the latter of which also are primarily of interest to historians and 'historical' scientists, such as geologists and evolutionary biologists.

Finally, the foregoing remarks are intended as an outline account of the meaning of the probability of hypotheses, not of their goodness in general or overall acceptability; for these two notions must be distinguished. On my account, the evaluative meaning of 'This hypothesis is (very, etc.) probable' is 'This hypothesis is (very, etc.) well-evidenced and so (very, etc.) good *qua* assertion'. But the notions of hypothetic goodness and preferability in general are wider than those of hypothetic probability and greater probability, as can be seen from a consideration of some of the criteria of the goodness of an hypothesis and of the betterness of one of a number of rival hypotheses.

To begin with, being probable is itself a necessary but not a sufficient condition of an hypothesis being good in general. An hypothesis cannot be a good one unless it is well-evidenced; but it may be well-evidenced and yet not a good one. Hence, the concepts of probability and goodness in general are not equivalent.

Many hold that another necessary condition of hypothetic

goodness is simplicity. This is not the place to inquire into the meaning of 'simplicity' as attributed to hypotheses, but Kneale's suggestion that an hypothesis is simpler accordingly as it contains a smaller number of independent concepts seems acceptable. He distinguishes simplicity in this sense from simplicity as attributed to functional generalizations, and plausibly suggests that a functional generalization is simpler accordingly as it contains fewer parameters. Some hold that the degree of simplicity of generalizations is a test of their degree of probability, and I shall examine this suggestion in due course. [4.1; Kneale, 229, 246 ff.] The point that I want to make now is just this. When it is said of two rival hypotheses which are equal in all other respects including their degree of probabilification, that the simpler is the better, the notion of betterness involved is plainly different from the notion of greater probability. For, by the supposition, the two hypotheses are alike in degree of probability but nevertheless different in degree of goodness. And again, whereas on my account the tests of degree of probability always relate to evidence, the test of degree of goodness here proposed, namely simplicity, has nothing to do with evidence.

A test of preferability for proportional hypotheses to which Braithwaite devotes a good deal of attention is greater advantageousness as a basis for action. He claims that one count on which this statistical hypothesis is judged better than that one is the fact that it is more advantageous to act on this one than to act on that one. It is not relevant to examine this claim now; what is relevant is simply to note that, here again, this 'betterness' is plainly different from 'greater probability', since the proposed test of the former, namely, greater advantageousness as a basis for action, has nothing to do with evidence. Braithwaite does not deny that greater probability is one ground for preferring one of a number of (proportional) hypotheses; his claim is rather that this criterion of betterness needs to be supplemented by that of greater advantageousness as a basis for action. Hence, he too implicitly distinguishes betterness from greater probability. [Braithwaite, 196 ff., 253] This thesis of his should not be confused, incidentally, with Kneale's account of the evaluative meaning of 'probable', discussed previously, according to which the evaluative meaning of 'p is probable' is 'p is good as a basis for action'.

1.2.5 *The Plan of the Rest of the Book*

It is now possible to define precisely the residual problem before us and to explain the plan of the rest of the book. The philosophical problem of probability is to explain the meaning of 'probable'. We have seen that this is partly evaluative and partly descriptive, the former being univocal but secondary and the latter being primary but equivocal. I have nothing more to say about the former. As to the latter, I have distinguished inductive from casual and hypothetic probability, and I have argued that these distinctions are precisely ones of descriptive and not of evaluative meaning. What remains, therefore, is to explain the descriptive meaning of 'inductive probability'. And this amounts to analysing the different sorts of inductive probabilification-judgement; for discriminating and analysing the different types of inductive probabilification-judgements, and explaining the descriptive meaning of 'inductive probability', are alternative descriptions of the same activity.

The number of actual and possible inductive probabilification-judgements is indefinitely large, and this may seem to pose at the outset an insuperable objection to carrying out this programme. However, the problem can be reduced to manageable proportions, first, by considering probabilification-judgement-formulas rather than probabilification-judgements; second, by classifying the formulas into a small number of types; and third, by selecting from among these a still smaller number of types as paradigms.

As to the first point: by considering formulas rather than judgements it is possible to ignore the indefinitely numerous actual and possible variations of subject-matter or content that are or can be found in judgements. It is for this reason that I have introduced formulas—an explanation that the reader may well feel to be overdue. The possibility of formalizing inductive reasoning is itself a question of some interest, and will be noticed accordingly in 6.2 in connexion with the question, Can there be an Inductive Logic?

As to the second point: it seems to me that the main types of formula can be defined by two fundamental and mutually associable distinctions introduced in 1.1.; namely, that between attribute-formulas and variable-formulas on the one hand, and that between primitive and derivative formulas on the other.

As to the third point: I shall discuss of attribute-formulas only subject-predicate ones and of variable-formulas only functional ones. We have seen that in fact there are many other subtypes, e.g. associative attribute-formulas and correlative variable-formulas; indeed, that there are as many possible generalizations about a class of things as there are descriptions of the observed members of that class. But I think that subject-predicate formulas and functional formulas may be taken respectively as paradigms of attribute-formulas and variable-formulas generally, since what is true of their probabilification is true of the probabilification of the other subtypes. And since I have argued that attribute-inductions and variable-inductions are jointly exhaustive of inductions, it follows that in analysing subject-predicate and functional formulas I shall in effect be explaining the descriptive meaning of inductive probability generally.

I shall consider in 2.1 and 3.1 the following primitive formulas: $(2')$ universal subject-predicate primitive, $\gamma\mathrm{PF}(fAg, f'Ag \cdot \gamma C_2)$; $(10')$ non-numerical proportional subject-predicate primitive, $\gamma\mathrm{PF}(fMg, f'Mg \cdot \gamma C_2 \cdot \gamma C_6)$; $(11')$ numerical proportional subject-predicate primitive $\gamma\mathrm{PF}(fm/ng, f'm/ng \cdot \gamma C_2 \cdot \gamma C_6)$; and $(7')$ functional primitive, $\gamma\mathrm{PF}((Aa)(Ab)b=a, (Aa')(Ab')b'=a \cdot \gamma C_2 \cdot \gamma C_3)$. Probabilification varies in degree, so that what is required is to formulate the rules governing its variations. In the case of primitive formulas, which are the more important ones, this depends on variations in degree of the conditions C_2 and C_3; the problem therefore is to identify these conditions. There is an important difference in this respect between conditions C_2, C_3 and C_4, which determine the degree in which the evidence probabilifies the conclusion, and conditions C_1, C_5 and C_6, which are preconditions of the evidence probabilifying the conclusion at all. C_3 and C_6, which have not been mentioned before, will naturally be explained in the proper places. Since I am not primarily interested in hypothetic probability, I have thought it not worth while to assign numbers to conditions of degree of hypothetic probability other than C_4, i.e. to the conditions applying to Examples (ii) to (vi) inclusive, above.

I shall consider in 2.2 and 3.2. the derivative formulas: $(3')$ singular subject-predicate derivative, $\gamma\mathrm{PF}(gx, \gamma\mathrm{P}(fAg) \cdot fx)$; and $(9')$ functional derivative, $\gamma\mathrm{PF}(b_n, \gamma\mathrm{P}((Aa)(Ab)b=a) \cdot a_n)$. A distinction is drawn between deductive and non-deductive derivative formulas. Rules governing the variation of degree of probabilification in the former class are rules of probable-deduction. In this connexion, it is necessary to discuss the heterogeneous (casual and inductive) formulas: $(5')$, $\delta PF(gx, \alpha P(fMg) . fx . C_1)$; and the corresponding numerical one, $(16')$, $\gamma PF(m/nP(gx), \gamma P(fm/ng) . fx . C_1)$. The homogeneous casual formulas: $(6')$, $\gamma PF(gx, fMg . fx . C_1)$; and the corresponding numerical one, $m/nPF(gx, fm/ng . fx . C_1)$, are also discussed.

This constructive account is followed in 4 by a critical one, in which I comment on what seem to me the most important rival suggestions about what makes inductions probable.

In 5.2, the constructive account is developed further, and inductive probabilification is shown to proceed by elimination; not however in the sense understood in the traditional theories of induction by elimination, some account of which is given in 5.1.

Finally, 6 is devoted to discussion of the notions of inductive reasoning and Inductive Logic, which raise questions of a more general philosophical interest; in the course of the discussion I criticize two further accounts of the meaning of (inductive) probability.

Note.—To enable the reader to refresh his memory of the meaning of the formulas and nomenclature, the main probabilification-judgement-formulas discussed in the text, together with exemplifying judgements, are collected and classified in the Appendix at the end of the book.

2 SUBJECT-PREDICATE INDUCTIVE PROBABILIFICATION- JUDGEMENT-FORMULAS

2.1 PRIMITIVE FORMULAS

2.1.1 *Operations Subsidiary to Induction, and the Primacy of Primitive Formulas*

Before formulating the rules governing the degree of probabilification of this type of judgement, there are two preliminary matters to be discussed. The first is the relation of induction to observation and description, and to naming, definition and classification. This is an interesting topic, and Mill devotes a whole book of his *Logic* to it. [Mill, 419 ff.] But since it does not seem to me to contribute much to the elucidation of the notion of inductive probability, I shall restrict myself to bringing out briefly the salient features of the interaction between these operations and induction. We shall see, however, that in Broad's view there is an important connexion between them and inductive probability. [Broad, R, II; Jevons, II, 344 ff.; Venn, P, 318 ff.; Wright, T, 140 ff.]

I have already pointed out some of the main facts about the relation of induction to observation and description. We have seen that for every generalization there logically must be a corresponding description; that generalization must not be confused with description, as is nevertheless done by those who conflate functional description with functional generalization or statistical induction

83

with statistical description; and that an essential difference between description and generalization is that the former is not, as the latter is, a sort of inference from evidence, notwithstanding that sensationalists represent it as being so.

Consider again the formula, (2): $E(fAg, f'Ag)$. The alleged fact, the description substituted on $f'Ag$, may really be a fact or true, or it may be no fact or false. If it is true, the corresponding generalization substituted on fAg will be supported or evidenced, and possibly well-evidenced or probabilified too. But if it is false, the generalization will not be supported or evidenced at all, *a fortiori* not well-evidenced or probabilified. Not to be supported at all is a more radical defect than not to be supported well; hence, a generalization may be criticized not only on the score that the alleged evidential fact, though indeed a fact, does not probabilify or verify it, but also on the score that the alleged evidential fact is no fact at all. There is perhaps a temptation to think that a false description is no description at all and an unsupported generalization no generalization at all. But this seems wrong. We rightly say e.g.: 'He described the episode to the best of his ability, but his account of it was quite false'; and 'The author makes the sweeping generalization that p, but unfortunately the supposed facts on which he bases it are no facts at all'.

Subject-predicate descriptions or observation-statements may be false on account of incorrect naming and/or incorrect attribution, and these errors may arise either from ignorance of the meanings of words or from inexact observation. One may assert falsely that $f'Ag$ because he mistakes what he observes for f when they are really h, when he ought to assert that $h'Ag$. This may happen e.g. when f and h are two species of plants that differ minutely and the man is untrained in observing plants. Or he may assert falsely that $f'Ag$ because he mistakes the meaning of the predicate term, and should rightly assert that $f'Ah$: e.g. he may call a sample of leaves 'bilobate' instead of 'bifid'. So that faulty observation and/or incorrect naming and/or incorrect attribution lead to false descriptions, and these lead in turn to unsupported corresponding generalizations.

Descriptions may also be defective through being excessively vague. I say 'excessively' because all general words are vague in some degree, and this is not a fault but a virtue in them, since they could not perform their functions otherwise. When the subject and/or predicate terms of a description are very vague, it is impossible to tell whether it is true or false and consequently whether the corresponding generalization is supported or not, *a fortiori* whether or not it is probabilified. Consider e.g. the generalization 'All democracies are free countries', of which both the subject and the predicate terms are very vague. Is the corresponding description 'All examined democracies are free countries' true or false? Suppose that the examined countries are Periclean Athens, Great Britain in 1870 and contemporary Yugoslavia. What degree of enfranchisement of its citizens entitles a country to be called a democracy? Some may say that the description is false because some of the examined countries are not democracies. And what number of the several liberties of expression of thought, association, enterprise, etc., and what degree of each, must the citizens of a country enjoy for it to qualify as a free country? Others may say that the description is false because some of the examined countries are not free.

Induction presupposes the existence of general words. For generalization presupposes the existence of descriptions such as 'All observed ravens are black', and these manifestly prerequire our possession of general words such as 'raven' and 'black'. Mill allows that this is true of generalizations, but argues that inductive reasoning from particulars to particulars can be effected without words. [Mill, 434 ff.] But since he also contends, as we have noticed earlier [1.1], that such reasoning may always be regarded as passing through a generalization, and that generalization presupposes general words, his exception of inference from particulars to particulars is not convincing. There is also another and deeper objection to this thesis which turns on the meaning of 'reasoning', and which will be brought forward when that topic is discussed. [6.1]

Conversely, the existence of one sort of general words, namely common nouns, presupposes induction. For we form e.g. the general name 'gold' when we have observed a constant conjunction between certain occurrent and dispositional properties, such as yellowness and malleability, and generalized that this observed conjunction holds true in unobserved cases also. But we form no common name for e.g. blue things, because we have observed no such constant conjunction between blueness and other properties.

85

Rather similar considerations apply to induction and definition. Definition presupposes induction thus: if we include 'mammal' in the definition of 'porpoise', it is not only because all the porpoises we have observed are mammals, but also because we have generalized that all porpoises are mammals and moreover judge the evidence for this generalization to be conclusive, and hence that it is true. For we do not include g in the definition of f when we judge the generalization $I(fAg)$ to be less than true, say very, very probable. Conversely, induction presupposes definition in a no less obvious way. It might be impossible to tell whether the generalization 'All democracies are free countries' was or was not supported because there was no agreed definition of 'democracy'; so that again there would be no knowing whether the corresponding description 'All observed democracies are free countries' were true or false because there would be no knowing whether Yugoslavia and Periclean Athens were or were not democracies. This of course is a different difficulty from that on the score of vagueness, mentioned above; there, it was supposed that 'democracy' was defined in terms of the enfranchisement of citizens, but that trouble arose out of the fact that the attribute 'having enfranchised citizens' is very vague in respect of degree.

Notice that if, having first judged the generalization 'All porpoises are mammals' to be true, we then proceed to include 'mammal' in the definition of 'porpoise', the statement 'All porpoises are mammals' ceases to be an empirical generalization. For we have already seen that a proposition logically cannot be simultaneously an empirical generalization and a necessary truth. [1.1] But it can be simultaneously a generalization and a contingent truth; this is the situation in the example before 'mammal' is included in the definition of 'porpoise'. And it can be successively a generalization and a necessary truth; the example illustrates precisely this process. Finally, the process can be reversed; if 'porpoise' were to be redefined omitting 'mammal', the proposition would be degraded from necessary truth to contingently true generalization.

The interaction between induction and classification is the most important of these topics. The classificatory sciences, such as Botany and Zoology, are pretty well coextensive with the attribute-inductive sciences; not, however, with the inductive sciences without qualification, for this is to ignore the existence of variable-inductions. It is the more curious that Aristotle, who both contributed largely to the classificatory sciences and founded the philosophy thereof, did not contribute correspondingly to Inductive Philosophy, or at least reach a sound view of ampliative induction.

Generalization presupposes classification through prerequiring the existence of general names. But it is pertinent to distinguish two types of general names: non-technical ones such as 'dog', and technical ones such as *primula veris*. There is a connexion with classification in both cases, but it is much more important in the latter case. In the former case, the connexion is simply this; every general name divides things into those which possess the attributes that name connotes and into those which do not possess them. In the latter case, the classification comes first and the technical nomenclature is based upon it. The example given illustrates the 'binomial' nomenclature of Botany, in which the name of a species is compounded out of the name of the genus which includes it (*primula*) and the specific difference (*veris*).

Broad argues that the probability of those generalizations which possess it prerequires the existence of natural kinds of substances and our discrimination of them. The logically possible combinations of attributes are not observed to occur in Nature with equal frequency; pig-faced women e.g. are very rarely seen. In other words, we observe that only certain attributes coexist, and we judge that these probably always coexist. These collocations of attributes are 'natural kinds' in Mill's sense, to which we give general names like 'raven' and 'swan'. Only inductions about such substances are judged to be probable. I shall criticize this theory, which resembles Keynes', in due course. [4.2] The point to notice now is simply the connexion that it alleges between classification and inductive probability. It may be objected that the theory ascribes the probability of inductions, not to the existence of certain classes in men's books or heads, but to the existence of certain kinds in Nature. But in fact the theory plainly requires both. It is necessary both that there should exist natural kinds and that we should have picked them out and named them. Otherwise, although 'All ravens are black' may in fact be a probable generalization, we shall not know, be able to judge, that it is. In Mill's terminology, we must have constituted 'natural classes' corresponding to the 'natural kinds'. [Mill, 460, 468, 470 f.]

Conversely, classification presupposes induction in the same way as definition does. We do not classify the porpoise as a mammal unless we have generalized that all porpoises are mammals and have judged this generalization to be conclusively evidenced and so true. Further, the descriptive meaning of the expression 'good scientific classification' is explicable in terms of induction. Mill formulates the criterion of good scientific classification as follows: 'The ends of scientific classification are best answered when the objects are formed into groups respecting which a greater number of general propositions can be made, and those propositions more important, than could be made respecting any other groups into which the same things could be distributed. A classification thus formed is properly scientific or philosophical, and is commonly called a Natural, in contradistinction to a Technical or Artificial, classification or arrangement.' [Mill, 466 f.] By 'general propositions' we must understand 'generalizations', not merely 'general descriptions'. E.g., it is good for scientific ends to class porpoises as mammals along with horses, men, etc., because many other true or probable generalizations can be made about all these sorts of animals, as that they are all vertebrates, warm-blooded, etc., besides the generalization that they are all mammals. But it is not good for scientific ends, though it may be good for some other end, to classify porpoises as animals whose names begin with P along with pike, pythons, etc., since very few if any assertions can be made about all animals whose names begin with P besides just that one fact. Mill is probably right in saying that classes formed in these two ways are what is most commonly meant by the expressions 'natural class' and 'artificial (or conventional) class' respectively; though of course the word 'natural' is notoriously slippery, as he himself well shows elsewhere. [J. S. Mill, 'Nature', in *Three Essays on Religion*, London, 1874] Similarly, such a resemblance among species of animals as being mammals is commonly called a scientifically 'important' one and such a resemblance as having a name beginning with P an 'unimportant' one.

Mill continues: 'And as it is one of the uses of such a classification [sc., a good one] that by drawing attention to the properties on which it is founded, and which, if the classification be good, are marks of many others, it facilitates the discovery of those others; we see in what manner our knowledge of things, and our classification of them, tend mutually and indefinitely to the improvement of each other'. [Mill, 468] I.e., a scientific classification is good when it not only effects the most economical or simple arrangement of existing knowledge, but also yields new knowledge. These, however, are not distinct criteria, for the second virtue is a natural consequence of the first. If we classify porpoises, horses, men, etc., together as mammals, we shall not only thereby systematize existing generalizations, e.g. that all these species are warm-blooded, vertebrates, etc., but also naturally be led to new ones, as when the discovery that all observed men possess ductless glands suggests not only that all men do so but also that all other species of mammals do so.

All this goes to show that, as generalization presupposes naming, definition and classification, so these presuppose generalization. If it is true that they are 'operations subsidiary to induction', as Mill calls them, it is no less true that induction is an operation subsidiary to them. But there is no vicious circle here; the appropriate figure is rather an ascending spiral. Given important and well-evidenced generalizations, we can make good classifications; and these in turn will suggest further important generalizations . . . and so on.

The second preliminary matter is this. I said in the conclusion of 1.2 that primitive formulas are more important than derivative ones. This is true; but what needs explaining is the paradox that, though primitive judgements have primacy over derivative ones, we practically never make them.

By a primitive inductive probabilification-judgement I mean a judgement of which the probabilified-proposition is an induction and the probabilifying-proposition a description. In such a judgement, the induction logically must be a generalization: see formulas (2′), (7′), (10′) and (11′). And by a derivative inductive probabilification-judgement I mean a judgement, the probabilified-proposition of which is an induction and the probabilifying-proposition of which contains an inductive probability-judgement. When the probabilified-proposition is a deduction from the probabilifying-proposition, the judgement is a deductive derivative one; and when it is not, the judgement is a non-deductive derivative one.

The deductive type has received more attention from philosophers than the non-deductive type. Species of it are illustrated by formulas (3′) and (9′), in which a probable generalization is applied to a particular case, and by the consilience of probable inductions. [2.2] But there are other important ways in which inductions are probabilified by other and previous probable inductions, and these accordingly present other types of derivative inductive probabilification-judgements. We shall see in 4.3 that this is true of cases in which inductions are judged probable because they have been attained by reliable methods of sampling or ampliative inference, and in 5.2 that it is also true of cases in which inductions are judged probable because possibly necessary qualifying conditions judged to be probably relevant have been eliminated. Indeed, the latter cases may be regarded as being of the same type as the former, since eliminating conditions judged to be probably relevant is a reliable method of inductive inference.

Now, in practice situations where we are unable to subsume our generalization under some wider probable or true induction, or to judge that the method of sampling that we are employing is (perfectly, very, etc.) reliable, or to judge that certain properties are (very, fairly, etc.) probably 'relevant' to the one we are interested in, are quite exceptional. I.e., the judgements that we actually make are practically always derivative, so that the situation in which we make primitive ones is an artificial abstraction, an epistemic State of Nature; we must imagine Adam making the first inductive probabilification-judgement. Nevertheless, it is evident that the whole elaborate structure of inductions probabilified by previous probable inductions logically must rest at bottom on inductions that are probabilified by true descriptions. It is in this sense that primitive inductive probabilification-judgements have primacy over derivative ones, and it is for this reason that it is desirable to discuss the former before the latter.

2.1.2 *Universal Formulas*

Rule (1). *An universal subject-predicate generalization is more probabilified as the observed sample is more varied.* This explains the meaning of the constituent γC_2 in the formula, (2'): $\gamma PF(fAg, f'Ag \cdot \gamma C_2)$. The rule sounds very simple, but there are complications which turn on the size of the sample and its relation to the variety thereof.

The first step is to explain the meaning of 'varied sample' and 'large sample'. Qualitative difference must of course be distinguished from numerical difference. If one BU is light and another BU is non-light, they differ qualitatively, in respect of weight. For simplicity, I shall consider only cases like this, in which the opposed attributes are contradictories. It will be convenient to write logical products as $h \times f$ or hf, and logical sums as $h + f$. E.g., the formula $h \times f Mg + i$ is read 'Most things that are h and f are g or i'; an exemplification is 'Most large BU are black or white'. Accordingly, a simple description-formula for a minimally varied sample is $hf'Ag . \bar{h}f'Ag$. But of course attributes may be contraries and a sample varied accordingly, as when it contains BU that are black, white, red and green and is thus varied in respect of colour. In this case too, however, the sample is correctly described by the same description-formula, since white, red and green are all cases of non-black.

Things are numerically different if they are not in the same place at the same time. We will take it that this is true of BU; but cp. the case in which one drop of water is placed on another and they coalesce, when we say that we have not two drops of water but one.

Then, a sample is (called) more varied when its individual members are made to differ in respect of a greater number of qualities, and of course larger when they are more numerous. Cp. these description-formulas of two samples: (i) $hgfx . \bar{h}gfy$; and (ii) $hgfw . \bar{h}gfx . igfy . \bar{i}gfz$. Sample (ii) is both larger than sample (i) since it contains four individuals as opposed to two, and more varied than sample (i) since it is varied in respect of two qualities as opposed to one. Naturally, Rule (1) must be understood to contain the following tacit qualification: 'varied, except in respect of the essential qualities connoted by the subject-term of the generalization'. For, if we want to make a probable generalization about the proportion of f that are g, we shall include in our sample hf as well as $\bar{h}f$ etc., but not of course $\bar{f}$ as well as f. But if h is an essential property of f, there logically can only be hf, not $\bar{h}f$.

Why is a generalization (judged to be) more probable accordingly as the observed sample is more varied? Essentially for this reason. The besetting danger in generalizing, the inductive fallacy *par excellence*, is making a generalization the scope of which is too wide relatively to the evidence for it. Thus, suppose that the sample is described by a statement of the form $hf'Ag$. Here, we judge that the possibly non-eliminable qualifying condition, h, is actually non-eliminable; i.e. that we are not justified in making a generalization of the wider scope fAg as opposed to one of the narrower scope $hfAg$. But suppose that its description is of the form $hf'Ag . \bar{h}f'Ag$. Here, we judge that the possibly non-eliminable conditions h and $\bar{h}$ are eliminable, and that we are to that extent justified in inferring to the unconditioned generalization fAg. Finally, suppose that the description of the sample is of the form $hf'Ag . \bar{h}f'Ag . if'Ag . \bar{i}f'Ag$. Here, we judge that the possibly non-eliminable conditions h, $\bar{h}$, i, and $\bar{i}$ are eliminable, and that we are more justified in inferring to fAg than in the preceding case. And so on. The pertinent rule of probabilification is: An unconditioned generalization is more probabilified as more possibly non-eliminable conditions are eliminated. But inspection of the two sample-description-formulas just given shows that this is equivalent to saying that an unconditioned generalization is more probabilified as the sample is more varied. This condensed preliminary account is expanded in 5.2, which is devoted to the connected key notions of condition and elimination.

A generalization is probabilified in a very low degree when the sample is large and in a slightly higher degree when it is very large. But it is superfluous to mention this in Rule (1) because the probabilificatory power of the size of a sample is simply a consequence of the probabilificatory power of its variety. For a (very, fairly, etc.) large sample logically must be (very, fairly, etc.) spatially varied, by virtue of the meaning of 'numerically different'. Numerically different balls must come from different parts of the urn. The low probabilificatory power of size is due to the fact that it induces variety in respect of only the one attribute, place. Moreover, increasing the size of the sample is an unsatisfactory because unsystematic way of inducing variety even in that solitary respect. If our sample is large, we know that it is varied in respect of place in some way or ways, but we do not know in what ways. It may be that both the left and the right halves of the urn are well represented in the sample, but that the bottom half of it is completely unrepresented. The normal and proper way of inducing spatial variety is of course to proceed systematically, selecting BU from both the left and the right half, from both the top and the bottom half, and so on.

Another possible objection to my account of the probabilificatory power of the number of the observed instances is this: it is true that number logically involves difference in respect of place, but false that this probabilifies the generalization in any degree, since we know *a priori* that place is irrelevant to all other attributes. Thus Keynes writes: 'There are certain properties of objects which we rule out from the beginning as wholly or largely independent and irrelevant to all, or to some, other properties. The principal judgements of this kind, and those alone about which we seem to feel much confidence, are concerned with absolute position in time and space, this class of judgements of irrelevance being summed up . . . in the Principle of the Uniformity of Nature. We judge that *mere* position in time and space cannot possibly affect, as a determining cause, any other characters; and this belief appears so strong and certain, although it is hard to see how it can be based on experience, that the judgement by which we arrive at it seems perhaps to be direct.' [Keynes, 255 f.; 226] To elucidate. h is said to be relevant to or associated with g among f if the proportion of hf that are g differs from the proportion of $\bar{h}f$ that are g, and irrelevant to or independent of it if these proportions are the same. If Keynes' contention is true, varying the sample in respect of place does not probabilify a generalization in any degree. For the point of varying the sample can be described as follows: the object is precisely to deal with the possibility that, among f', h, i, etc., are relevant to g. Thus, if we find that $hf'Ag$. $\bar{h}f'Ag$, we conclude that h is eliminable, and that the unconditioned generalization fAg is to that extent probabilified. But now, substitute on f 'BU', on g 'H' and on h 'located in the top half of the urn'. Then, on Keynes' doctrine, including hf as well as $\bar{h}f$ in the sample has no point, since we know already that the proportion of hf' that are g will be the same as the proportion of $\bar{h}f'$ that are g. Consequently, observing that $hf'Ag$. $\bar{h}f'Ag$ does not probabilify in any degree the unconditioned generalization fAg; for we do not thereby ensure the actual eliminability of a possibly non-eliminable condition, since we knew beforehand that h was not a possibly non-eliminable condition, i.e. that h is always eliminable from any generalization whatsoever.

My reply to this objection is that it is not only false but paradoxical. The same example will serve to illustrate its falsity. It is perfectly possible that, among BU, being in the top half of the urn is relevant to being H; for it may be that the heavy BU tend to settle in the bottom half of the urn, and that being heavy is positively associated with being solid. Indeed, place and date are precisely the two most obvious and important respects in which to vary our samples. As Keynes himself says about the generalization mentioned by Hume, 'All eggs are good': 'He should have tried eggs in the town and in the country, in January and in June'. [Keynes, 219] I shall consider further Keynes' and Broad's remarks about the (ir)relevance of place and date in 5.2, where the question will be shown to be connected with some important points about the dependence of the degree of probability of generalizations on the type of population that they are about.

A sample that is much varied tends to be fairly large. For the number of individuals in the sample logically cannot be less than twice the number of respects in which the sample is varied, and is normally a much greater multiple of it. For the limiting case is that in which the variation is effected by dichotomous division and we include in the sample only one individual possessing each attribute, thus: $hfw, hfx, ify, \bar{i}f\bar{z}$ ... etc. But normally we vary by dividing into more than two classes, as when we vary our sample of BU in respect of colour by taking black, white, red and green ones, and include in it more than one individual possessing each attribute, say ten black, ten white ... etc. Hence, a varied sample normally possesses as a very small part of its inductive probabilificatory power the probabilificatory power of a large sample. By contrast, as we have seen, a large sample necessarily possesses a very small part of the inductive probabilificatory power of a varied sample. Let us now compare these findings with those of some other philosophers.

Bacon holds that ordinary induction 'by simple enumeration' is worthless, and recommends instead induction 'by exclusion'. [Bacon, 290 f., 14] By the former he means generalizing from samples that are merely large; just what he means by the latter is a more difficult question. The antithesis is also traditionally expressed by contrasting induction by confirmation with induction by infirmation. My view may seem on the face of it to be very like his, since on the one hand both represent the number of the observed instances as having very little inductive probabilificatory power, and on the other both claim that the proper way to establish a generalization with probability is eliminative. But we shall see that in fact what Bacon understands by induction by elimination is something quite different from what I understand by it. [5]

At the other extreme are philosophers who hold that the degree of probability of generalizations depends solely on the size of the sample. Russell e.g. formulates the 'principle of induction' thus: 'The greater the number of cases in which a thing of the sort A has been found [always] associated with a thing of the sort B, the more probable it is . . . that A is always associated with B'. [Russell, P, 104] Here, there is no mention of the variety of the instances at all. To this my view is evidently quite opposed; it seems to me that, when generalizing, there is small safety in numbers.

I have argued that the fact that the sample is large probabilifies the generalization at all only because making the sample large logically involves making it varied, though only in one respect. Keynes argues along somewhat similar lines that large samples possess inductive probabilificatory power through inducing variety in the sample. His argument, which has been reproduced uncritically in many textbooks of Logic, seems to me to be open to the following objections.

For a start, there is a crucial ambiguity in his exposition. Cp. the following passages: (a) '. . . the advantage of additional instances, derived from experience, arises not out of their number as such, but out of their tendency to . . . increase the negative analogy. . . . The more numerous the instances, the less comprehensive are their superfluous resemblances likely to be.' (b) 'Every new instance *may* diminish the unessential resemblances between the instances and by introducing a new difference increase the Negative Analogy. For this reason, and for this reason only, new instances are valuable.' [Keynes, 228, 233] In (a) he says that large samples are probably varied, but in (b) he says that they are only possibly so. Manifestly, only the former claim will serve his purpose; but the existence of the latter formulation perhaps indicates that he is not too sure of the former, with good reason.

Even if the former claim were true, the fact that the sample is large would not probabilify the generalization much, for making the sample large would be an unsatisfactory because unsystematic way of making it various. For in making it large we should be varying it in respect of unknown attributes. The description of a large sample would be of the form, say: $?_1 f'Ag . \bar{?}_1 f'Ag . ?_2 f'Ag . \bar{?}_2 f'Ag$ . . ., etc., where $?_1$, $?_2$, etc. designate different unknown attributes. But all these might well be unimportant attributes, i.e. attributes judged to be probably irrelevant to or independent of g, in the senses of 'irrelevant' and 'independent' explained above. And if this were so, the generalization $I(fAg)$ would be only slightly probabilified by the variety of the observed instances. For we shall see later [5.2] that generalizations are probabilified in a respectable degree by varying the sample, not in respect of any qualities, but in respect of those judged probably relevant or important; and that the degree of probability of the generalization depends in part on the degree of the antecedent probability of relevance of attributes that are eliminated.

In any case, it is false that large samples are probably varied in respect of a number of attributes. This is an important question of fact, not of Philosophy, and it is answered unequivocally by the statisticians, who study the pertinent facts, and whose findings are as follows. [Tippett, 77 ff.; Yule, 332 ff.] The composition of a sample may differ from that of its parent population, so that it is unrepresentative, from two sorts of causes. First, from the 'fluctuations of chance'; it is possible, though casually improbable, for a sample to be large and random but quite unrepresentative. This fact is alternatively expressed by saying that samples are liable to random errors. Second, from bias in the method of selection, so that the sample is not random; i.e. it is not the case that every possible sample of the size of the one we have, had an equal chance of being selected. Selection by human agency e.g. is a notoriously biased method of sampling. The sort of thing that is found is that, if I choose haphazard a sample of wheat-plants (f) from a field in order to determine what proportion of them are diseased (g), I select a disproportionate number of tall ones (h) because these catch my eye. This is alternatively expressed by saying that samples are liable to errors of bias as well as to random ones. Consider the extreme case in which I select nothing but tall plants. If this happens, but I do not realize that it has happened, and generalize that, say, $f2/3g$, I evidently commit the inductive fallacy of inferring to $f2/3g$ from $hf'2/3g$ rather than from $\bar{h}hf'2/3g$; in other words, of failing to vary my sample. Of course, if h is irrelevant to g among f', this will not matter; but if it is relevant, it will matter. In this instance, it is plausible to suppose that, among observed wheat-plants, being tall is in fact relevant to being diseased.

If a sample is random, it is demonstrable that, the larger it is, the less it is exposed to risk from random errors. For, as we have already seen, it is casually probable that a large random sample approximately matches its population. Further, this probability increases with the size of the sample; this is the essential import of Bernoulli's Theorem. But the same is not true of errors of bias. A simple thought-experiment will show why. If, in taking a sample of 100 wheat-plants, I pick all tall ones because they catch my eye, why should the situation be any different if I increase the size of my sample to 1,000? In any case, the verdict of those who study the pertinent facts is that there is no reason to expect the result to be any different. 'It is implicit in my definition of errors of bias that they cannot be "drowned" by taking very large samples in the way that random errors can. . . .' [Tippett, 93]

The statisticians teach that the proper ways of eliminating errors of bias are two. First, employing a reliable method of random sampling, which involves using some 'randomizing' apparatus, such as a lottery or Tippett's Numbers. This technique is appropriate to cases where the population is known to be certainly or probably homogeneous, a word the meaning of which I shall explain shortly. We shall also re-encounter in due course the important conception of a reliable method of random sampling. [4.3] Second, deliberately varying the sample in respect of properties judged to be probably relevant to the predicate-property. This technique is appropriate to populations known to be certainly or probably non-homogeneous. Actually, the technique favoured for non-homogeneous populations is a combination of both procedures, called stratified sampling. The population is divided in thought into 'strata' in respect of properties judged probably relevant to the predicate-property, individuals are selected from each stratum by a reliable method of random sampling, and included in the sample in the proportion in which the strata exist in the population. This is the technique employed e.g. in the Gallup Polls. When the aim is to determine, say, what proportion of electors will vote Conservative in an election, the first step is to divide in thought the population into male and female; old, middle-aged, young; rich, medium, poor, etc. Individuals are then selected by, say, lottery from each of these sub-classes; and the sample is composed by including these individuals in it in the proportions in which these subclasses are found in the class of electors.

Hence, Keynes is mistaken in claiming that large samples are probably varied in respect of numerous attributes; all that can be truly asserted is that they are necessarily varied in respect of one attribute, namely place. He is consequently led to overestimate the probabilificatory power of induction by simple enumeration. Nevertheless, I agree with him that it is only because large samples are varied that induction by simple enumeration possesses any probabilificatory power at all.

In conclusion, I wish to stress that I am considering, as alone relevant to my theme, the *inductive* probabilificatory powers of the variety and number of the observed instances. Nicod e.g. claims to vindicate induction by confirmation against those who, like Bacon and in particular Keynes, depreciate it in favour of induction by infirmation. [Nicod, 203 f., 266 ff.] But this is misleading. For Nicod's argument is in terms of casual, not inductive, probabilification. The fundamental criticism to be made of his book is that, despite its title, it is not about induction at all. We have seen above [1.1] that this goes too for Jevons' account of 'inductive reasoning', and we shall see below [4.2] that it touches Williams' account of 'inductive' probability also.

2.1.3 *Proportional Formulas*

Rule (2). *A proportional subject-predicate generalization is more probabilified as the observed sample is more varied.* The pertinent formulas here are: (10'), $\gamma PF(fMg, f'Mg . \gamma C_2 . \gamma C_6)$; and (11'), $\gamma PF(fm/ng, f'm/ng . \gamma C_2 . \gamma C_6)$. It will be instructive to compare proportional with universal generalizations in respect first of disproof, then of proof.

As to disproof, there is this important disparity. The fact that $f'I\bar{g}$ demonstratively disproves the universal generalization $I(fAg)$, but not the proportional generalization $I(fMg)$. For though the formula $fAg . f'I\bar{g}$ is self-contradictory, the formula $fMg . f'I\bar{g}$ is not. A special case of $f'I\bar{g}$ is $\bar{g}fx$, which accordingly suffices to disprove a universal generalization. The fact that such a single negative instance can disprove a universal generalization whereas a single positive instance cannot prove it, is expressed by Bacon in the maxim *maior est vis instantiae negativae*; but it is evident from what has been said that it does not apply to proportional generalizations. Unlike universal generalizations, proportional generalizations are never demonstratively disproved, though they may indeed be conclusively disproved. They are (judged to be) more or less improbabilified, or falsified, in the following conditions: the fact that it is not the case that most observed f are g makes it (very, fairly, etc.) improbable that most f are g in the degree that the condition C_2 is satisfied; and in the upper limiting case the same fact makes it false that most f are g.

As to proof, comparison of Rule (2) with the Rule (1) shows that the criteria of the probability of proportional and universal generalizations are the same. But comparison of formulas (10′) and (11′) with formula (2′) also reveals that the former involve a condition that the latter does not, namely C_6. This must now be explained.

C_6 is the condition of proportional stability in the sample. [Keynes, 391 ff.; Kneale, II, 315; Lewis, 300; Yule, 368 f.] What does this mean? Explaining its meaning is precisely one of the main difficulties; it will be convenient to begin with Keynes' account. He closely follows Lewis, to whom he gives the credit for first appreciating the need for such a condition, and whose measure of degree of stability he accepts. Suppose that we have a large sample, the description of which is of the form $f'm/ng$. We divide up or stratify this sample in thought in respect of numerous attributes judged to be probably relevant to g, thus: $hf, \bar{h}f, if, \bar{i}f \ldots$ etc. We then select from each of these strata large random sub-samples of equal size, thus: $hf', \bar{h}f', if', \bar{i}f' \ldots$ etc. Then, the proportion (m/n) in the sample is stable (or, its degree of stability is normal) if the observed distribution of the proportion in the sub-samples fits tolerably closely to the distribution of the proportion that we should theoretically expect to get if the subsamples were large random samples from a population of composition m/n.

Obviously, this condition can only apply to proportional, not to universal, subject-predicate generalizations. For in the latter the sample must be of the form $f'Ag$, and the subsamples of the form $hf'Ag, \bar{h}f'Ag \ldots$ etc. On the other hand, it is important to notice that analogous conditions apply, not merely to proportional subject-predicate generalizations, but to all attribute and variable generalizations that are not universal. E.g., they apply to partial, but not to perfect, associative generalizations; and to partial correlative generalizations, but not to functional generalizations. But it will suffice to attend to the proportional subject-predicate type only.

Why is this condition required? Because without it we cannot speak simply of *the* proportion of f' or f that are g at all. Although C_6 varies in degree, since a ratio can be more or less stable, its variations do not determine the degree of probability of a proportional generalization; that is determined entirely by those of C_2. Lewis, indeed, argues that stability, which he calls 'uniformity', determines degree of inductive probability, which he calls 'reliability'. But I believe this view to be mistaken; the situation is rather that, as Keynes says: '. . . until a *prima facie* case has been established for the existence of a stable probable-frequency, we have but a flimsy basis for any statistical induction at all. . . .' [Keynes, 415] I.e., unless the proportion in the sample is tolerably stable, we (judge that we) may not make a proportional description of the sample, nor consequently a corresponding proportional generalization about the population, at all. However, there is, as Keynes observes, an intimate connexion between the degree of stability of a ratio or other statistical parameter in a sample and the degree of variety in it. For we have seen that the proportion (or mean, or coefficient of correlation) in the sample is stable if and only if the distribution thereof in varied subsamples is of a certain form. Determining the degree of stability of the parameter is essentially a matter of analysing the sample. But if the sample contains varied subsamples, it must of course be itself varied. Perhaps it is this intimate connexion between C_6 and C_2 which raises the belief that the former determines the probability of proportional generalizations.

It seems to be generally agreed that C_6 is necessary to proportional generalizations; what is open to discussion is just how 'stability' is to be understood. There is possibly a temptation to think that we may not assert that $f'm/ng$ or generalize correspondingly that fm/ng unless the proportion in all possible subsamples is the same as that in the sample, i.e. unless $hf'm/ng$. $hf'm/ng$. $if'm/ng$. $if'm/ng$ . . . etc. In other words, a proportional description and corresponding generalization cannot be made unless the sample is absolutely homogeneous with respect to the relevant property, g. But this is certainly wrong. For a start, the notion of absolute homogeneity is self-contradictory, since there logically must be some possible subsample, the composition of which differs from that of the sample; the composition of the possible subsample gf, e.g., is of course $gfΛg$, not gfm/ng. Again, even if the proposed test were logically possible, it is practically impossible, since we cannot establish that all possible subsamples of a large sample are of the same composition as the sample. Finally, given that the Lewis/Keynes account of stability is basically correct, we see that the test of stability that we actually apply is very different; we are satisfied if most subsamples have about the same composition as the sample and the distribution of the rest is as just described. Indeed, when statisticians speak of a sample or population as homogeneous with respect to g, they mean just this; to say that a class, f, is homogeneous with respect to g is to say that the proportion of f that are g is stable in the sense explained, and conversely. Naturally, neither notion applies to classes in which all f are g or $\bar{g}$, of which all possible subclasses logically must be of the same composition. Such classes, and only they, are absolutely homogeneous; but this is an uninteresting truism. In sum, the workaday notion of homogeneity must be discriminated from the otiose notion of absolute homogeneity, which is an inductive philosopher's figment, and an illogical one at that.

The latter resembles the concept of irregularity or randomness, which plays a leading part in von Mises' theory of probability. [2.2] It is one of the defining conditions of what he calls a 'collective', of which he writes: 'The limiting values of the relative frequencies in a collective must be independent of all possible place selections'. [Mises, 33] But there are noteworthy differences. A sample is absolutely homogeneous if the relative frequency or proportion in all possible subsamples howsoever selected is the same as that in the sample; but a collective is irregular if the limiting value of the relative frequency in all possible subsequences selected by place is the same as that in the collective.

We must consider next the relation of preponderant to universal subject-predicate generalizations. In principle, every unconditioned preponderant generalization is replaceable by a corresponding conditioned universal one; but in practice this is not so, on account of the difficulty in some cases of supplying the requisite qualifying conditions. Thus, Mill avers that the generalization 'Most persons who have uncontrolled power employ it ill' may be transformed into 'All persons who have uncontrolled power employ it ill, provided they are not persons of unusual strength of judgement and rectitude of purpose'. [Mill, 394] The example is interesting because, as he rightly points out later, the bulk of our knowledge of human nature consists of unconditioned preponderant generalizations; or, in his terminology, 'The empirical laws of human nature are merely approximate generalizations'. [Mill, 562 ff.] And this of course is the sort of knowledge that really interests him, as it does Locke and Hume also. Perhaps Mill is right in thinking that the preponderant generalization he instances can be easily transformed into an universal one on the lines he suggests. But consider by contrast the generalization 'Most persons are right-handed'; in the present state of our knowledge, it is not practically possible to transform it into its corresponding universal, because all the requisite qualifying conditions are not known.

When it can be done, there are good reasons for replacing preponderants by universals; but there are also reasons for not doing so. The first reason in favour is that universals can be deductively systematized in an ordinary way, whereas preponderants cannot. E.g., from $I(gAh . fAg)$ we may deduce $I(fAh)$; but from $I(gMh . fMg)$ we may deduce no preponderant induction. The only conclusion that can validly be drawn from two preponderant propositions is this: from $fMh . fMg$ we may infer that gIh. I say that preponderant generalizations cannot be deductively systematized 'in an ordinary way', because Braithwaite's discussion of 'tendency statements' seems to show that they can be organized in what he calls a 'tendency quasi-deductive system'. [Braithwaite, 361 ff.] I cannot take up more than one point of interest in his discussion. He denies that the notion of 'tendency' is equivalent to the notion of 'preponderance'. It seems to me, however, that in one use of the word, 'tendency' does mean just this: 'People tend to be right-handed' surely means the same thing as the generalization 'Most people are right-handed'. There are, however, other uses of the word: e.g. 'Raising the price tends to diminish the demand'.

The second reason in favour is that, when they are applied to an individual case, true or probable universal generalizations establish the conclusion with a higher degree of probability than do true or probable preponderant generalizations. Consider the following two pairs of formulas: First, $VF(gx, I(fAg) . fx)$ as contrasted with $(6')$, $\gamma PF(gx, fMg . fx . C_1)$. The former formula is read: 'The fact that all f are g and that x is an f makes it true that (verifies) x is a g'; here, the constituent $I(fAg)$ is a true induction-formula. Second, a variant of $(3')$, $\alpha PF(gx, \alpha P(fAg) . fx)$, as contrasted with $(5')$, $\delta PF(gx, \alpha P(fMg) . fx . C_1)$. I shall say more about formulas (5′) and (6′) shortly. [2.2] Consideration of these pairs of formulas will reveal a third reason for preferring universal to their corresponding preponderant generalizations. Namely, in order to subsume an individual instance under the latter we must know that C_1 is certainly or probably satisfied, which may be difficult; whereas in order to subsume an individual under the former we do not need to know this.

The reasons against replacing preponderants by universals are these. First, as already noticed, it may be practically impossible or very difficult to do so because we do not know or cannot easily discover the requisite conditions by which the universals must be qualified. But second, even though we know these, we may not be able to establish that the individual possesses these attributes; yet unless we can establish this fact, we have no right to apply the universal to it. Thus, suppose that we can replace a true preponderant generalization of the form $I(fMg)$ by its corresponding true conditioned universal generalization $I(hfAg)$. We cannot apply the latter to x unless we can establish that hfx; but this may be practically impossible, or at least difficult. Notice particularly that we are not justified in applying a generalization of this form to x if we know only that fx, not that hfx. If we know that all consumptive librarians certainly or probably die before reaching sixty years, we cannot apply this knowledge to Tom if we know only that he is a librarian. We must know that he is a consumptive librarian; but there may be practical obstacles in the way of our discovering whether he is consumptive or not. This topic will be raised again in examining Hume's claim that degree of analogy is a criterion of degree of inductive probability. [4.1]

2.1.4 *Statistical Laws, and Statistical Theory*

In this connexion, I wish to touch briefly on the question of statistical (or indeterministic) *vs.* universal (or deterministic) laws of Nature. It is familiar that some thinkers, including Einstein, are not entirely at ease about statistical laws, an example of which is the Second Law of Thermodynamics as interpreted by and since Boltzmann; and that others have retorted upon them that their objections rest on nothing more than a reluctance to accept new ways of thinking.

It seems to me that statistical laws are objected to on at least two different grounds. First, it may be held that preponderant statements are essentially provisional and as such have no place in science; whatever their utility in other spheres, here they are tolerable only as temporary makeshifts which will be replaced as soon as possible by corresponding conditioned universal ones. An expression of this view is the following passage of Mill's: 'Propositions in the form, Most A are B, are of a very different degree of importance in science, and in the practice of life. To the scientific inquirer they are valuable chiefly as materials for, and steps towards, universal truths. The discovery of them is the proper end of science: its work is not done if it stops at the proposition that the majority of A are B, without circumscribing that majority by some common character, fitted to distinguish them from the minority.' [Mill, 387] I have just enumerated the chief considerations for and against this thesis. But I suggest that there is another ground of objection, which is perhaps obscurely felt rather than explicitly stated.

This objection may be rendered shortly: Laws of Nature must be universal, hence they cannot be statistical. Thus, Broad e.g. writes of '. . . *laws* (i.e. universal propositions) as against propositions of the form $n\%$ of the S's in nature are P's . . .' [Broad, R, II, 13] I suggest that this objection rests on an ambiguity in the word 'universal'. It is true that in one use of 'universal' a statistical law logically cannot be universal; this is the use in which 'universal law' means 'law expressed by an "All . . . " sentence', i.e. the use in which propositions are described as universal in Formal Logic. But it is also true that in another use of 'universal' a law of Nature logically must be universal. In this use, 'universal' means 'holding true in or applying to all Nature, i.e. in all times, places and circumstances'. In this use, 'universal law' is opposed, not to 'statistical law', but to 'law of restricted application'. Cp. Newton's Law of Gravitation, which holds (or was thought to hold) in all times, places and circumstances with Galileo's law of falling bodies, which holds only on the Earth, and which is in fact deducible from and hence explicable by Newton's law. My point is simply that the sense of 'universal' in which a law of Nature logically must be universal by virtue of the connotation of that name, is not the sense of 'universal' in which a statistical law logically cannot be universal. There is no logical reason why the Second Law of Thermodynamics should not be universal in the required sense as well as the Law of Gravitation. This second objection to statistical laws of Nature therefore fails.

Finally, a word about the bearings of modern statistical theory on the present inquiry. The foregoing discussion shows that one branch of modern statistical theory, namely, the Theory of Sampling, is highly relevant to my theme, and I shall have more to say about it later. [4.3] It may be thought that another branch is so too, namely, the theory of statistical-experimental techniques such as Fisher's Analysis of Variance. But this is not the case. It is true that induction and these techniques share an important common feature, in that the basic difficulty which both have to contend with is the variable or non-homogeneous character of the material investigated. But there is also an essential difference, in that these techniques are not methods of making inferences from samples to populations. Their function is rather to prove causation, e.g. that an improved crop-yield may be attributed to the use of a certain variety of barley, or of a certain sort of fertilizer, and not to variations in other conditions such as the soil.

The rationale of these techniques belongs to the theory of experiment, and it is instructive to regard them as developments from Mill's Method of Difference. Mill thinks that the only effective way of proving causation is the Method of Difference, in which we prove that an antecedent event A is the cause of a subsequent event X by establishing that: (i) when X occurred A preceded it; (ii) when X did not occur A did not precede it; and (iii) there was no other difference between situation (i) and situation (ii) besides the compresence of X and A in (i) and their con-absence in (ii). But he appreciates, and indeed stresses, the practical impossibility of establishing (iii), especially in the social sciences: what hope is there, he asks, of proving e.g. that protection promotes the wealth of nations by finding or producing two nations which are alike in every respect except that one is both protected and prosperous whereas the other is neither? I return to Mill's Methods later. [4.2]

The practitioners and theorists of modern statistical-experimental techniques teach that the best that can be done towards meeting this difficulty is to use 'precision control' and 'randomization', as follows. Two samples are selected from the population under investigation, the 'experimental sample', which is to be exposed to the causal influence in question, and the 'control sample', which is not to be so exposed. The samples are composed thus. First, a double list is prepared of individuals paired according to known characteristics, both members of one pair being e.g. of the same race, occupation and income (precision control). Then the samples are made up from this list by assigning each member of each pair to each sample at random (randomization). [Tippett, 102 ff.; Yule, 444 ff.; J. Madge, *The Tools of Social Science*, London, 1953, ch. 5]

2.2 DERIVATIVE FORMULAS

2.2.1 *Deductive Derivative Formulas*

I shall discuss in order deductive derivative formulas, and then non-deductive derivative ones. It will be recalled that, in a deductive derivative judgement, the probabilified-proposition must be a deduction from the probabilifying-proposition, and the probability-judgement in the latter must be a probable induction; whereas in a non-deductive derivative judgement these conditions need not be satisfied. The rules governing variation of degree of probabilification of the probabilified-proposition in the former sort of judgements are the rules of probable-deduction, i.e. rules describing how the degree of probability of a conclusion is determined by the degree of probability and nature of the probable premises which entail it.

Consider first the formulas: (3'), $\gamma\text{PF}(gx, \gamma\text{P}(fAg) \cdot fx)$; and (4'), $\gamma\text{PF}(fAg, \gamma\text{P}(hAg) \cdot fAh)$. The pertinent rule is *Rule* (3). *In judgements of the types of formulas* (3') *and* (4'), *the degree of probabilification of the probabilified-proposition is the same as, and hence varies directly as, the degree of probability of the probability-judgement in the probabilifying-proposition.* Thus, cp. with formula (3') the formula: $\beta\text{PF}(gx, \beta\text{P}(fAg) \cdot fx)$. Both (3') and (4') are important formulas; the former in particular represents the application of a probable universal generalization to a particular case, which of course is a thing we very often do.

Take next the formula, (12'), $\gamma\text{PF}(p, (r \supset p) \cdot \gamma\text{PF}(r, q))$. An exemplification of it is 'Since, if all metals are malleable all gold is malleable, and the fact that all observed silver, copper, lead and iron are malleable makes it probable that all metals are malleable, it is probable that all gold is malleable'. The pertinent rule is

Rule (4). *In judgements of the type of formula* (12'), *the degree of probabilification of the probabilified-proposition is the same as, and hence varies directly as, the degree of probabilification of the probabilified-proposition in the probabilifying-proposition.* Thus, cp. with formula (12') the formula: $\beta PF(p, (r \supset p)) . \beta PF(r, q))$. These are noteworthy formulas because they involve two important conceptions: first, the consilience of (probable) inductions; and second, one sense of 'indirect probabilification'.

As to the former conception, the generalization 'All gold is malleable' is shown to be probable by being shown to be deducible from, and hence explicable by, a probable generalization of wider scope, 'All metals are malleable'. In other words, a proposition that is a primitive induction from the direct evidence for it is shown to be also a derivative induction. This situation should be compared with the similar one discussed above, in which a number of probable generalizations are shown to be deducible from and hence explicable by a non-empirical hypothesis. [1.2; Kneale, 106 ff.] Both sorts of situation often arise, so that the emphasis placed on the consilience of inductions by Whewell, Mill and Apelt is fully justified. Nicod writes: '. . . induction gains autonomously a kind of momentum which increases in strength as it progresses. Its power has a "snow-ball" or cumulative effect.' [Nicod, 239] This is true and important, and the preceding considerations reveal one, but not the only, reason why. We can use inductions previously established as true or probable to verify or probabilify other inductions.

As to the latter conception, in formula (12') q directly probabilifies r and indirectly probabilifies p. Corresponding to the notions of direct and indirect probabilification are of course those of direct and indirect evidence. Consider the evidential-statement-formula, (12), $E(p, (r \supset p)) . E(r, q))$. In it, q is (called) direct evidence for r and indirect evidence for p. As Hume says: 'In all cases we transfer our experience to instances of which we have no experience . . . either *directly* or *indirectly*'. [Hume, T, 105; Braithwaite, 17]

Special cases of formulas (3') and (12') respectively are the formulas: $VF(gx, I(fAg)) . fx)$; and $VF(p, (r \supset p)) . VF(r, q))$. In the former, fAg is a conclusively evidenced generalization which is accordingly judged not probable but true; in the latter, q is conclusive evidence that r, so that r and hence p are judged true. In these cases, of course, there is no question of probable-deduction, since there is no probability-judgement in the probabilifying-proposition. On the other hand, they are concerned with the entailments of inductions. Borrowing a useful distinction of von Wright's, we may say that the study of such formulas as these belongs to the Logic of Inductive Truth, and that the study of such formulas as $(3')$, $(4')$ and $(12')$ belongs to the Logic of Inductive Probability. [Wright, T, 31]

I turn next to the formula, $(13')$, $\gamma PF(p, (r \supset \beta P(p)) . (q \supset \beta P(r)) . q)$. An exemplification of it is: 'Since, if there was smoke here there was very probably fire here, and if there is soot here there was very probably smoke here, and there is soot here, there was probably fire here'. The pertinent rule is *Rule* (5). *In judgements of the type of formula* $(13')$, *the degree of probabilification of the probabilified-proposition varies inversely as the number of hypothetical probabilification-judgements in the probabilifying-proposition.* Thus, cp. with formula $(13')$ the formulas: $\beta PF(p, (q \supset \beta P(p)) . q)$; and $\delta PF(p, (s \supset \beta P(p)) . (r \supset \beta P(s)) . (q \supset \beta P(r)) . q)$. This sort of formula illustrates another sense of 'indirect probabilification' and 'indirect evidence', distinct from that involved in formula $(12')$. The evidential-statement corresponding to the exemplification of formula $(13')$ just cited is: 'Since the presence of smoke here would be evidence of the presence of fire here, and the presence of soot here would be evidence of the presence of smoke here, and there is soot here, that is evidence that there was fire here'. The fact that this evidential-statement and formula $(13')$ are respectively a deductive derivative statement and a deductive derivative judgement-formula, turns on the fact that 'evidences' and 'probabilifies' are transitive relations.

The existence of this type of evidential-statements and probabilification-judgements has long been recognized both in ordinary language and, accordingly, in Philosophy. The everyday expression 'chain of evidence' is a metaphorical description of the former, the 'links' in the chain being the constituent hypothetical evidential-statements. Bentham speaks in this connexion of 'self-infirmative chains of evidence'. [Mill, 391 ff.; Wigmore, 13 f.] I take his calling them 'self-infirmative' to show his grasp of Rule (5). Locke and Hume too recognize that the more 'removed' or 'distant' the conclusion from the evidential fact, the less probable it is. [Locke, 339 f.; Hume, T, 144 ff.] In his discussion, Hume equates 'chain of evidence' with 'chain of causes'; this is connected with a far-reaching confusion in his epistemology between 'evidences' and 'causes'. [5.1] Both he and Locke instance hearsay evidence, and it will be informative to consider this illustration. Consider the judgement: 'Since, if Tom says that p it is very probable that p, and if Dick says that Tom says that p it is very probable that Tom says that p, and Dick does say that Tom says that p, it is probable that p'. This exemplifies formula $(13')$. And in it, Dick's statement is not only indirect evidence that p, but also, as we have seen earlier, dependent evidence that p. [1.2]

The last type of deductive derivative formula that I shall notice is, $(14')$, $\gamma PF(fAg, \beta P(hAg \cdot fAh))$. A possible exemplification of it is: 'Since all mammals are very probably vertebrates and all porpoises are very probably mammals, all porpoises are probably vertebrates'. The pertinent rule is *Rule* (6). *In judgements of the type of formula* $(14')$, *the degree of probabilification of the probabilified-proposition varies inversely as the number of probability-judgements in the probabilifying-proposition*. Thus, cp. with formula $(14')$ the formulas: $\beta PF(fAg, \beta P(hAg) \cdot fAh)$; and $\delta PF(fAg, \beta P(iAg \cdot hAi \cdot fAh))$. The former of this pair is a variant on formula $(4')$. Judgements substituted on formula $(14')$ may conveniently be called 'probable syllogisms', and judgements substituted on the last formula 'probable polysyllogisms'. They are important formulas, because they are involved in the classificatory or attribute-inductive sciences in a way that I shall try to bring out shortly.

Before passing on to non-deductive derivative inductive probabilification-judgements, I shall add some general remarks on deductive ones; they arise naturally out of what I have just said about probable syllogisms. Probability-judgements are value-judgements, so that in studying these deductive judgements we are studying the entailments of one sort of value-judgements. This is not a matter to which philosophers have paid much attention; the sort of entailments on which they concentrate are of course those of statements, i.e. propositions that can be true or false, this study forming what is usually called Deductive (or Formal) Logic. However, there is no ground for surprise that value-judgements should have entailments, or that the study of them should be philosophically interesting. Somewhat similarly, Hare draws attention to the fact that commands have entailments. He also points out that, though some philosophers deny this fact, Aristotle is not one of them, since he speaks of practical as well as of theoretical syllogisms. [Hare, 26] To which I add that Aristotle also recognizes the existence of probable syllogisms, i.e. syllogisms with probable premisses, as well as of ordinary syllogisms, i.e. syllogisms with true premisses. I shall revert to his views shortly.

Examination of the deductive derivative formulas discussed above shows that we often have, not premisses that are all probable, as in formula (14'), but a mixture of probable premisses and true ones, as in formulas (3') and (4'). In these cases, the conclusion is probable and not true; a fact which is less trivial than it sounds. For consider first formula (3'), $\gamma PF(gx, \gamma P(fAg) . fx)$, and suppose that fx is a description-formula, as is in fact usually the case with this formula. Then, the implication of the rule just given is that a deduction from a (certain sort of) value-judgement and a description is a value-judgement and not a description. Cp. Hare's discussion of inferences from two premisses, one of which is in the imperative mood and the other of which is in the indicative mood. [Hare, 27 f.] Consider next formula (4'), $\gamma PF(fAg, \gamma P(hAg) . fAh)$, and suppose that fAh is a true generalization-formula, not a description-formula. This case differs from the preceding one, since the premisses are both value-judgements, truth being here the upper limit of probability. However, both cases are covered by a rule formulated by Nicod thus: '. . . the probability conferred by an inference, of any sort, upon its conclusion is at most equal to that of the least probable of its premisses'. [Nicod, 212] In fact, this rule applies to non-deductive as well as to deductive derivative judgements, and should be compared with two rules of Leibniz's that I shall give directly. What emerges, then, from these considerations is that the general problem of deductive derivative probabilification-judgements is, How is the degree of probability of the conclusion affected by the degree (or degrees) of probability of the premiss (or premisses)?

The study of the entailments of inductive probability-judgements is only a part of the study of the entailments of probability-judgements generally. E.g., in the formula (14'), $\gamma PF(fAg, \beta P(hAg . fAh))$, it is immaterial whether both premisses are inductive probability-judgements, or one is inductive and the other hypothetic, or both are hypothetic. Again, the study of the entailments of inductive probability-judgements is narrower than the study of the entailments of inductions generally. For when the evidence for them is conclusive as opposed to merely (very, etc.) good, the inductions which are the premisses are claimed to be true; in which case we have, of course, not probable syllogisms as in formula (14′), but the familiar true syllogisms. As I pointed out above, the studies of true and probable inductive syllogisms are conveniently called respectively the Logic of Inductive Truth and the Logic of Inductive Probability. Further, the name Inductive Logic may conveniently be used for these two studies collectively; we shall see later [6.2] that it has no stable meaning at present.

The deductive derivative formulas that I have discussed form only a very small part of the entailments of inductive probability-judgement-formulas. They are in fact those entailments which naturally force themselves on the attention when one is making a systematic analysis of inductive probability; for they present themselves in connexion with such questions as the deductive systematization of probable inductions, and chains of evidence, which are important for such an analysis. However, one could make a systematic analysis of the entailments of probability-judgements generally and for its own sake, a study which could well be called the Logic of Probability. A natural way to set about it would perhaps be to take the existing Logic of Truth or Statement Logic, replace all or some premiss-statements by judgements that are in varying degrees probable, and see how the degree of probability of the conclusion-judgement is affected. It would remain to formulate, and if possible systematize, the rules governing these variations in the degree of probability of the conclusions. E.g., I have mentioned in connexion with formula (14′) probable syllogisms and polysyllogisms. But a typical question in the Logic of Probability as just defined might also be, What conclusion is to be drawn from the premisses: 'He is very probably a fool or a knave; if he is a fool he cannot help, and if he is a knave he probably will not care'? These premisses exemplify the formula: $\beta P(r \lor s)$. $(r \supset \sim p) . \gamma P(s \supset \sim q)$. Whether such a theory of probable-deduction is possible or interesting naturally cannot be decided *a priori*. Possibly someone will think it worth while to investigate the question; but it is beside my purpose to do so here.

This hypothetical investigator will find that one natural division of this Logic of Probability is the Logic of Casual Probability, the subject-matter of which is an important one, namely, the Calculus of Probabilities. For the theorems of this calculus are simply casual deductive derivative probability-judgements. As Kneale says, '. . . the calculus of chances is just the procedure for deriving [casual] probabilities from others which are supposed to be given, and it is concerned solely with consistency'. [Kneale, 124] I shall explain the meaning of 'casual probability' shortly. But despite the importance of its subject-matter, there is no reason to think that this Logic of Casual Probability involves any special philosophical problems. For the Calculus of Probabilities does not differ in any essential respects from other calculi, so that the sort of philosophical problems that may arise out of it are those that arise out of any deductive or mathematical system, e.g. questions of consistency, independence and completeness.

Our investigator will also find that attempts have been made from time to time on other divisions of the Logic of Probability as defined above, though not it seems to any great effect. Thus, Aristotle distinguishes a sub-province of Logic, called 'Dialectic', concerned with the study of probable syllogisms, or 'enthymemes', i.e. syllogisms with probable premisses, or 'topics'. This study is pursued in his *Topics*, as is that of true syllogisms in his *Analytics*. Again, the scholastic logicians study probable syllogisms under the rubric 'modal syllogisms', opposing the latter to 'pure', i.e. true, syllogisms. They investigate such questions as: 'Whether, with one premiss certain [i.e. true] and the other probable, a certain [true] conclusion may be inferred'. [Venn, L, 317] We have seen that the answer to this question is in fact, No; cp. formulas (3') and (4'). The relation of Probability to Modality is a question of some interest, and I shall consider it later in criticizing a contemporary modal theory of Probability, namely, Toulmin's. [6.1] The name 'probable syllogism' is used by Crakanthorpe, who devotes a book of his *Logic* to the subject. [Keynes, 440] Finally, it comes as no surprise to find Leibniz giving some attention to this matter. He formulates e.g. the following rules: 'A conclusion can never be more probable than the premiss from which it is derived'; and 'If a conclusion is deduced from several probable premisses, it is less probable than each of them'. [Leibniz, 180] The first rule should be compared with Nicod's rule, above. I take the second one to refer to probable syllogisms and polysyllogisms; it should accordingly be compared with my Rule (6), above.

In 6.2 I shall examine the notions of a Logic of Probability, of an Inductive Logic, and related conceptions. It will appear that they have at present no fixed meanings. But I can conveniently summarize the foregoing remarks by anticipating the constructive part of what I shall have to say about these notions; i.e. by indicating the uses to which it seems to me that these expressions can usefully be put, and by assigning them their places in the general scheme of philosophical studies.

We may begin with the study Axiology and its divisions. This is the philosophical study of value-judgements, and is to be distinguished accordingly from the philosophical studies of commands, performative utterances, etc., and particularly of statements, the name for the philosophical study of which is Epistemology. A branch of Epistemology is (Deductive or Formal) Logic, which is distinguished from other branches thereof by being about deductive derivative statements or truths; whence it may also be called the Logic of Truth or Statement Logic. And so generally, the name 'logic' connotes the study of deductions, entailments or logical implications. Divided on one principle, one branch of Axiology is the Philosophy of Probability, which differs from other branches thereof, such as Ethics and Aesthetics, in being about probability value-judgements as opposed to ethical or aesthetic value-judgements. But divided on another principle, one branch of Axiology is Evaluative Logic, which differs from other branches thereof in being about deductive derivative value-judgements as opposed to primitive or non-deductive derivative value-judgements. It follows from what has been said about the subject-matter of Axiology that Evaluative Logic must be distinguished both from Statement Logic and from Imperatival (or Deontic) Logic.

Divided on one principle, one branch of the Philosophy of Probability is the Philosophy of Inductive Probability, which differs from other branches thereof in being about inductive as opposed to casual or hypothetic probabilification-judgements, and which constitutes the subject of this essay. But divided on another principle, one branch of the Philosophy of Probability is the Logic of Probability, which differs from other branches thereof in being about deductive derivative probabilification-judgements as opposed to primitive or non-deductive derivative ones. These considerations show why 'Logic of Probability' is an unsatisfactory name for what I call Philosophy of Probability, and also why it is incorrect to regard the philosophical study of Probability as a whole as falling within the province of Logic. Inspection of the contents of most textbooks of Logic nevertheless reveals that the prevailing view is that it does so fall.

One branch of the Logic of Probability is the Logic of Inductive Probability, which differs from other branches thereof in being about deductive derivative inductive probabilification-judgements as opposed to casual or hypothetic deductive derivative ones. The subject-matter of the Logic of Casual Probability is important, since the theorems of the Calculus of Probabilities are deductive derivative casual probabilification-judgements.

Still continuing the process of division, one branch of the Logic of Inductive Probability is the Logic of Inductive Truth, which differs from other branches thereof in being about deductive derivative inductive verification-judgements as opposed to probabilification-judgements, inductive verification-judgements being the upper limiting case of inductive probabilification-judgements, in the sense that they occur when the evidence for an induction is judged to be conclusive. The rules of the Logic of Inductive Truth are simply those of the wider Logic of Truth or Statement Logic. In other words, the rules for the deductive systematization of true inductions are the same as those for the deductive systematization of true descriptions. Historically, I think this is important. For Aristotle's Syllogistic is surely a logic of inductive truth rather than a logic of descriptive truth. He seems to have regarded his logic as formulating the principles of organization of the classificatory sciences, in which he himself was actively engaged. But we have seen [2.1] that the operation with which classification is significantly connected is generalization rather than description; the 'classificatory sciences' are nearly enough identical with the 'inductive sciences'. But since inductions are more often probable than true, a logic of the classificatory sciences such as Aristotle envisaged ought to include what may be called Probability Syllogistic as well as ordinary Truth Syllogistic. To put the point another way, the *Organon* ought genuinely to include the *Topics* as well as the *Analytics*; whereas in fact Aristotle really finds no place for the *Topics* in his philosophy of science. [W. D. Ross, *Aristotle*, 5th ed., London, 1949, pp. 20 f., 56 ff.; D. J. Allan, *The Philosophy of Aristotle*, London, 1952, Pt. IV] I imagine the underlying reason for this to be that, as we have seen earlier [1.1], Aristotle has no notion of ampliative induction and consequently, as we shall see shortly, no notion of inductive probability either. Hence, in his view, the statements of the sciences are only true, so that the theory of their deductive systematization must take the form of a logic of truth.

Finally, as I said above, it is convenient to refer to the Logic of Inductive Probability and the Logic of Inductive Truth collectively as Inductive Logic; the investigations in 3.2 and in parts of the present 2.2 belong to this study. I turn now to non-deductive derivative formulas.

2.2.2 *Non-deductive Derivative Formulas, and Casual Probability*

Take the formula, $(15')$, $\delta PF(fAg, \alpha P(f'Ag) . \gamma C_2)$. An exemplification is: 'The fact that all examined boys in the school very, very probably have chicken-pox, and that they are a varied sample, makes it fairly probable that all the boys in the school have chicken-pox'. The pertinent rule is *Rule* (7). *In judgements of the type of formula* $(15')$, *the degree of probabilification of the probabilified-proposition varies directly as the degree of probability of the probability-judgement in the probabilifying-proposition, and as the degree of variety in the sample.* Thus, cp. with formula $(15')$ the formulas: $\epsilon PF(fAg, \beta P(f'Ag) . \gamma C_2)$; and $\gamma PF(fAg, \alpha P(f'Ag) . \beta C_2)$. It is to be understood that the probability-judgement in the probabilifying-proposition is inductive, else the whole judgement is not inductive. In practice, it might well be hypothetic rather than inductive, as diagnoses from symptoms often are. It is worth noticing in this connexion that Inductive Philosophy apparently originated in reflection on medical diagnosis; the de Lacy locate the first sources of Epicurean empiricism in the works of the Hippocratic corpus (5th–4th centuries B.C.). [Philodemus, 120 ff.; Stocks, 203]

This completes my account of derivative subject-predicate formulas that are purely inductive and so homogeneous. But in the interests of general clarity about inductive probability, it is essential to take into consideration certain heterogeneous derivative formulas that are partly inductive. They are in fact all casual and inductive formulas, so that in the course of the discussion it will be necessary to explain the meaning of 'casual probability'.

Take first the formula, $(5')$, $\delta PF(gx, \alpha P(fMg).fx.C_1)$. An exemplification is: 'Since most BU are very, very probably H, and this is a·BU, and C_1 is satisfied, it is fairly probable that this is H'. The relevant rule is *Rule* (8). *In judgements of the type of formula* $(5')$, *the degree of probability of the probabilified proposition varies directly as the degree of probability of the probability-judgement in the probabilifying-proposition, and as the quantity of the latter judgement approaches to universality.* Thus, cp. with formula $(5')$ the following formulas. First, $\epsilon PF(gx, \beta P(fMg).fx.C_1)$. And second, writing 'nearly all' as N, $\gamma PF(gx, \alpha P(fNg).fx.C_1)$. Formula $(5')$ is partly inductive because, as has been said, the probability-judgement-formula in the probabilifying-proposition-formula is understood to be inductive. It should be compared with formula $(6')$, $\gamma PF(gx, fMg.fx.C_1)$. The essential difference between them is that in $(6')$ the constituent formula fMg is a true description-formula, whereas in $(5')$ the corresponding constituent formula $\alpha P(fMg)$ is a probable-induction-formula. Accordingly, $(6')$ is an homogeneous casual formula; I shall discuss it shortly. $(5')$ is an important formula, since it illustrates the application of a probable preponderant generalization to an individual case. Hence, most of our inductive inferences about Tom, Dick and Mary exemplify it. For we have seen that most of what we call our knowledge of human nature consists of preponderant generalizations which are more often probable than true, e.g. 'In all probability almost everyone resents ingratitude'.

Take next the formula, $(16')$, $\gamma PF(m/nP(gx), \gamma P(fm/ng).fx.C_1)$. An exemplification is: 'Since m-$n$ths BU are probably H, and this is a BU, and C_1 is satisfied, it is (inductively) probable that it is (casually) probable in the degree m-$n$ths that this is H'. The pertinent rule is *Rule* (9). *In judgements of the type of formula* $(16')$, *the degree of (casual) probability of the first-order probabilified-proposition is the same as, and hence varies directly as, the quantity of the probable induction in the probabilifying-proposition; and the degree of (inductive) probability of the second-order probabilified-proposition is the same as, and hence varies directly as, the degree of probability of the induction in the probabilifying-proposition.* Thus, cp. with formula $(16')$ the formula: $\beta PF(m/nP(gx), \beta P(fm/ng).fx.C_1)$. The essential differences between formulas $(16')$ and $(5')$ are these. In $(5')$ the probable induction in the probabilifying-proposition is non-numerical, whereas in $(16')$ it is numerical. Consequently, in $(16')$ we get what is sometimes called a probability of a probability, but is better called a probability-judgement about a probability-judgement or a second-order probability-judgement; Nisbet speaks of 'probable chance'. [Nisbet, 10] But in ($5'$) we get no higher-order judgement, since we amalgamate, so to speak, the casual and the inductive probabilities involved. We do not say 'It is (inductively) very, very probable that it is (casually) probable that p'; we say instead 'It is fairly probable that p'. As far as I can see, there are no probability-judgements of orders higher than the second, and the first-order judgement in a second-order judgement is always a numerical casual one. However, formula ($16'$) is not the sole type of second-order judgements, since these can be hypothetic as well as inductive. To explain. I have discussed above the probabilification of proportional or statistical hypotheses, such as '51% births are male'. [1.2] But proportional hypotheses are often expressed in the (descriptively) equivalent form of probability hypotheses, such as 'There is a probability of 51% of a birth's being male'. Suppose now that this probability hypothesis is probabilified in the way sketched in Example (vi). It is then in order to make the judgement: 'It is (hypothetically) probable that there is a (casual) probability of 51% of a birth's being male'. Finally, formula ($16'$) should be compared with the corresponding homogeneous casual formula, $m/n\mathrm{PF}(gx, fm/ng \cdot fx \cdot C_1)$. As with formulas ($5'$) and ($6'$), the essential difference is that in it the constituent formula fm/ng is a true description-formula, whereas in ($16'$) the constituent formula $\gamma\mathrm{P}(fm/ng)$ is a probable induction-formula.

I shall now discuss the two casual primitive probabilification-judgement-formulas, the numerical and the non-numerical; i.e. make an excursion to explain the descriptive meaning of 'casual probability'.

The relevant rules of probabilification are these. First, in judgements of these types, the degree of probabilification of the probabilified-proposition is greater as the quantity of the proportional description in the probabilifying-proposition approaches to universality. Thus, cp. with formula ($6'$), $\gamma\mathrm{PF}(gx, fMg \cdot fx \cdot C_1)$, the formula $\beta\mathrm{PF}(gx, fNg \cdot fx \cdot C_1)$. Second, in judgements of these types, the degree of probabilification of the probabilified-proposition is numerical only when the quantifier of the proportional description in the probabilifying-proposition is numerical. This is precisely the difference between formula ($6'$) and the formula

$m/n\mathrm{PF}(gx, fm/ng . fx . C_1)$. Third, in judgements of these types, the probabilified-proposition is not probabilified at all unless C_1 is satisfied, i.e. unless x has been randomly selected from among f. As Peirce says: 'When the partial rule that the proportion ρ of the Ms are Ps is applied to show with probability ρ that S is a P, it is requisite, not merely that S should *be* an M, but also that it should be an instance drawn *at random* from among the Ms'. [Peirce, 192] Hence, the formula $\gamma\mathrm{PF}(gx, fMg . fx)$ is unsound; though the formula, (6), $\mathrm{E}(gx, fMg . fx)$ is not.

In casual primitive judgements the probabilified-proposition logically must be singular. It will be recalled that in inductive primitive judgements, however, the probabilified-proposition logically must be general; see formulas (2'), (10') and (11'). Thus, Tippett writes concerning 'the statistician's definition of probability as a ratio of frequencies' that '. . . statistical probability is a device (a verbal trick!) for attaching to the random individual the characteristics of the whole distribution. In this way, a population is epitomized in an individual. . . .' [Tippett, 119] The expression 'statistical probability', like 'mathematical probability', is synonymous with my 'casual probability'. The other vital differences between casual and inductive primitive judgements are as follows. Only degrees of casual probabilification are always in principle, if not always in practice, measurable in the strict sense and expressible by a fraction. Above all, their criteria of degree of probabilification are different, as witness the difference between the three rules of probabilification just formulated and Rules (1) and (2). This of course is precisely the distinction of descriptive meaning between casual and inductive probability.

To understand formulas (5'), (6') and (16'), it is necessary to be clear about the different possibilities respecting the status of the proportional proposition-formula in the probabilifying proposition-formula. Consider the following three cases. *Case (a)*. The proportional proposition is a true description. This is so e.g. in the judgement 'Since m-$n$ths BU are H and this is a random BU, there is a probability of m-$n$ths that this is H', which exemplifies the formula $m/n\mathrm{PF}(gx, fm/ng . fx . C_1)$. This judgement is purely casual and so homogeneous, and the constituent proportional proposition is established simply by observation and counting.

Case (b). The proportional proposition is a probable induction.

This is the case with formulas $(5')$ and $(16')$, which are heterogeneous, i.e. only partly inductive, because partly casual as well. However, the constituent probable induction may be established in different ways, as the following examples will show. *Example* (i). Take the judgement: 'Since *m-n*ths BU are probably H and this is a random BU, there is probably a probability of *m-n*ths that this is H'. Here, the constituent judgement '*m-n*ths BU are probably H' is likely to be a probable primitive induction; cp. the formula, $(11')$, $\gamma PF(fm/ng \cdot f'm/ng \cdot \gamma C_2 \cdot \gamma C_6)$. I.e., it will be established by observing, appraising and generalizing from the statistical evidence of the observed BU.

Example (ii). Take now the judgement: 'Since one-sixth of all throws with this die are probably ace, and the next throw is a random throw, there is probably a probability of one-sixth that the next throw will be ace'. Here, the constituent judgement may have the same status as in Example (i) and be a probable primitive induction. But there are other possibilities as well. I may have reasoned: 'Since one-sixth of all throws with all dice that are regular and homogeneous cubes are probably ace, and this is a die that is a regular and homogeneous cube, one-sixth of all throws with this die are probably ace'. Here, the constituent judgement is a probable deductive derivative induction; cp. the formula, $(3')$, $\gamma PF(gx, \gamma P(fAg) \cdot fx)$. The example illustrates the consilience of (probable) inductions. By applying a previously established probable generalization about all dice that are regular etc. to the particular case of this die, I obtain a probable proportional derivative induction which I can apply in turn to the particular case of the next throw with this die.

Case (c). The proportional proposition is a true induction, i.e. an induction the evidence for which is judged to be conclusive. This case resembles Case (a) in that the probabilified-proposition is true, and Case (b) in that it is an induction. Consider e.g. the judgement: 'Since *m-n*ths BU are H and this is a random BU, there is a probability of *m-n*ths that this is H'. It will be perceived that we use the same sentence to express this judgement as we use to express the different judgement in Case (a); the two types of judgement are therefore likely not to be distinguished. However, if we use notation already explained, the difference between the corresponding formulas is plain enough. For the formula in this case, (c), is: $m/nPF(gx, I(fm/ng) \cdot fx \cdot C_1)$, which is not the same as the formula in Case (*a*). The above judgement also resembles that in Case (*a*) in that the degree of probabilification of the conclusion is determined exclusively by the quantifier of the proportional proposition. But it also resembles that in Case (*b*) in that it is an heterogeneous and not an homogeneous judgement, and in that its constituent proportional proposition cannot be established simply by observation and counting, since it is an induction and not a description. The latter may in fact be established in different ways according as it is a primitive or derivative true induction; this point has been sufficiently explained under Case (*b*).

Something must next be said about the meaning of C_1. 'Random selection or sampling' is defined as follows: 'We may give a formal definition of random sampling by saying that the selection of an individual from a universe is random when each member of the universe has the same chance of being chosen. Similarly, a sample of *n* individuals is random when it is chosen in such a way that, when the choice is made, all possible samples of *n* have an equal chance of being selected.' [Yule, 336; Jeffreys, 48 f.] It will be perceived that 'random sampling' is defined in terms of 'equal probability'. This sense of 'randomness' should be distinguished from that which it bears in von Mises' definition of probability, discussed above. [2.1] The two senses are quite distinct, and in fact von Mises' *Regellosigkeit* is more naturally translated 'irregularity'.

The preceding definition of 'random sampling' naturally raises the further question: When does every possible individual, or sample of *n* individuals, have an equal chance of being selected? As we have already seen [2.1], the answer given is: When a reliable method of random sampling is employed. But this in turn naturally raises the further question: When is a method of random sampling (called) reliable? The answer given to this is: A method of random sampling is said to be (very, fairly, etc.) reliable if, when it has been applied to a (very, fairly, etc.) great variety of populations of known compositions, it has selected every possible individual, or sample of size *n*, with approximately equal frequency. [Yule, 346] I shall argue later [4.3] that 'reliable' in this context has the same descriptive meaning as 'inductively probable'. When *x* has been selected from among *f* by a (very, fairly, etc.) reliable method of random sampling, we know that it is (very, fairly, etc.) inductively probable that C_1 is satisfied. Hence, judgements of the form, $(6')$, $\gamma PF(gx, fMg \cdot fx \cdot C_1)$, are less common in practice than judgements of the form, $(17')$, $\delta PF(gx, fMg \cdot fx \cdot \alpha P(C_1))$. The latter is of course an heterogeneous formula, being partly casual and partly inductive. The pertinent rule is *Rule* (10). *In judgements of the type of formula* $(17')$, *the degree of probabilification of the probabilified-proposition is greater as the degree of probability of the probability-judgement in the probabilifying-proposition is greater, and as the quantifier of the proportional description in the probabilifying-proposition approaches to universality.* Thus, cp. with formula $(17')$ the formula: $\delta PF(gx, fNg \cdot fx \cdot \beta P(C_1))$.

Before leaving this question of the satisfaction of C_1, we should notice the following difficulty. Consider again the judgement discussed above: 'Since one-sixth of all throws with this die are probably ace, and the next throw is a random throw, there is probably a probability of one-sixth that the next throw will be ace'. What justification is there for the claim that the next throw is (or is probably) a random throw? Evidently, not that the next throw has been selected from among all possible throws with this die by a (perfectly, fairly, etc.) reliable method of random sampling, such as lottery-sampling; for such techniques are obviously inapplicable to this case. The difficulty turns on an important distinction between types of population or universe. Whereas the classes of e.g. BU, or present inhabitants of London, are called by the statisticians 'existent' populations, the classes of e.g. throws (i.e. all possible throws) with this die, or of births, are called by them 'hypothetical' populations. [Yule, 333] I shall argue in due course that there is an interesting connexion between the degree of probability of generalizations and the nature of the populations that they are about. [5.2] The above-mentioned difficulty about ensuring that an individual or sample is selected at random from an hypothetical population is noticed, but not met, by Yule and Kendall. [Yule, 345] Since I too am unable to provide a solution, I must leave it to the reader to make what he can of it.

The last of these heterogeneous, casual and inductive, formulas that I propose to consider is formula $(18')$: $\eta PF(gx, \alpha P(bMg \cdot fMb) \cdot fx \cdot C_1)$. An exemplification is: 'Since it is very, very probable that most holders of absolute power become tyrants and that most successful revolutionary leaders become holders of absolute power, and N is a random successful revolutionary leader, there is an appreciable probability that N will become a tyrant'. The pertinent rule is *Rule* (11). *In judgements of the type of formula* (18'), *the degree of probabilification of the probabilified-proposition is greater as the degree of probability of the inductions in the probabilifying-proposition is greater, and as the quantities of the latter approach to universality.* Thus, cp. with formula (18') the formula: ηPF(gx, βP(hNg . fNh) . fx . C$_1$).

Formula (18') is important, because it shows how we apply to an individual case a number of probable preponderant generalizations, as opposed to a single such generalization as illustrated by formula (5'). As the example shows, this is a thing we often do. A point that needs explaining is just how this type of inference goes. Take first the simpler case in which the proportional statements in the probabilifying-proposition are true descriptions, not probable inductions; the formula corresponding to (18') is: ϵPF(gx, hMg . fMh . fx . C$_1$). This inference is to be analysed into two steps: first, γPF(hx, fMh . fx . C$_1$); and second, ϵPF(gx, hMg . γP(hx) . C$_1$). *Mutatis mutandis*, the two steps in (18') are: first, δPF(hx, αP(fMh) . fx . C$_1$); and second, ηPF(gx, αP(hMg) . δP(hx) . C$_1$).

2.2.3 *Some Accounts of Casual Probability and Related Concepts*

I shall conclude with some remarks on philosophers' accounts of casual probability and related matters. Since I am more concerned in this book to be constructive than to be critical, I shall be as brief as possible. It will be convenient to proceed more or less chronologically.

It appears from the preceding discussion that casual probability is a fairly simple conception. It is consequently not surprising to find its meaning tolerably well explained early in the history of Western Philosophy. By contrast, inductive probability was first analyzed in an elementary way and distinguished from casual probability by Hume, and not commonly recognized by philosophers as a distinct notion before the 19th century. The existence of inductive inference, on the other hand, was recognized and discussed much earlier. And hypothetic probability has not received much attention from philosophers, and been distinguished from casual and inductive probability, until the last quarter-century. In this case too, however, the existence of hypothetic inference was recognized much earlier.

We will begin with Aristotle (384–322 B.C.), whose account of probability is as follows: '. . . that which people know to happen or not to happen, or to be or not to be, usually (ὡς ἐπί τὸ πολύ) in a particular way, is a probability (εἰκός): e.g., that the envious are malevolent or that those who are loved are affectionate'. [Aristotle, 522 f.]

Aristotle may be interpreted, then, as saying that the meaning of 'the probable' (τὸ εἰκός) is 'the preponderant' (τὸ ὡς ἐπί τὸ πολύ). Keynes puts the same point another way when he fathers the relative frequency theory of probability on Aristotle. However, Aristotle's account is open to the following criticisms. First, this is an account of the meaning, not of probability in general, but of casual probability. Aristotle has no conception of inductive or hypothetic probability. The former is not surprising since, as we have seen earlier [1.1], Aristotle has no notion of ampliative inductive inference; his ἐπαγωγή does not mean this. As to the latter, however, we have seen [1.2] that he does recognize the existence of hypothetic inference. Second, his definition commits the naturalistic fallacy; he should say rather that 'the preponderant' gives the descriptive meaning of 'the casually probable', not the meaning in general, i.e. the evaluative and descriptive meaning. Third, his account of the descriptive meaning of casual probability is defective inasmuch as he omits the condition of random selection, C_1. The last two criticisms touch most of the authors discussed below; I shall not repeat them in the case of each writer.

Consider next Philodemus (1st century B.C.), spokesman for the Epicureans. He too understands by 'probability' τὸ ὡς ἐπί τὸ πολύ; i.e. he equates probability with casual probability. [Philodemus, 82 f.] He does indeed also use the word εὐλογία, understanding by it 'plausibility'. [Philodemus, 190]

It is surprising that the Epicureans, like Aristotle, have no notion of inductive probability; for, unlike him, they have a clear notion of ampliative induction or analogical inference, their terms for which are ἐπιλογισμός, μετάβασις καθ' ὁμοιότητα or ὁ καθ' ὁμοιότητα τρόπος. [Philodemus, 189 f.; Stocks, 198] The explanation is that they think generalizations, when rightly made, to be necessary and not probable. Thus, Philodemus writes e.g.: '. . . we Epicureans take this to be necessarily connected with that from the fact that this has been observed to be a property of that in all cases that we have come upon. . . .' [Philodemus, 105, 123,

137; Stocks, 198 ff.] I suppose that this aberration is due to their confusing universality with necessity; to their supposing e.g. that because 'All men are animals' is necessary, 'All men are mortals' is so too. Hence, the criterion that Philodemus gives of what may be called 'inductive necessity' is properly that of inductive probability. His criterion is this: '. . . it is not necessary to include all appearances in our experience, and we should not rely merely on chance appearances. We must consider many homogeneous and varied ones, so that from our experience of them and from the accounts of history concerning them we may take the inseparable constituent of each of them individually, and from these we may infer to all the others. For example, if men are found to differ in all other respects, but in one respect they have been observed to have no difference, why shall we not say confidently on the basis of the men that we have ourselves met with and those of whom we have historical knowledge, that all men are liable to old age and disease?' [Philodemus, 70 f.] This is, for its date, an excellent account, and it is only to be regretted that the Epicureans do not advance it as the criterion of inductive probability. For the criterion given by Philodemus is of course identical with my C_2. [2.1]

And so it seems that the only concept of probability known to the Greeks generally is that of casual probability, though the Epicureans have an excellent grasp of inductive reasoning. It is worth adding that the Sceptics too seem to be well-informed on these topics. One of the few things known about the doctrines of Carneades and Clitomachus (2nd century B.C.) is that they recognized the existence of degrees of probability and the frequent necessity of acting on probabilities rather than certainties. They seem also to have arrived at their views in the course of opposing popular beliefs in divination, magic and astrology. The views of Sextus Empiricus (2nd century A.D.) on these matters are also interesting, and of course we know much more of them, since his works survive. [Philodemus, 171 ff.; Stocks, 194 ff.] The facts that Sextus was a physician and that Carneades and Clitomachus wrote to oppose divination, illustrate the point that it was largely through critical reflection on the arts of Medicine and Divination that men were led to study the nature of inference from omens, symptoms, evidences and signs. And of course minds of an empirical and sceptical habit naturally find the field of study congenial; after all, Hume too was an Empirical Sceptic.

The author we shall consider next is de Moivre. In his *Doctrine of Chances* (1718) he writes: 'The probability of an event is greater or less according to the number of chances by which it may happen compared with the number of all the chances by which it may either happen or fail. Thus if an event has three chances to happen and two to fail, the probability of its happening may be estimated to be 3/5 and the probability of its failing 2/5.' [Quoted in Kneale, 119]

Kneale thinks that this marks the first appearance of numerical (casual) probability-judgements. [Kneale, II, 310] There is certainly no trace of them in the discussions of Aristotle and Philodemus, who are content to explain the meaning of (casual) probability in terms of the non-numerical quantifier 'Most'.

In speaking of 'the number of chances by which an event may happen', de Moivre has in mind judgements of the type: 'Since one-sixth of all throws with this die are ace, and the next throw is a random throw, there is a probability of one-sixth that the next throw will be ace'. It will be recalled that I distinguished this type of judgement from judgements of the type 'Since one-sixth BU are H, and this is a random BU, there is a probability of one-sixth that it is H'. The basis of the distinction I drew was the way in which the proportional proposition in the probabilifying-proposition is established. In the latter case, the proportional proposition 'One-sixth BU are H' may be either a description or a generalization judged to be true. In the former case, the proportional proposition 'One-sixth of all throws with this die are ace' may likewise be a primitive induction judged to be true; but it may also be a deductive derivative induction from 'One-sixth of all throws with all dice that are regular and homogeneous cubes are ace, and this is a die that is a regular and homogeneous cube'. In throwing dice, and in games of chance generally, we tend to establish the relevant proportional proposition in the latter way. I.e., we do not establish it by throwing the die a number of times and generalizing from this direct statistical evidence. Rather, we first establish that this die is a regular and homogeneous cube, and then subsume the case under the wider generalization about throws with dice that are regular and homogeneous cubes. When we do this, our judgement that there is a probability of one-sixth that the next throw with this die will be ace, is in Kneale's phrase 'relatively *a priori*'.

[Kneale, 197 ff.] It is because he has games of chance in mind that de Moivre employs the term 'chances'.

It is sometimes said that the correct formulation of primitive casual judgements is not e.g. 'Since two-thirds BU are H, and this is a random BU, there is a probability of two-thirds that this BU is H', but rather 'Since two-thirds BU are H, there is a probability of two-thirds that any (or a) BU is H'. See e.g. Kneale's remarks about what he calls 'probability rules in matters of chance'. [Kneale, 117 f.] However, this manner of formulation seems to me to obscure the essential point, which is how in judgements of this type we establish the degree of probability that some actual individual possesses some or other attribute. Of course, in this formulation 'any' means 'any random'. And this being so, we can if we wish insert the recommended formulation as an extra constituent in the judgement, thus: 'Since two-thirds BU are H, there is a probability of two-thirds that any random BU is H; but this is a random BU; therefore, there is a probability of two-thirds that it is H'. But it is not necessary to do so, nor is anything lost if it is not done.

I pass now to the views of Hume, as expounded in his *Treatise of Human Nature* (1739). We noticed earlier [1.2] that Hume discriminates different 'kinds' of probability; namely, the probabilities of chances, of causes, of analogy, and unphilosophical probability. I now propose to consider further the first pair, which represent the chief of these distinctions, in order to answer two questions. First, what precisely, on Hume's account, is the difference between the probability of chances and the probability of causes? And second, is this distinction of Hume's the same as the distinction between casual and inductive probability?

The answer to the first question appears readily from the examples that he gives. His instance of the probability of chances is, with slight modifications: 'Since two-thirds of throws with this die yield a number greater than 2, and the next throw is a random throw, there is a probability of two-thirds that it will yield a number greater than 2'. [Hume, T, 127 ff.] And his instance of the probability of causes may be rendered: 'Since nineteen-twentieths of observed ships that sail from London return safely, and this is a random ship sailing from London, there is a probability of nineteen-twentieths that she will return safely'. The difference between the two instances resides solely in the ways in which the proportional propositions in the probabilifying-propositions are established. In the latter, 'I have found, by long observation, that of twenty ships which go to sea, only nineteen return'. [Hume, T, 134] But in the former, there is no question of 'long observation' of the proportion of throws with this die that yield a number greater than 2. We establish the proposition, Hume says, by reflecting that the die must fall with one and only one of its six faces uppermost; that there is no reason to suppose that it will fall with any one face upward rather than another; and that of these six equally probable alternatives, four are favourable to obtaining a number greater than 2.

The answer to the second question is as follows. Unfortunately, Hume fails to appreciate that inductive probability is actually involved in his own instance of the probability of causes; that the constituent proportional proposition in his example is really the true or probable generalization 'Nineteen-twentieths of ships . . . etc.', and not, as he states, the description 'Nineteen-twentieths of observed ships . . . etc.'. He thus falls into what Keynes represents as the root error of the relative frequency theorists. [Keynes, 95 ff.; Venn, L, 207 f.] Namely, in saying that 'relative frequency' is *the* (descriptive) meaning of 'probability', they fail to see two points. First, that we much more commonly make heterogeneous casual and inductive judgements of the forms, $(5')$, $\delta PF(gx, \alpha P(fMg) \cdot fx \cdot C_1)$ and $\gamma PF(gx, I(fMg) \cdot fx \cdot C_1)$ than homogeneous purely casual judgements of the form, $(6')$, $\gamma PF(gx, fMg \cdot fx \cdot C_1)$. Second, that the sense of 'probable' in which the probability-judgement-formula in the probabilifying-judgement-formula in $(5')$ is probable, is not the same as the sense in which the probabilified-proposition-formula in $(6')$ is probable.

Despite his failure to see these points, Hume does in fact recognize that generalizations are frequently called probable rather than true. He states that this sort of probability arises from 'imperfect experience', meaning, when the number of observed instances is (judged to be) insufficient to make the generalization in question certain or true. He observes, significantly, that '. . . the species of probability here explained [is] the first in order'. But he proceeds at once to depreciate its importance as compared with that of a second sort of probability, namely casual probability, which arises from 'contrariety in our experience', meaning, when the conjunction we observe of g with f is 'frequent' (i.e. preponderant) rather than 'constant' (i.e. universal). [Hume, T, 131]. These few remarks of Hume's constitute, so far as I can discover, the first explicit philosophical recognition of the existence of Inductive Probability and the first theory of the 'source' or ground of the several degrees of it; namely, the number of the observed instances in favour of the generalization.

It is natural to wonder whether Bacon has not anything of value to say in his *Novum Organum* (1620) about inductive probability, or at least about inductive reasoning. But in fact he has not. As to inductive probability, the reason is that he wrongly holds that inductions ought to be and, when established by the method that he recommends, are, true or certain rather than probable. And as to inductive inference, the reason is that he falsely maintains 'true' (i.e. proper) induction to be a mechanical process of establishing causal laws by elimination or 'exclusion'. [Bacon, 14, 20 f.; Kneale, 48 ff.; Lalande, 40 ff.] I say 'falsely' because, although sound generalization may indeed be correctly described as 'eliminative', it is not eliminative in the sense or way that Bacon describes.

[5.1] Mill in his *Logic* (1st ed. 1843) is at one with Bacon on these two fundamental points, so that the same criticisms apply to both authors. But to avoid misunderstanding, I should add that their being wrong on these two central issues by no means involves that they have nothing to contribute to Inductive Philosophy. Their strength lies in their incidental discussions rather than in their positive theories; those of Mill in particular are full of valuable insights. Nor are they the only inductive philosophers whose constructive doctrines are unacceptable, yet have much to teach us on this range of topics.

Laplace, in a celebrated passage of his *Philosophical Essay on Probabilities* (1819), writes as follows: 'The theory of chance consists in reducing all the events of the same kind to a certain number of cases equally possible, that is to say, to such as we may be equally undecided about in regard to their existence, and in determining the number of cases favourable to the event whose probability is sought. The ratio of this number to that of all the cases possible is the measure of this probability, which is thus simply a fraction whose numerator is the number of favourable cases and whose denominator is the number of all the cases possible.' [Laplace, 6 f.]

It will be perceived that Laplace explicitly states that this fraction is the measure, not the definition, of (casual) probability. Consideration of the passage from de Moivre quoted above shows that this is in effect his view also. However, Laplace is often misrepresented on this point. E.g., in a well-known text-book on the Calculus of Probabilities we find the following under the head, 'Classical Definition of Mathematical Probability': '*Definition of Mathematical Probability*. If, consistent with condition *S*, there are *n* exhaustive, mutually exclusive, and equally likely cases, and *m* of them are favourable to an event *A*, then the mathematical probability of *A* is defined as the ratio *m/n*.' [J. V. Uspensky, *Introduction to Mathematical Probability*, New York, 1937, pp. vii, 6] Considered as a definition of 'probability', this is of course open to the charge of circularity, as Poincaré points out. [Poincaré, 156] For the word to be defined occurs in the defining expression. It will be noticed, incidentally, that whereas Uspensky writes of 'equally likely (or probable) cases', Laplace himself writes of 'equally possible' ones; a paradoxical locution, since we do not ordinarily speak or think of possibility as possessing degrees.

This talk of equally probable (or possible) cases naturally prompts the question, When are cases (or alternatives) equally probable? As is well known, Laplace answers, When they are not known not to be. This criterion is known as the Principle of Indifference (or of Insufficient Reason). It does not originate with Laplace, for J. Bernoulli e.g. writes in his *Ars Conjectandi* (1713) that the tickets in a lottery are equally likely to be selected '. . . because there is no apparent reason why this or that one should be drawn rather than any other'. [Quoted in Kneale, 147] The principle has been subjected to criticisms that seem to me, and apparently to most philosophers, conclusive. They are given by Keynes and Kneale, and there is no point in retailing them here. [Keynes, 41 ff.; Kneale, 147 ff.] Fundamentally, the trouble with the principle is that it admits total ignorance as the test of the equal probability of alternatives; whereas in fact we must of course have knowledge before we can judge them to be equally probable. It is plausibly suggested that Laplacians confuse the true assertion, that alternatives are equally probable if we know that there is no reason to think them unequally probable, with the false assertion that they are equally probable if we do not know that there is any reason to think them unequally probable. The latter formulation is evidently compatible with our knowing nothing about the matter whatever, whereas the former is not. [Kneale, 172 f.] As to the forms that our knowledge takes, we have seen earlier that they are various. The simplest case is that in which we use direct statistical evidence; we judge e.g. that the alternatives heads or tails when this penny is thrown are equally probable because, in a long succession of throws, heads and tails have been observed to occur with approximately equal frequency. But we may also judge that these alternatives are equally probable because we know that this penny is a regular and homogeneous body, and that the laws of motion involve that when regular and homogeneous bodies of this sort are thrown by human agency (i.e. in a purely random way), they land with one or the other face upwards with approximately equal frequency in the long run.

It seems to me that the opening sentence of the citation from Laplace is also open to criticism. For it involves that we can measure degrees of casual probability, and perhaps even make casual probability-judgements at all, only when we judge certain alternatives to be equally probable. Kneale too agrees that '. . . the measure of [casual] probability is to be defined by reference to equiprobable alternatives'. [Kneale, 149] But this is surely not so. From observation of the outcomes of a very great variety and number of throws with this die, I judge that one quarter of all throws with it are aces. I then apply this true generalization to the individual case of the next throw, and judge: 'Since one quarter of all throws with this die are aces, and the next throw is a random throw, there is a probability of one quarter that it will be an ace'. Here, the six possible alternative outcomes of a throw with this die are not equally probable; ace is favoured. Yet we can make a perfectly good casual probabilification-judgement about the next throw, and measure the probability of its being ace.

There seem to be two plausible explanations of Laplace's doctrine on the point. First, he may have been thinking of casual probability too much in terms of games of chance, which would be natural considering that the Calculus of Probabilities originated in attempts to solve problems in such games. For in these, the alternatives not merely are, but logically must be, equally probable, else they are not (rightly called) 'games of chance'. Games played with loaded dice or notched cards are not games of chance. In Nature, on the other hand, it is exceptional to find alternatives that are equally probable; consider an example already discussed, that of the sex-ratio. And these natural alternatives are of course vastly more numerous and more important than the artificial alternatives encountered in games of chance. Second, there is possibly some confusion between two ways in which equal probability may enter into casual probabilification-judgements. On the one hand, no primitive casual judgement is sound unless the individual in question had an equal chance of being selected with every other. This is the random selection condition, C_1, which accordingly applies to all such judgements. On the other hand, it may happen that the alternatives also are equally probable; but this, so far from having to be the case in a sound probabilification-judgement, is in fact not true of the great majority of such judgements that we make. I am tentatively suggesting that it is because he in some way confuses the second way in which equal probability may enter into sound casual judgements with the first way in which it must enter into them, that Laplace unduly restricts the scope of such judgements to cases in which the alternatives are equally probable.

E. F. Apelt, in his *Theory of Induction* (1854), distinguishes 'philosophical' from 'mathematical' probability. [Apelt, 34 ff.; 1.2] According to v. Wright, this distinction is first drawn by Apelt's master, the Kantian J. F. F. Fries, in his *System of Logic* (1811), and is also to be found in the works of a number of 19th-century philosophers, notably in the *Account of the Theory of Chances and Probabilities* (1843) of A. Cournot. These philosophers hold that an essential difference between the two concepts is that mathematical probability is measurable in the strict sense, whereas philosophical probability is not. [Wright, T, 296 f.]

From this it appears that, by the middle of the last century, the distinction first adumbrated by Hume between (what I call) casual and inductive probability was fairly widely recognized among philosophers. For it is pretty plain that this 'philosophical probability' means 'inductive probability'. At that time, 'philosophical' still meant 'scientific', and what these authors have in mind is the probability of inductive laws, especially of the functional or 'numerical' sort. We have already noticed that they are right in holding that measurability constitutes a major distinction between these two senses of 'probable'. [1.2]

An interesting modification of the relative frequency theory of (the meaning of) probability is due to Peirce, the best statement of whose views is to be found in his study, *A Theory of Probable Inference* (1883). In essence, it consists in replacing the notion of the relative frequency of events by that of the relative truth-frequency of propositions. Peirce claims to find the germs of his theory in the *Essay concerning Human Understanding* (1690) of Locke and the *Logic of Chance* (1st ed. 1866) of Venn. [Peirce, 158, 160; Locke, 334; Venn, L, 162 ff., 304 f.] The theory is justly described as 'pragmatic'; it is currently very fashionable, for which reason, as well as that of its intrinsic interest, I shall examine it in detail later. [4.3] We have also touched on it earlier in criticizing Keynes' notion of 'partial implication'. [1.2]

It will suffice for the moment to expound the gist of it, which is adequately conveyed by the following passage: 'To say . . . that a proposition has the probability ρ means that to infer it to be true would be to follow an argument such as would carry truth with it in the ratio of frequency ρ'. [Peirce, 193] E.g., 'Since there is a North wind, it is probably cold' means 'Most cases of the truth of "There is a North wind" are cases of the truth of "It is cold"'.

At present, I will make only two comments, and reserve the rest until later. This relative truth-frequency form of the relative frequency theory has one conspicuous *prima facie* advantage over the ordinary form. The latter is unable to provide any account of the probability of general propositions, and hence of generalizations or primitive inductions. For we have already noticed that the probabilified-proposition in primitive casual judgements of the form, (6'), $\gamma PF(gx, fMg \cdot fx \cdot C_1)$, logically must be singular. But the relative truth-frequency theorist can argue e.g. that 'Since all observed BU are H and varied, it is probable that all BU are H' means 'Most cases of the truth of "All observed so-and-so's are such-and-such and varied" are cases of the truth of "All so-and-so's are such-and-such"'. [Venn, L, 304 f.] However, the advantage turns out to be unreal. For, in giving this account of the probability of primitive inductions, the relative truth-frequency theorist commits himself to the position that degrees of inductive probability are always at least in principle measurable in the strict sense by a fraction. Given that we know that all observed BU are H and varied, and also that two-thirds of cases of the truth of 'All observed so-and-so's are such-and-such and varied' are cases of the truth of 'All so-and-so's are such-and-such', we must conclude that there is a probability of two-thirds that all BU are H. But this is false, as has been said more than once, and as we have just seen to have been common ground to numerous philosophers for a century. And since this logical consequence of the relative truth-frequency theory is false, the theory itself must of course be false too.

The most recent exponents of the relative frequency theory of probability are R. v. Mises and H. Reichenbach. In his *Probability, Statistics and Truth* (1st ed. 1928), v. Mises offers the following definition of the meaning of 'probability': 'It is possible to speak about probabilities only in reference to a properly defined collective. A collective means a mass phenomenon or an unlimited sequence of observations fulfilling the following two conditions: (i) the relative frequencies of particular attributes of single elements of the collective tend to fixed limits; (ii) these limits are not affected by any place selection. . . . The limiting value of the relative frequency of a given attribute, assumed to be independent of any place selection, will be called "the probability of that attribute within the given collective". Whenever this qualification of the word "probability" is omitted, this should be accepted as an abbreviation and the necessity for reference to some collective must be strictly kept in mind.' [Mises, 38] I have already explained the term 'independence of place selection' or 'irregularity' incidentally to discussing C_6, the condition of proportional stability. [2.1] With v. Mises' should be compared this earlier definition of Venn's: '. . . we may define the probability . . . of an event happening in a particular way as the numerical fraction which represents the proportion between the two different classes in the long run . . . The run must be supposed to be very long indeed, in fact never to stop. As we keep on taking more terms of the series we shall find the proportion still fluctuating a little, but its fluctuations will grow less. The proportion, in fact, will gradually approach towards some fixed numerical value, what mathematicians term its *limit*. This fractional value is the one spoken of above.' [Venn, L, 163 f.] The important difference between the two definitions is that 'irregularity' enters into v. Mises' but not into Venn's. This is also a main difference between v. Mises' definition and Reichenbach's, as presented in his *Experience and Prediction* (1938). [Reichenbach, 302 ff., 324 ff.]

Von Mises' theory has been subjected to a number of criticisms. I shall notice only one which involves inductive probability. In the first place, v. Mises claims to be defining the (descriptive) meaning of 'probability'; yet his definition itself reveals, upon examination, that there is more than one (descriptive) meaning of the word. Thus, it seems at first sight that the concept which his definition fits is, of course, casual probability, and that he is asserting this to be the unique meaning of 'probability'. However, his definition actually presupposes the existence of inductive probability too. For we logically cannot ever observe a limiting value of relative frequency, or the independence of all possible place selections of such a limiting value, or in short a collective. All we can observe is a limited succession of events; and if we conclude that such a succession is, or may be regarded as, part of a collective, this is an inductive inference from the evidence of that succession. For, as Broad asks: 'How are we justified in passing from the empirical premise that the frequency with which a certain die has fallen with 6 uppermost in the N times which, so far as we know, it has been thrown is so-and-so, to the conclusion that, if it were thrown infinitely many times, the frequency would approach indefinitely near to the limiting value so-and-so? Again, how can we establish empirically the very sweeping universal negative proposition that there is *no* way of selecting an infinite sub-class from the original class of throws which would have a different limiting frequency for the same alternative? If we have any rational ground for believing such conclusions on such evidence, must it not involve principles of probability in some important sense of "probability" not contemplated by von Mises?' [Quoted in Wisdom, 193] Thus, v. Mises is in the same sort of position as one would be who should claim that the descriptive meaning of 'probable' is given by the formula, $(16')$, $\gamma PF(m/nP(gx), \gamma P(fm/ng) . fx . C_1)$. For the objection to this claim is, of course, that the formula itself indicates that there is no such thing as *the* descriptive meaning of 'probable', since the sense in which the constituent formula $m/nP(gx)$ is probable is (descriptively) different from the sense in which the constituent formula $\gamma P(fm/ng)$ is probable.

In his *Logical Foundations of Probability* (1950), R. Carnap distinguishes two concepts of probability, which he calls respectively 'probability$_1$' and 'probability$_2$'. We saw earlier that by 'probability$_1$' he means 'degree of confirmation', and that the chief aim of his treatise is to explain the meaning of this expression. 1.2] By 'probability$_2$' he means 'relative frequency in the long run'. [Carnap, 25] But he adds that the two concepts are related, inasmuch as the meaning of 'probability$_1$' is explicable, not only as 'degree of confirmation', but also as 'an estimate of relative frequency [in the long run]'. [Carnap, 164] He writes: 'Thus we find an important connection between the two probability concepts: in certain cases *probability$_1$ may be regarded as an estimate of probability$_2$*. The relation between probability$_2$ and probability$_1$ is hence seen to be a special instance of the logical relation which holds generally between an empirical, e.g. physical, quantitative concept and the corresponding inductive-logical concept of its estimate with respect to given evidence.' [Carnap, 173]

He goes on to discuss Reichenbach's account, and correctly observes that the essential difference between their theories is, that whereas he (Carnap) holds that probability$_1$ and probability$_2$ are distinct concepts, Reichenbach maintains that 'probability' is fundamentally univocal. For although Reichenbach does indeed distinguish probability in the sense of limit of relative frequency (corresponding to Carnap's probability$_2$) from 'the logical concept of probability' or 'weight' (corresponding to Carnap's probability$_1$), he nevertheless argues that the meaning of the latter notion is explicable in terms of the former. [Reichenbach, 297 ff.] Carnap comments: 'It seems to me that it would be more in accord with Reichenbach's own analysis if his concept of weight were identified instead with the *estimate* of relative frequency'. [Carnap, 176]

Compare with this doctrine of Carnap's the definition of 'probability' offered by C. I. Lewis in his *Analysis of Knowledge and Valuation* (1946): 'We have suggested that instead of defining probability in the empiricist fashion so as to identify the measure of it with an actual objective frequency, we should . . . in order to be in accord with what is commonly and most usefully meant by "probability", identify it with a *valid estimate* of a frequency. That is, instead of holding that "The probability that c, which is an instance of the property ψ, will also have the property ϕ, is a/b", means, "The frequency of instances of ϕ among instances of ψ is a/b", we should take it to mean, "The frequency of instances of ϕ amongst instances of ψ is validly estimated from the data " 'D' " as a/b".' [Lewis, 303]

There is evidently truth in Carnap's account, inasmuch as from the evidence that in an observed sample of throws with this die the relative frequency of ace is $1/5$, we can only judge that it is inductively probable that, if we go on throwing it, the relative frequency will tend to the limiting value $1/5$ 'in the long run'. This is the same point that Broad makes in criticizing v. Mises' definition. (See above) But it is not therefore correct to say 'in certain cases probability$_1$ may be regarded as an estimate of probability$_2$'. The truth is rather that the notion of inductive probability may be illustrated, among other ways, by that sense of 'probable' in which we speak of an estimate of the limiting value of a relative frequency as made probable by the observed value of that relative frequency.

The gist of Lewis' account is that 'a probability is a valid estimate of a frequency from the given data'. [Lewis, 291] But what does 'valid' mean in this context? Manifestly, 'inductively probable'; Lewis has in mind the cases typified by formula (11′), $\gamma \mathrm{PF}(fm/ng, f'm/ng . \gamma C_2 . \gamma C_6)$. Hence, as a definition, the statement quoted is of course open to the charge of circularity. Moreover, it in effect equates 'probability' with 'inductive probability', and so reveals too narrow a view of the (descriptive) meaning of 'probable'. Elsewhere in his account of Probability, Lewis speaks of inductive probability as 'reliability'. Finally, his account is too narrow considered even as an account of the meaning of 'inductive probability'. For it is not true that the only things that are the subjects of inductively probable estimates are relative frequencies or ratios. In other words, (11′) is not the only type of primitive inductive probabilification-judgement-formula; there is also e.g. the formula, (7′), $\gamma \mathrm{PF}((\mathrm{A}a)(\mathrm{A}b)b = a, (\mathrm{A}a')(\mathrm{A}b')b = a . \gamma C_2 . \gamma C_3)$. I imagine that Lewis' preoccupation with relative frequencies springs from his common-sense recognition of the existence of casual as well as of inductive probabilities. Indeed, I suspect that what Lewis by his definition, and Carnap by his doctrine that probability$_1$ is sometimes an estimate of probability$_2$, really wish to draw attention to, is the existence of heterogeneous judgements of the form, (16′), $\gamma \mathrm{PF}(m/n\mathrm{P}(gx), \gamma \mathrm{P}(fm/ng) . fx . C_1)$.

Lewis' use of 'reliable' and 'valid' as synonyms for '(inductively) probable' is suggestive. The relation of reliability to (inductive) probability will be taken up later. [4.3] But it is worth noticing here certain resemblances and differences between probability and validity. The important resemblance, of course, is the evaluative nature of both words; 'valid' in this respect belongs with 'good', 'sound', 'reliable' and the other familiar substitutes for 'probable'.

The important difference, on the other hand, is that whereas that which is (called) probable is always a proposition and never an argument, that which is primarily (called) valid is an argument, and only secondarily a proposition that is the conclusion of such an argument. But some philosophers overlook this difference. When Peirce e.g. contends that what are probable are primarily arguments and secondarily propositions that are conclusions of such arguments, he is patently trying to interpret the meaning of 'probable' by analogy with that of 'valid'. The same is true of Keynes, whose account of 'the probability-relation' I have shown earlier to have important affinities with Peirce's views. [1.2]

Reichenbach and Carnap also offer accounts of the meaning of 'hypothetic probability'. [For a summary of their doctrines, see Nagel, 62 ff.] I remarked earlier that, although most students of these problems from the time of Huyghens onwards have recognized the existence of 'the probability of theories', some dispute it: I also outlined my own view of the descriptive meaning of this expression. [1.2]

Carnap attempts to explain 'degree of probabilification' of an hypothesis as its 'degree of confirmation'. But I have already argued that the latter expression is illogical, since it is said to mean 'degree of evidencing', and there are in fact no degrees of evidence. [1.2]

Reichenbach holds the meaning of 'probable' to be univocal and to mean always 'limiting value of relative frequency'. His attempt to explain the meaning of 'hypothetic probability' by means of this notion comes to this: he defines 'the degree of probability of an hypothesis' as 'the limiting value of the relative frequency of the true testable consequences deduced from the hypothesis and pertinent initial conditions, among the true pertinent initial conditions'. The sort of hypotheses that Reichenbach and Carnap have in mind are mainly non-empirical or 'abstract' scientific theories.

It will be perceived that Reichenbach's is a relative truth-frequency theory of the Peircian type. As Peirce tries to explain the meaning of 'inductive probability' in terms of 'relative truth-frequency in the long run', so Reichenbach tries to explain the meaning of 'hypothetic probability' in terms of the same conception. And the same criticism applies to his account as to Peirce's. I argued above that Peirce's account must be rejected because it involves the false consequence that degrees of inductive probability can be measured in the strict sense and expressed by a fraction. Similarly, Reichenbach's account must be rejected because it involves the no less false consequence that degrees of hypothetic probability can be so measured. For we saw earlier that Toulmin is surely right in saying that such judgements as 'The probability of the kinetic theory of gases is 17/18' make no sense.

Lastly, a few words on W. Kneale's constructive account of the meaning of 'casual probability' as contained in his *Probability and Induction* (1949), and on some connected remarks by R. B. Braithwaite in his *Scientific Explanation* (1953). [Kneale, 167 ff.; Braithwaite, 118 ff.; Wisdom, 196 ff.] Kneale summarizes his views in the following passage: 'It seems, then, that we are entitled to define the [casual] probability of an α thing's being β as the proportion of the range of α-ness which belongs also to the range of β-ness. . . . In trying to make clear what is meant by range we have had to distinguish different kinds of measurement. If α-ness determines a closed class, the measure of its range is the number of individuals belonging to that class. If, on the other hand, it determines an open class, the definition of the measure of its range is more complicated. First we must introduce the notion of a primary set of equipossible alternatives, and then we must allow for two distinguishable cases. If the smallest primary set of equipossible alternatives is finite, the measure of the range is the number of items in this set. If, however, the smallest set is infinite, because each alternative involves a different value for some continuous variable or variables, the measure of the range is to be conceived as the measure of a region in configuration space.' [Kneale, 190] He admits that his views derive from those of F. Waismann as given in his *Logical Analysis of the Concept of Probability* (1931), and ultimately from those of J. von Kries as contained in his *Principles of the Calculus of Probabilities* (1886). The reader will notice that the theory is elaborate, and rather than attempt a complete exposition and criticism of it, I shall concentrate on the point that seems to me central.

According to Kneale, then, 'degree of casual probability' always *means* 'ratio of ranges of possibilities', but the *measure* of one of the pertinent ranges differs accordingly as we are talking about 'closed' (i.e. finite) classes or 'open' (i.e. infinite) ones. We will consider the two cases in order. Take the casual probability-judgement: 'There is a probability of 51% that this (random) BU is H'. Here we are dealing with a finite class, namely BU, and the measure of the range of BU-ness is simply the number of BU. Hence, the degree of this probability is simply the proportion of BU that are H among BU. By contrast, consider the judgement: 'There is a probability of 51% that this (random) birth is male'. Here we are dealing with an infinite class, namely births. We cannot proceed as in the case of the finite class, saying that the measure of the range of birth-ness is the number of births, so that the degree of probability of this (random) birth being male is the proportion of births that are male among births. For this is to make nonsense of the probability-judgement, since a fraction with an infinite denominator has no meaning. Consequently, the definition of 'degree of probability' as 'ratio of ranges of possibilities' can be saved only if the measure of the relevant range in this type of case is, not the number of members of the pertinent class, but something else that is at any rate not infinite. The elaborate definition of the measure summarized by Kneale in the second half of the above citation is designed to fill this bill.

The reason for the sharp distinction that they draw between the two types of case is, then, our authors' belief that the statement 'The proportion of male births among births is 51%' is ('literally') meaningless, because 'in ordinary algebra a/b is only defined when a and b are finite numbers. . . .' [Braithwaite, 123] But is this not paradoxical? We surely do make statements of this type, as indeed Braithwaite seems to allow; and when we do so we may say if we like, as he does, that we are using 'proportion' in a 'non-literal sense'; but in any case we must recognize that we are using it in a different sense from that in which we are using it when we say 'The proportion of BU that are H among BU is 51%'. [Braithwaite, 118]

What I am suggesting is then this. The word 'proportion' has different senses accordingly as it figures in descriptions on the one hand and in inductions or hypotheses on the other. And it is only when it appears in a description that there is applicable to it the rule of significance that holds in ordinary Algebra, that numerator and denominator must both be finite. But such statements as 'The proportion of male births among births is 51%' must, of course, be either inductions or hypotheses; they cannot be descriptions since the infinite class of births cannot be observed. Hence, the distinction between finite and infinite populations and between the different senses of 'proportion' is chiefly important as indicating the fundamental distinction between descriptions on the one hand and inductions and hypotheses on the other. So that, in fine, I suspect that the basic distinction that Kneale is really after is, not that between casual probability-judgements about finite populations and casual probability-judgements about infinite populations, but rather that between homogeneous (casual) judgements and heterogeneous (casual and inductive, or casual and hypothetic) ones. The formulas which the two illustrative judgements exemplify are respectively: $51\% \, \mathrm{PF}(gx, f \, 51\% \, g \cdot fx \cdot C_1)$; and $51\% \, \mathrm{PF}(gx, \mathrm{I}(f51\% \, g) \cdot fx \cdot C_1)$, where the constituent $\mathrm{I}(f51\% \, g)$ is a conclusively evidenced and so true generalization-formula. (I am ignoring the case in which the constituent proportional formula is a true hypothesis-formula.)

It should be noticed, in conclusion, that the two divisions of casual probabilification-judgements into (a) those about finite populations vs. those about infinite populations, and (b) those in which the proportional statement in the probabilifying-proposition is a description vs. those in which it is a (true or probable) induction or hypothesis, do not completely coincide. For, although a proportional statement about an infinite population, such as that of births, must be an induction or hypothesis and cannot be a description, a proportional statement about a finite class, such as that of BU, may be either a description on the one hand or an induction or hypothesis on the other.

I will sum up this excursion into the descriptive meaning of 'casual probability' by recapitulating the main points. Historically considered, 'probable' was for long taken to be synonymous with 'casually probable'. Although ampliative inductive reasoning was discussed as early as the time of Philodemus, inductive probability was first discriminated as a separate sense of 'probability' by Hume, and attempts at systematic analyses of it date only from the 19th century. Somewhat similarly, although the existence of hypothetic inference was already recognized by Aristotle, and that of hypothetic probability by e.g. Huyghens in the 17th century, systematic analyses of the latter have not been attempted until quite recent times, notably by Reichenbach and Carnap.

In the probability-judgements that we actually make, it often happens that more than one of the three different descriptive meanings of 'probable' are involved; I call these heterogeneous judgements. And this is one reason why, in making a systematic analysis of the meaning of 'inductive probability', I have had to give some account of casual and hypothetic probability. For one sort of heterogeneous judgements is the partly inductive sort; they cannot be ignored by the philosopher of inductive probability, since not the least important feature of the logical behaviour of 'inductive probability' is precisely the ways in which it interlocks with casual and hypothetic probability. The other reason for dwelling at some length on casual and hypothetic probability is the necessity of examining the philosophical attempts to explain one of the three concepts of probability in terms of one of the others. Of chief importance to the philosopher of inductive probability are naturally attempts to explain the meaning of inductive probability in this manner. Such are the efforts, from Laplace to D. Williams, to explain it in terms of casual probability; and the endeavours of the hypothetists to explain it, or explain it away, by hypothetic probability. But there is also e.g. Reichenbach's attempt to explain hypothetic probability in terms of casual probability.

Finally, I believe that the historical fact of these attempted explanations or reductions is partly explicable by the existence of heterogeneous judgements in which the three descriptive meanings of 'probable' interlock in more or less intricate and subtle ways. For the existence of such judgements naturally enhances the risk of conflating them and the difficulty of discriminating them. The other explanation which has frequently been offered in recent literature is that we have here an instance of the insidious fallacy, *unum nomen, unum nominatum*. I.e., men have taken it for granted that, since there is but the one word 'probability', so there is but one concept, idea or meaning that it stands for. There is certainly much force in this contention, but I doubt whether it constitutes the complete explanation, which in my opinion requires reference to the existence of heterogeneous judgements as well. However all this may be, the meanings of casual and hypothetic probability, and their relations to inductive probability, have been sufficiently clarified for present purposes, so that from now on we can concentrate attention on the latter concept.

3 FUNCTIONAL INDUCTIVE PROBABILIFICATION-JUDGEMENT-FORMULAS

This topic has been neglected by philosophers of induction, so that in treating it one is inevitably to some extent breaking new ground. V. Wright scarcely exaggerates when he writes: 'It is astonishing how little has actually been done in this important field of research. Bacon's description of the *tabula graduum sive comparative* and Mill's account of the Method of Concomitant Variations are almost all that is available. . . .' [Wright, T, 83] Students have concentrated almost exclusively on subject-predicate generalizations, and indeed on the universal species of these; for, as v. Wright further observes, the establishment of proportional or statistical generalizations has likewise received less attention than the importance of the question warrants.

3.1 PRIMITIVE FORMULAS

Consider the formula, $(7')$, $\gamma \mathrm{PF}((\mathrm{A}a)(\mathrm{A}b)b = a, (\mathrm{A}a')(\mathrm{A}b')b = a \cdot \gamma \mathrm{C}_2 \cdot \gamma \mathrm{C}_3)$. An exemplification is: 'Since, for all observed values of the length and breadth of this leaf, its breadth in cms. is equal to its length in ins., and the observations have been made under varied conditions, and the observed values of the variables are numerous and evenly distributed over the range of observation; it is probable that, for all values of the length and breadth of this leaf, its breadth in cms. is equal to its length in ins.' The relevant rule is *Rule* (12). *In judgements of the type of formula* $(7')$, *the degree of probabilification of the probabilified-proposition varies directly as the variety of the conditions of observation; and as the number, and degree of evenness of distribution over the range of observation, of the observed values of the variables.* The formula and the rule show that one determinant of inductive probability, C_2, is common to both variable- and attribute-generalizations. But the condition C_3 is peculiar to variable-inductions, which is why there is a fundamental difference of descriptive meaning between attribute and variable primitive inductive probability-judgements.

The meaning of C_3 is very simple, and is most conveniently explained graphically. Cp. the following three figures:–

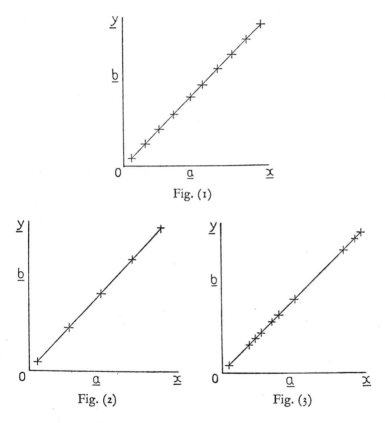

Fig. (1)

Fig. (2)   Fig. (3)

The difference between the cases illustrated by Fig. (1) and by Fig. (2) respectively is that in the former the observed values of the variables, which are represented by points, are more numerous than in the latter; whereas the difference between the cases illustrated by Fig. (1) and by Fig. (3) respectively is that in the former the observed values of the variables are more evenly distributed over the range of observation than in the latter.

Nor is the meaning of C_2 in the context of judgements of this type difficult to grasp. Thus, before making a generalization about the functional connexion between the absolute pressure and the volume of a given mass of gas, we must vary the conditions, e.g. the temperature, and see whether this possibly necessary qualifying condition is eliminable. In fact, as we have seen [1.1], it is not, so that the proviso 'at a constant temperature' is included in the formulation of Boyle's law. The position here is essentially the same as with attribute-generalizations. If the preceding very simple example about the values of the length and breadth of this leaf contained one qualifying attribute, as does Boyle's law, it would exemplify the formula: $\gamma PF((Afa)(Ab)b = a, (Afa')(Ab')b = a . \gamma C_2 . \gamma C_3)$.

Some generalizations are both attribute- and variable-generalizations; in such cases we generalize, so to speak, in two dimensions simultaneously. [Mace, 319 ff.] Consider e.g. the generalization: 'Provided the amplitude is small, the periods of all simple pendulums vary directly as the square root of their lengths'. Clearly, this is a doubly general judgement. Concentrating first on this simple pendulum, we vary its length (say, by lengthening the wire by which the weight is suspended); observe that for different lengths there are different periods; discover that these observed covariations are tolerably accurately described by the simple function stated; and generalize that for all covariations of these magnitudes of this pendulum the same functional relationship holds. We can then go through the same routine with a number of other simple pendulums, and so generalize in the other dimension as well. The essential here, of course, is to vary the observed pendulums; we should do well to experiment with e.g. pendulums of different materials, as Newton did in his famous experiment to prove the equal gravitation of all substances. Plainly then, the probabilification of these two-dimensional generalizations involves no epistemological problems over and above those involved in that of attribute- and variable-generalizations considered separately. Notice, incidentally, that this generalization contains two qualifying conditions; namely, that the pendulums are simple and that the amplitudes of the swings are small.

The probability of both subject-predicate and functional generalizations may be said to be affected by 'the number of the observed instances'. But this phrase bears a different meaning in the two cases, since the instances are instances of different things. In functional generalizations, the observed instances are observed values of variable magnitudes, such as lengths and periods; cp. Rule (12). But in subject-predicate generalizations, the observed instances are observed things, such as pendulums.

The qualifying conditions in variable-generalizations which I have mentioned above are equally applicable to attribute-generalizations. But there is one important sort which is applicable to variable-generalizations only, namely, specifications of the range within which the functional relation holds. E.g., if breadths of this leaf in cms. are observed to be equal to lengths thereof in ins. between the limits 2·5 ins. and 9·5 ins., this qualification must be included in the corresponding generalization for the same reason as must such qualifications as 'at a constant temperature' or 'at sea-level'. The corresponding probabilification-judgement exemplifies the formula:
$$\gamma PF((A\overset{m}{\underset{a=n}{a}})(Ab)b = a,\ (A\overset{m}{\underset{a=n}{a'}})(Ab')b = a \cdot \gamma C_2 \cdot \gamma C_3),$$
in which the expression $A\overset{m}{\underset{a=n}{a}}$ is to be read 'For all values of a between n and m'. The reason why this sort of qualification is often necessary is indicated by Hume: 'A certain degree of heat gives pleasure; if you diminish that heat, the pleasure diminishes; but it does not follow, that if you augment it beyond a certain degree, the pleasure will likewise augment; for we find that it degenerates into pain'. [Hume, T, 174] This matter of the observed range of variation bears vitally on interpolation and extrapolation, as we shall see shortly. [3.2]

My account of this type of judgement is seriously over-simplified in that it represents mathematical descriptions as fitting the facts exactly; in Figs. (1), (2) and (3) the line (representing the function) passes exactly through the points (representing the observations). In practice, of course, we commonly neither expect nor get such precision. A more accurate idea of how functional descriptions and generalizations are actually made is conveyed by the following passage of Poincaré's: 'I wish to determine an experimental law. This law, when I know it, can be represented by a curve. I make a certain number of isolated observations; each of these will be represented by a point. When I have obtained these different points, I draw a curve between them, striving to pass as near to them as possible and yet preserve for my curve a regular form, without angular points, or inflections too accentuated, or brusque variation of the radius of curvature. This curve will represent for me the probable law and I assume not only that it will tell me the values of the function intermediate between those which have been observed, but also that it will give me the observed values themselves more exactly than direct observation. This is why I make it pass near the points, and not through the points themselves.' [Poincaré, 169] Notice in passing the interesting paradox, that the very observations themselves are 'corrected' in the light of the function selected. Some hold that degree of precision or exactness of fit of the curve (function) to the points (observations) is a criterion of the degree of probability of functional generalizations, and I shall examine their suggestion in due course. [4.1]

Johnson writes: 'The theory of what I have called the functional extension of demonstrative induction constitutes a link between the Demonstrative and the Problematic forms of inference. For certain rules (of a strictly formal character) are required for deducing, amongst all the functions which fit the observed covariations, the *most probable function* of the variable cause-factors by which an effect-factor may be calculated. The oldest and most usual method of determining this function is known as the *method of least squares*. Its validity depends upon a certain assumption with regard to the form of the Law of Error, i.e. of the function exhibited by divergences from a mean or average, when the number of co-variational instances is indefinitely increased; and a different method must be employed for each corresponding different assumption. . . . The inductive inference examined in the above [i.e. functional induction] is thus shown to be based upon purely formal and demonstrative principles of probability. . . . It is therefore legitimate, and even necessary, to include the functional extension of the figures of induction under the general title of demonstrative inferences.' [Johnson, II, 252 f.]

This claim of Johnson's seems to me false but important, since it arises out of and illustrates once again a confusion between casual and inductive probability. It is not easy to expose the confusion briefly, since reference must be made to Laws of Error and to the Methods of Means and of Least Squares. The situation is very shortly as follows. The Method of Least Squares is designed to counter the accidental or random, as opposed to the systematic or constant, errors to which observations of the values of variable magnitudes may be supposed to be subject. The method, as presented by Gauss, rests on certain factual assumptions about the occurrence of these errors, i.e. about the form of the Law of Error. These are that any observation is subject to an infinite number of infinitely small errors, that the occurrences of these errors are independent events, and that the occurrences of positive and negative errors are equally probable. These assumptions permit the Calculus of Probabilities to be applied to the matter, and it is demonstrable that the most probable function is the one that yields the least sum of squares of errors, and that this function is the arithmetic mean.

The essential point for our purposes is then this. In the expression 'the most probable function', 'probable' means 'casually probable' and not 'inductively probable', since we are here concerned with deductive reasoning in matters of chance. That we are not at all concerned here with inductive probability also becomes plain when we reflect that all this relates to functional description or colligation and not to functional induction. For, provided that the factual assumptions about the occurrence of accidental errors are true (as of course they may well not be), the Method of Least Squares enables us to select from among all the functions that fit the observations that functional description which is casually the most probable. But it does not follow that the functional generalization corresponding to this description is inductively probable. Johnson's mistake is precisely to suppose that this is so, so that functional inductions are proved to be probable by deductive probable reasoning about chances.

Again, we can see that what the Method of Least Squares enables us to select is the most (casually) probable functional description, and not the most (inductively) probable functional generalization, from the following consideration. In the literature, the function (or law) that is called 'the most probable' is also called 'the best (i.e. closest) fit'. [Yule, 311, 314] But what the curve (function) more or less closely fits are of course the points (observations); so that we are plainly concerned here with mathematical description.

Historically, this application of the Calculus of Probabilities to mensuration, called the Theory of Errors, considerably preceded its application to inference from samples to populations, called the Theory of Sampling, and was developed mainly to meet the needs of Astronomy. Philosophers, however, have devoted much more attention to the latter theory than to the former, because they have hoped to find in it a solution to the traditional problem of induction. The former, indeed, constitutes an unduly neglected chapter in the Philosophy of Science.

An interesting consequence of the fact that we frequently have to be content with the most probable values of magnitudes, in the sense explained, is that there arises from it one more interconnexion between two of the senses of 'probable', namely casual probability and hypothetic probability. For we saw [1.2] that the degree of probability of some hypotheses is determined in part by the variety and number of the facts that they explain, and that these facts are often observed magnitudes. I gave the simple example of the probabilification of the principle of the rectilinear propagation of light by its explaining a variety of depths of shadows. However, it will now be clear that these 'facts' may not be, and indeed in the actual establishing of scientific hypotheses commonly are not, the true values of certain magnitudes obtained by making one observation of each value, but rather the most (casually) probable values thereof obtained by taking the arithmetic mean of several observations of each value. In this way, the probabilification of certain sorts of hypotheses presupposes casual probability. There is a superficial similarity between the position here and the phenomenalist thesis that we noticed and rejected above [1.2]; what is common to both is the contention that the observation-statements or descriptions, on which probable inductions and hypotheses rest, are themselves only probable. But a moment's reflection will be enough to make it evident that the resemblance ends here.

There is an intimate connexion between these remarks about 'the most probable function' and those immediately preceding them about 'precision'. For, when we draw a regular curve (representing the functional induction) between rather than through the points (representing the observations) we proceed on the same assumptions as underlie the Methods of Means and Least Squares. Namely, we suppose that equal positive and negative chance errors are equally probable and so occur with approximately equal frequency in the long run, etc. As Whewell says, there is in this regard an essential analogy between these methods and what he calls 'the Method of Curves'. [Whewell, 396 ff.] Hence too, the expression 'the [most] probable law' in the passage from Poincaré cited above likewise means casually probable, and has nothing to do with inductive probability.

This graphic process of eliminating observational errors that Poincaré describes is one method of graduation. It is desirable to add, in conclusion, that there exist other methods of graduation which are more mechanical in character and less dependent on the judgement and experience of the investigator. These are processes founded on the Method of Differences, i.e. techniques which involve proceeding to higher orders of differences and the use of e.g. Newton's formula. But it is beside my purpose to describe these processes or to discuss their rationale here. [Yule, 462 ff.]

3.2 DERIVATIVE FORMULAS

Consider the formula, $(9')$, $\gamma PF(b_n, \gamma P((Aa)(Ab)b = a) . a_n)$. An exemplification is: 'Since it is probable that, for all values of the length and breadth of this leaf, its breadth in cms. is equal to its length in ins., and its present length is 3·5 ins., it is probable that its present breadth is 3·5 cms.' The relevant rule is *Rule* (13). *In judgements of the type of formula* $(9')$, *the degree of probabilification of the probabilified-proposition is the same as, and hence varies directly as, the degree of probability of the probability-judgement in the probabilifying-proposition.* Thus, cp. with formula $(9')$ the formula: $\beta PF(b_n, \beta P((Aa)(Ab)b = a) . a_n)$.

In judgements of this type, the probabilified-proposition is a probable interpolation. There is an obvious analogy between formula $(9')$ and Rule (13) on the one hand and formula $(3')$ and Rule (3) on the other. As formula $(9')$ is a singular subject-predicate deductive derivative formula, so formula $(3')$ is a singular functional deductive derivative formula. The criterion of the degree of probability of the probabilified-proposition in the two cases is the same, and in both cases what we do is apply a probable general rule to a particular case falling under it.

I ought to add that this is not the only method of interpolation. In the method here considered, we may, of course, represent the functional generalization by a curve and simply read off the required value of the dependent variable, rather than deduce it from the functional generalization and the pertinent value of the independent variable. But in an alternative method, no functional generalization is made at all. We simply interpolate as required between the observed values of the dependent variable, using the technique of simple interpolation when the differences between the successive observed values thereof are constant, and the Method of Differences previously mentioned when they are not constant. [3.1] I am concerned with the former method only. But the existence of the latter method requires an amendment to the definition that I offered earlier of 'a functional interpolation'. For I suggested that it should be defined as 'a functional deductive derivative induction'; whereas it is now clear that this definition is too narrow. [1.1]

Take now the judgement: 'Since it is very probable that, for all values of the breadth of this leaf and all values of its length between 2·5 ins. and 9·5 ins., its breadth in cms. is equal to its length in ins.; and since its present length is 9·55 ins., so that the degree of extrapolation is small; it is fairly probable that its present breadth is 9·55 cms.' The appropriate rule is *Rule* (14). *In judgements of the type of the one just given, the degree of probabilification of the probabilified-proposition varies directly as the degree of probability of the probability-judgement in the probabilifying-proposition, and inversely as the degree of extrapolation.* The condition or criterion, degree of extrapolation, may be represented as C_7, and the several degrees of it symbolized as with other conditions αC_7, γC_7, etc. The meaning of 'degree of functional extrapolation' is again very simple and most conveniently explained graphically. Cp. the following figures:–

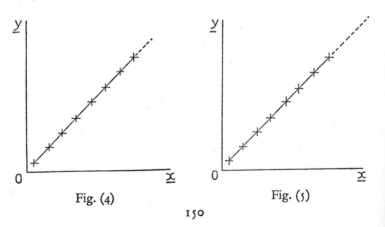

Fig. (4)   Fig. (5)

In these figures, the points again represent observed values of magnitudes and the continuous lines represent functional generalizations. The points at each end of the continuous lines accordingly represent the limits of the ranges of observed covariation. And the degree of extrapolation is represented by the length of broken line; it will be seen to be greater in Fig. (5) than in Fig. (4).

The probabilified-proposition in the judgement under consideration is then a probable functional extrapolation. The essential feature of this sort of judgement is that, on the evidence of a functional generalization that is qualified in respect of range, we judge that the dependent variable has the value so-and-so when the independent variable has the value such-and-such lying outside the range of that generalization. They are consequently non-deductive derivative inductive judgements. They are non-deductive, because the required value of the dependent variable obviously cannot be deduced from the generalization and the relevant value of the independent variable when the latter lies outside the range of that generalization. Yet they are nevertheless derivative inductive judgements, because the probability-judgement in the probabilifying-judgement is inductive, and the probabilified-proposition is derived in part from it, in the sense that it constitutes part of the reason for it, although it is not one of the premisses entailing it. The important difference between extrapolations and the sort of interpolations that I discussed above is precisely that the latter are deductive derivative inductions whereas the former are non-deductive ones.

Functional extrapolations are not the only sort of extrapolations, though they are the most familiar sort. For we in effect extrapolate whenever we make a derivative induction that exceeds the scope of the relevant generalization. One who has generalized from observation of European swans that all European swans are white, and asserts on the evidence of this generalization that the first swan that he will see in Australia will be white, is also extrapolating. Thus there are attribute-extrapolations as well as variable-extrapolations. The difference between the two cases resides simply in the respect in which we extrapolate. In the leaf example, we extrapolate in respect of the range of values within which the functional relation has been observed to hold. But in the swan example, we extrapolate in respect of place. I shall touch on this question of attribute-extrapolation again later, when it will be found that some interesting questions arise out of extrapolations in respect of time and space in particular. [5.2]

The degree of probability of an extrapolation decreases very rapidly as the degree of extrapolation increases, and quickly reaches zero. In Mill's terms, 'a merely empirical law' may be extended with any degree of probability only to 'adjacent cases'. [Mill, 360 ff.] For, as Jevons remarks, '. . . to extend our inference far beyond the limits of experience is exceedingly unsafe'. [Jevons, II, 123] Thus, a functional extrapolation of the degree represented in Fig. (5) would be judged not to be probable in any degree. The same would be said of my man who declares that the first swan he will see in Australia will be white. But if he had made a similar induction about the colour of the first swan that he would see in Turkey, it might be allowed to possess some degree of probability.

Although there is, as we have just seen, an essential difference between functional extrapolations and the sort of interpolations that I have discussed earlier, there is also an important resemblance in the criteria of their probability. For the degree of probability of an interpolation is determined by that of the functional generalization in the probabilifying-proposition (Rule (13)). And the degree of probability of the latter is determined in part by the number and degree of evenness of distribution of the observed values of the variables (Rule (12)). And again, the degree of probability of a functional extrapolation is determined in part by the degree of the extrapolation (Rule (14)). But these criteria of probability for interpolations and extrapolations evidently come to pretty much the same thing. For, the more numerous and evenly distributed over the range the observed values of the variables (points), the closer an interpolated point will be to some point representing an observation. (See Figs. (1), (2) and (3).) And the less the degree of extrapolation, the closer an extrapolated point will be to an end point representing one limit of the range of observation.

It is necessary to distinguish between two different ways in which a proposition may be established. On the one hand, we may establish it by simply extrapolating a functional generalization, or what Mill calls an 'empirical law' and Jevons calls an 'empirical formula'. On the other hand, we may establish it by deduction from the law of Nature to which that generalization is reducible, conjoined with some additional premisses. I shall illustrate the distinction by considering the case of long-range historical predictions, a subject of topical interest to which philosophers have rightly given considerable attention in recent years.

In the Preface to his *Democracy in America* (1835), de Tocqueville writes as follows. He first makes from the historical evidence the generalization that there has existed among the nations of Western Europe over the past 700 years a trend towards complete social equality, and he then predicts from this generalization that in the not too remote future (say, for argument's sake, about 1935) there will exist among those nations the same complete social equality as he has found in the U.S.A. Thus, what he does is first make a functional generalization and then extrapolate it. But since the degree of extrapolation is large, namely, from 1835 to 1935, his conclusion is not in any degree probable, still less certain or true. For we have just seen that extrapolations can properly be made to adjacent cases only. To be sure, he himself regards his proposition as something much more profound than a mere empirical law: 'The gradual development of the equality of conditions is therefore a providential fact, and it possesses all the characteristics of a Divine decree: it is universal, it is durable, it constantly eludes all human interference, and all events as well as all men contribute to its progress'. [A. de Tocqueville, *Democracy in America*, tr. H. Reeve, ed. H. S. Commager, Oxford, 1946, p. 5] But an empirical law is none the less all it is.

The statement 'There was a trend (or tendency) towards social equality in Western Europe between 1135 and 1835' is of course not a description but a generalization, since it asserts something about the degrees of social equality obtaining at unexamined as well as at examined times within this period. Nor is it a singular existential statement, as its grammatical form might suggest. For to assert the existence of a temporal trend is to make a functional generalization in which time is the independent variable. Such generalizations may be numerical, as in e.g. a population trend-statement in which the size of the population is expressed as a function of the time, or non-numerical. It is a prominent feature of the sort of temporal trend-statements that I am discussing now, sometimes called 'laws of historical development', that they are not only non-numerical but also very difficult to establish or refute. For they assert increases or decreases in degree of such things as 'equality of conditions' and 'civilization'. But it is often not made clear what are the criteria of an increase in degree of, say, civilization; or, even when these tests are stated, they tend to be such that it is very hard to find out whether or not they have been satisfied.

Functional generalizations, no less than subject-predicate ones, may be shown to be consilient with or explicable by generalizations of wider scope. A special case of this arises when a temporal trend-statement is shown to be consilient with or 'reducible' to an inductive law of Nature. The effect and the point of such reductions is that already noticed in treating of the consilience of inductions; namely, that the trend-statement is thereby more securely established. [2.2] For after reduction the trend-statement is not merely probabilified or verified by the direct evidence for it, but verified by being shown to be entailed by a true inductive law. Thus, de Tocqueville's trend-statement might be reduced to the proportional or statistical law of human nature 'Most men desire complete social equality', or more simply, 'Most men are envious'. Mill argues in this way about progress. He accepts as true or probable the functional generalization that there has been progress (in some sense) between, say, 1453 and 1843, and holds that this trend can be explained, proximately by Comte's Law of Three Stages as middle axiom, and ultimately by the (alleged) true or genuine law of human nature, that men have a propensity to improve. He calls this procedure of reducing trends to laws the 'inverse deductive, or historical method'. [Mill, 594 ff.]

However, a trend cannot be reduced to, or deduced from, a law of Nature alone; at least one additional premiss is requisite. The generalization that there was a trend towards social equality in Western Europe between 1135 and 1835 is not explained solely by the law that most men desire complete social equality. But it is explained or entailed by this law and, say, the facts that in 1135 there was very little social equality or respect for the wishes of the majority, but that thereafter the majority was increasingly successful in making its wishes prevail. So too Galileo's empirical law of falling bodies cannot be explained by Newton's law of gravitation alone, but can be explained by it and his laws of motion and a knowledge of the mass and radius of the Earth.

The point that I am chiefly concerned to make is this. Suppose a certain prediction first to be made simply by extrapolating a temporal trend, as in the example from de Tocqueville. But suppose further that the trend is subsequently reduced to an inductive law of Nature. Then, the prediction is no longer a mere extrapolation, but a deductive derivative induction; for it is deduced from an inductive law of Nature and some additional premisses. For since the law of Nature logically must hold good at all times, being 'universal', any prediction however remote falls within its scope or range. And so generally, it is possible to extrapolate from empirical laws but not from laws of Nature, since the former logically must be conditioned whereas the latter logically cannot be so.

Some suppose that when the relevant law of Nature has once been identified, we can proceed without more ado to make with perfect confidence statements about the remote future. Mill e.g. seems to think that, simply from the alleged law about the human propensity to improve, he can deduce that the world will be in a better and happier state in, say, 1943. But, as Popper observes, this is to overlook the obvious but vital point that we cannot deduce predictions any more than trends from laws of Nature alone; we need as well some additional premisses specifying the 'initial conditions'. [K. R. Popper, 'The Poverty of Historicism', Pt. III, *Economica*, London, May 1945, Sect. 28] Thus, one obviously could not properly argue in 1835: 'Most men desire complete social equality; therefore there will be complete social equality by about 1935'. But one could properly argue: 'Most men desire, etc. In Western Europe there already exists a fair degree of social equality. Moreover, under democracy the will of the majority prevails, and the nations of Western Europe will probably remain or become democracies. Therefore, there will probably be complete social equality in Western Europe in about a century.' Or alternatively: 'Most men desire, etc. In Western Europe there already exists, etc. Moreover, under democracy, etc. Therefore, provided that the nations of Western Europe remain or become democracies, there will be complete social equality in Western Europe in about a century.'

The latter argument illustrates the not unimportant case of conditional prediction or prediction under a proviso. In the former argument, the conclusion is unconditional, but probable as opposed to true or certain. The reason for this is, of course, that the third premiss is a probability-judgement; this point has been explained in discussing Nicod's rule. [2.2] Both examples show why predictions from laws of Nature are often precarious; namely, because although the law is certain, some of the additional premisses are not. In the example, it may well be that the nations of Western Europe will neither remain nor become democracies. By contrast, a prediction of e.g. an occultation of one of Jupiter's moons is regarded as virtually certain, because no doubt is entertained concerning the premisses specifying the initial conditions, namely, the present positions of that moon and of Jupiter, etc. Such doubt as there is arises from recognition of the possibility and minutely small degree of probability of some fact occurring that would falsify the prediction, e.g. the destruction of the Earth by collision with a runaway star. Notice in this connexion that those who wrongly hold that predictions are deduced from laws of Nature alone are involved in the false consequence that such predictions are always true and never probable. For a law of Nature logically must be true, and a deduction from a true premiss must of course be true too.

Other things being equal, we regard a functional extrapolation as more probable accordingly as the range of the functional generalization involved is greater. Let us consider further the special case of predictions from temporal trends. Take the following convenient if rather absurd illustration. Observation of the size of the population of community A over the period 1935–1955 enables us to judge it to be very probable that, over this period, the number of the population of A is equal to the number of the year. And observation of the size of the population of community B over the period 1755–1955 enables us to judge it to be very probable that, over that period, the number of the population of B is equal to the number of the year. I.e., the direct evidence for the two functional generalizations is equally good. Then, we unquestionably judge that the prediction that the population of B will be 1956 in the year 1956 is more probabilified by the latter evidence than the prediction that the population of A will be 1956 in 1956 is probabilified by the former evidence. Why is this?

I think that the reason is as follows. We hold that secular trends are explicable by or reducible to laws of Nature, and so regard the prediction about the population of B, not as a mere extrapolation from an empirical law, but as deducible from some law of Nature conjoined with additional premisses. Short-term trends, on the other hand, we do not think to be thus reducible, and so regard the prediction about the population of A as a simple extrapolation. We take this view about the reducibility of a secular trend whether we can specify the explanatory law and extra premises or not. In the example, we may find that the trend is explainable by the inductive law of human nature, 'Men do not change their policies without reason', conjoined with additional premises to the effect that the rulers of B decided in 1755 or earlier to keep the number of the population of B equal to the number of the year by means of expulsions or importations as required, and that nothing happened between 1755 and 1955 which gave them a reason for altering their policy or prevented them from implementing it. If this is so, then in judging it to be probable that the population of B will be 1956 in 1956 we are in effect judging it to be improbable that anything will happen in the period 1955–1956 which will give the rulers a reason for altering their policy or prevent them from implementing it. And the greater probability of the prediction in the case of B than in the case of A will be due to the fact that we judge the degree of this improbability to be greater than the degree of probability of the extrapolation in the case of A.

But even if we cannot identify the explanatory law, and are content simply to regard the trend in case B as explicable by an unknown law and auxiliary premises, we still regard the prediction in case B as more probable than that in case A, for the same reason. Mill discusses the parallel case of the rising of the Sun. He supposes us to have generalized from observations that the Sun has risen every 24 hours for the past 5,000 years, but to be ignorant of the explanation of this empirical law by the rotation of the Earth about its axis and other facts. In this situation, he points out: 'Having evidence that the effects had remained unaltered, and been punctually conjoined for 5,000 years, we could infer that the *unknown* causes on which the conjunction is dependent had existed undiminished and uncounteracted during the same period'. [Mill, 362] So that in judging it to be virtually certain that the Sun will rise to-morrow, we are in effect judging it to be virtually certain that nothing will supervene to diminish or counteract these unknown causes between now and then.

It remains to ask, Why do we think that secular trends are reducible to laws whereas short-term ones are not? I think, because we are prepared to accept that the latter, but not the former, are multiplied coincidences. That the number of the population in a community should chance to be the same as that of the year in 20 successive years is perhaps credible; but that this should be so in 200 successive years is too much. The reasoning here is therefore of a kind discussed by Mill under the title 'the elimination of chance', about which I shall say something later. [5.1]

4 OTHER ALLEGED
DETERMINANTS OF
INDUCTIVE PROBABILITY

My next task is to criticize what seem to me to be the most important alternative suggestions about what makes inductions probable.
These suggestions divide naturally into proposed additional criteria, proposed grounds of inductions, and pragmatic theories of
inductive reasoning. It will be convenient to examine them in this
order.

4.1 SUGGESTED ADDITIONAL CRITERIA

We will consider first five proposed criteria of the probability of
attribute-, specifically subject-predicate, inductions; then two proposed criteria of the probability of variable-, specifically functional,
inductions.

4.1.1 *Criteria for Subject-Predicate Formulas*

I will begin with Keynes' views on analogy, comprehensiveness
and scope. He writes: 'In an inductive argument . . . we start with
a number of instances similar in some .espects AB, dissimilar in
others C. We pick out one or more respects A in which the instances are similar, and argue that some of the other respects B in
which they are also similar are likely to be associated with the
characteristics A in other unexamined cases. The more comprehensive the essential characteristics A, the greater the variety
amongst the non-essential characteristics C, and the less compre-

hensive the characteristics B which we seek to associate with A, the stronger is the likelihood or probability of the generalization we seek to establish. These are the three ultimate logical elements on which the probability of an empirical argument depends,—the Positive and the Negative Analogies and the scope of the generalization.' [Keynes, 219 f.]

I agree with what he says about 'negative analogy' or variety; cp. Rules (1) and (2), above. We need therefore to consider 'positive analogy' only. Keynes' thesis may be summarized as follows. A generalization has a higher initial probability accordingly as its subject-term is more specific and/or as its predicate-term is less specific. His terminology is confusing and his notation complicated, but the main ideas are fairly clear. By the initial or *a priori* probability of generalizations he means the probability that they possess independently of that conferred on them by the evidence of observed instances. [Keynes, 224] In his view, then, the following formulas can be ranged in order of increasing degree of initial probability thus: (i) $I(fAg)$; (ii) $I(b \times fAg)$; (iii) $I(fAg + i)$; (iv) $I(b \times fAg + i)$. Exemplifications are respectively: 'All BU are blue'; 'All glass BU are blue'; 'All BU are blue or green'; 'All glass BU are blue or green'. In (i), the subject-term is less specific (or more comprehensive) and the predicate-term is more specific (or less comprehensive) than in (ii), (iii) or (iv); it therefore has a lower degree of initial probability than these. The initial probability of (ii) is greater than that of (i) because its subject-term is more specific. The initial probability of (iii) is greater than that of (i) because its predicate-term is less specific. The initial probabilities of (ii) and (iii) are presumably equal. And the initial probability of (iv) is greater than that of (ii) because its predicate-term is less specific, and greater than that of (iii) because its subject-term is more specific.

Further, Keynes identifies the degree of specificity of the subject-term with the degree of positive analogy between the observed instances. If the conclusion is of the form, say, $I(ihfAg)$, then the observed instances for this generalization must agree in being i, h and f as well as g; whereas if it is of the form $I(fAg)$, the observed instances need to agree only in being f as well as g. Finally, he thinks of the scope of the generalization as being determined more by the scope of the predicate-term than by that of the subject-term; what the latter determines is primarily the positive analogy.

Thus, in Keynes' view, the scope of (iii) is wider than that of (i) because the predicate-term is less specific.

It is important to remember that Keynes is here attempting 'no more than to state in precise language what elements are commonly regarded as adding weight [probability] to an empirical or inductive argument'. [Keynes, 218] And it seems to me that the root error of the foregoing account is precisely the notion that the probability of a generalization is determined in part by 'the nature of the conclusion which we seek to draw' or 'the character of the generalization *a priori*' as well as by the evidence for it. [Keynes, 224 f.] Generalizations are made probable only by the evidence for them; they do not possess different degrees of (initial) probability accordingly as their subject- or predicate-terms are more or less specific.

The explanation of the error is to be found, I believe, in the following passage: 'We see . . . that some generalizations stand *initially* in a stronger position than others. In order to attain a given degree of probability, generalizations require, according to their scope, different amounts of favourable evidence to support them.' [Keynes, 225] The implication is that these two statements are equivalent, whereas in fact they are not. I.e., Keynes confuses two different points. First, that it is more difficult to establish, say, the less specific generalization, (i), with a given degree of probability than it is to establish the more specific generalization, (ii), with the same degree of probability. Second, that (ii) has a higher degree of initial probability than (i). The first is true, but the second is false. The reason why the first is true is of course that it requires a greater variety and number of instances to make it, say, very probable that all BU are blue than it does to make it very probable that all glass BU are blue. Specifically, the former requires that both glass and non-glass BU shall have been examined, whereas the latter does not.

It is interesting to find Mill and Popper arguing in exactly the opposite sense to Keynes about the effect of the specificity of the subject-term on the probability of the generalization. Mill contends that the generalization 'Every event has a cause' is certain [true] because its subject-term is as little specific as possible, the word 'event' being one of the most general that our language contains. [Mill, 373] We shall see in 4.2 that the alleged truth of this generalization plays a leading part in Mill's theory of induction.

Similarly, Popper argues in deliberate opposition to Keynes that a generalization is more probable as its subject-term is less specific or more general; for a wider generalization is more testable or confirmable than a narrower, and he equates degree of inductive probability with degree of testability. [Popper, 75 ff., 200 ff.] The same objection naturally applies to these doctrines as to Keynes'.

In conclusion, it is desirable to compare Keynes' view on the bearing of the scope of a generalization on its probability with what seems to me to be the true view of this matter. Keynes holds, to repeat it, that the scope of a generalization is determined primarily by the specificity of its predicate-term, and that its initial probability is greater as the specificity of that term is less. In fact, however, the significant connexion is between the specificity of the subject-term, not of the predicate-term, and the probability of the generalization; moreover, what counts is the specificity or scope of the subject-term, not in itself, but relatively to the evidence. It can indeed be said that the suitability of the scope of the generalization to the evidence is the crucial question in attribute-inductions, since this is the same question as that of the variety of the observed instances. For to say that the scope of the generalization $I(fAg)$ is too wide relatively to the evidence for it is precisely to say that the observed instances, f', have been insufficiently varied to establish this generalization as probable. They are all, say, h as well as g; so that the appropriate generalization is one of narrower scope, namely $I(hfAg)$.

I shall take next another doctrine about how degree of analogy determines degree of inductive probability, namely, what may be called the traditional doctrine of inductive reasoning by analogy. [Jevons, II, 244 f.; Reid, 35 ff.; Mill, 364 ff.] The gist of the doctrine is this. There is a species of primitive inductive inference from a particular to another particular, in which the degree of probability of the conclusion is greater accordingly as the degree of resemblance between the two particulars is greater; and the resemblance between particulars is greater when they have a greater number of common properties. Thus, cp. the following two formulas: $\delta PF(gx, jihgfy . jihfx)$, and $\gamma PF(gx, kjihgfy . kjihfx)$. Mill adds the refinement that the degree of probability is less accordingly as the degree of difference between the individuals is greater, this again being a question of the number of attributes in respect of which they disagree; and where there is both similarity and dissimilarity, the degree of probability of the conclusion is greater accordingly as attributes in respect of which the individuals agree are more numerous than attributes in respect of which they differ. Thus, cp. with the two preceding formulas the formula: $\epsilon PF(gx,$ $lkjihgfy . \overline{l}kjihfx)$. But I shall ignore this refinement. My criticisms of the doctrine are as follows.

I have contended earlier [1.1] that all primitive inductions are generalizations, and conversely; so that all singular inductions are derivative. Hence, I do not accept that there is any such distinct species of primitive inductive inference from a particular to a particular; and agree rather with those who maintain that what may appear on the face of it to be so is found on closer inspection to involve only the primitive and derivative inductive reasoning elucidated earlier. Let us now see why this is so.

It is indeed a sufficient objection to the doctrine as it stands that is plainly false. Consider the following variant on the stock example: 'The fact that the Earth is a planet, nearly spherical, more than 100 years old, not made of aluminium, and inhabited, and that Mars also possesses the first four attributes, makes it in some slight degree probable that Mars is inhabited'. We should say that, on the contrary, the fact that these four attributes are common to the two planets is worthless evidence, does not make it in any degree probable, that Mars possesses the Earth's fifth attribute too.

This objection to the doctrine is apt to be met by the following modification: it is stipulated that the attributes common to the two individuals must be 'important' or 'material' ones, i.e. ones 'connected' with the problematic one ('inhabited'). Consider e.g. this judgement: 'The fact that the Earth has an atmosphere, has water, has a moderate temperature-range, and is inhabited, and that Mars also has the first three attributes, makes it probable that Mars is inhabited'. This of course is much more plausible. But then the question must be raised, How is it known that these three attributes are (probably) 'connected' with that of being inhabited? By generalization, of course; we have judged, we will suppose, that the presences of these three attributes are probably the severally necessary and collectively sufficient conditions of the presence of life. So that the real form of the argument turns out to be: 'The fact that all places that possess these three attributes are probably inhabited, and that Mars is a place that possesses these three

163

attributes, makes it probable that Mars is inhabited'. But this is a deductive derivative judgement exemplifying the by now familiar formula, $(3')$: $\gamma PF(gx, \gamma P(fAg) \cdot fx)$. So that the conclusion 'Mars is (probably) inhabited' turns out to have been reached, not by a distinct species of primitive inductive reasoning, namely analogical inference from a particular (the Earth) to a particular (Mars); but by deduction from a generalization. Yet the claim that analogical inference is a species of primitive inductive inference distinct from generalization is, I think, of the essence of what I have called the traditional doctrine of inductive reasoning by analogy.

As a last-ditch defence of the traditional doctrine it may be argued as follows. It may be conceded that the conclusion 'Mars is probably inhabited' is simply a deduction from the judgement 'All places that possess these three attributes are probably inhabited' conjoined with the statement 'Mars is a place that possesses these three attributes'. But it may yet be maintained that the evidence which makes the generalization probable is simply the fact that the Earth, which possesses the three attributes, is also inhabited. I.e., the claim that the argument is a primitive induction is abandoned; but the claim that it proceeds ultimately from a particular (the Earth) to a particular (Mars), though avowedly by way of a generalization, is retained. But this will not do either. For it involves claiming that a generalization can be probabilified by the evidence of a single observed instance; specifically, that we may rightly judge: 'The fact that the Earth is a place that possesses the three attributes in question and is also inhabited makes it probable that all places that possess them are also inhabited'. But this is impossible, since attribute-generalizations are probable when and only when the observed instances are varied, and a single instance logically cannot be varied. The generalization can only be probabilified, therefore, by the evidence of a variety and number of observed places.

It appears, then, that the pretended singular primitive inductive probabilification-judgement from the evidence of a single observed instance, is actually deductively derived from an implicit probable generalization based on the evidence of a variety and number of observed instances. It is worth noting in passing that similar considerations apply to other sorts of cases where we seem on the face of it to make a primitive probabilification-judgement on the evidence of a single instance. Consider Mill's famous question: 'Why is a single instance, in some cases, sufficient for a complete induction, while in others myriads of concurring instances, without a single exception known or presumed, go such a very little way towards establishing an universal proposition?' [Mill, 206] In reply to the first part of his question, which is alone relevant here, take the following case. In 1894, Rayleigh and Ramsay discovered a new element, argon, determined the density of a single specimen of it, and concluded that this was certainly the density of all argon. Why was this considered to be perfectly in order? Certainly not because a single observed instance is held to be capable of making a generalization probable or, as here, true; but because there is present another unexpressed premiss, namely, the true generalization 'All elements are constant in respect of density'. So that the conclusion about the density of all argon is not, as it appears to be at first sight, a primitive induction from a single instance, but a deductive derivative induction from the above true generalization conjoined with the premisses 'Argon is an element' and 'This examined specimen of argon has density so-and-so'.

Finally on analogy as a criterion of inductive probability, let us look at what Hume has to say about 'the probability derived from analogy'. [Hume, T, 142, 153 f.; Lewis, 299] Hume contends that degree of resemblance is a, but not the, criterion of the degree of probability of derivative inductions. Thus, cp. the following two judgements. First, we have judged that all fat men are very probably jolly, and we consider that this man is exactly like the examined fat men who constitute the instantial evidence for this probable generalization; in this case, we conclude that this fat man is very probably jolly. Second, we have made the same probable generalization, but consider that this fat man is only very like the examined fat men; in this case, we conclude that this fat man is probably jolly. This degree of analogy is not the sole determinant of the degree of probability of the conclusion because the latter is also affected by the degree of probability of the generalization (cp. 'All fat men are fairly probably jolly') and by the degree of its approximation to universality (cp. 'Most fat men are very probably jolly').

Hume's account differs from the traditional doctrine of inductive reasoning by analogy in two main respects. First, his is clearly intended to relate to derivative judgements, and he makes no claim that analogical inductive reasoning is a distinct species of primitive inductive reasoning. He has in mind judgements exemplifying e.g. formula (3′), $\gamma PF(gx, \gamma P(fAg) . fx)$, and formula (5′), $\delta PF(gx, \alpha P(fMg) . fx . C_1)$. Second, whereas the traditional doctrine represents the degree of resemblance between individuals as determined by the number of attributes in the possession of which they agree, Hume represents it as determined rather by the degree of resemblance in respect of the attribute ('fatness') or attributes in the possession of which they agree.

My first criticism of Hume's thesis is that it is not applicable to derivative attribute-inductions generally. Consider the case in which we apply the probable generalization 'All BU are very probably H' to the case of this BU. Analogy as Hume conceives it cannot enter in here, because the notion of this instance agreeing in greater or less degree with the examined instances in respect of the attribute of being a BU makes no sense: all these individuals either are BU or they are not, and there is no more or less about it. Hume's account applies at best to attributes that can vary in degree, such as fatness; here it does of course make sense to say that there is a greater degree of resemblance in respect of fatness when all the observed instances are fat and this man is fat too, than there is when they are all fat but this man is only fairly fat.

But I do not think that Hume's suggestion is true even of the class of cases to which it is applicable. For it seems to me an all-or-nothing question into which degree does not enter. If we decide that this man is sufficiently like in respect of fatness to the observed cases which constitute the evidence for the judgement 'All fat men are very probably jolly', we apply the judgement to his case and conclude that he is very probably jolly. But if we decide that he is not sufficiently like, we do not apply the judgement to his case at all, and conclude nothing as to his being jolly. We do not, as Hume suggests, conclude with a lower degree of probability than in the former case that he is jolly. The merit of Hume's account is that it reminds us that the familiar operation of applying an attribute-generalization to a particular case or class of cases is not mechanical; it requires intelligence in the form of a decision about whether the degree of resemblance between the case or cases and the cases forming the evidence for the generalization is high enough to warrant the application of the generalization here. But he is mistaken in thinking that degree of analogy in this sense affects the degree of probability of the conclusion.

I propose to take next some remarks by Keynes and Lewis respecting the amount of evidence as a criterion of probability. [Keynes, 71 ff., 312 f.; Lewis, 292 f., 298 f.] Keynes contends that the degree of 'weight' of an argument [proposition] increases as the amount of evidence. But weight is not the same thing as probability. For although an increase of amount always increases the weight, it may diminish the probability; for the additional evidence may be wholly or mostly against the proposition. He considers the question, Ought one always to maximize the amount of the evidence, and hence the weight of the proposition?, and concludes that no universal rule on this matter is possible. He cites Locke as holding the contrary opinion: 'He that judges without informing himself to the utmost that he is capable, cannot acquit himself of judging amiss.' [Locke, Bk. II, Ch. xxi, Sect. 67]

Lewis, on the other hand, argues that the degree of reliability (meaning, inductive probability) of a proposition increases as the 'adequacy' (meaning, amount) of the evidence. He writes: 'The meaning of "adequacy" here will be obvious: if the past experience collated with respect to the frequency in question be extensive, then the assessment of the expectation will be in that respect correspondingly reliable: and if the data be meagre, then in general it will be correspondingly unreliable. In particular, we have the obvious rule that *additional* data which are pertinent always increase the reliability in some degree (regardless of any effect that they may have on the expectation coefficient); though this increase in reliability may not be in direct proportion to any measure of the additional information.' [Lewis, 298 f.] He has in mind judgements typified by formula (16'): $\gamma PF(m/nP(gx), \gamma P(fm/ng) . fx . C_1)$, where it is understood that the constituent formula $\gamma P(fm/ng)$ is a probable generalization-formula.

It will be well to attend first to Lewis' claim; for he explicitly proposes amount of evidence as a criterion of degree of inductive probability, not of the mysterious concept of 'weight'. In his first statement, then, he is claiming that the degree of probability of the generalization-formula $I(fm/ng)$ is determined by the number of f'. For, in the case of generalizations, 'amount of evidence' means of course simply 'number of observed instances'. But this claim has been disposed of earlier: we have already seen that a generalization may be probabilified only in a very low degree by a large sample, as when its members differ only in respect of place; but on the other hand probabilified in quite a high degree by a fairly small sample, namely, when its members differ in respect of many attributes. [2.1]

His second statement too is incorrect for the reason given by Keynes (above). For although the first lot of instantial evidence may make it very probable that fm/ng, the additional lot may make this slightly improbable; so that the appropriate subtractive compositive judgement leads us to conclude that both lots jointly make it only probable that fm/ng. [1.2]

In general, there are two distinct types of case in which the evidence may be copious but the evidenced proposition, p, be in no degree probable. First, when the pieces of evidence are collectively but not severally worthless evidence for p. This happens when the total evidence comprises one lot of pieces for p and another lot of pieces against p, and the probabilificatory powers of the two lots are equal. Second, when the pieces of evidence are collectively and severally worthless evidence for p. E.g., a great number of men assert that p; but all the statements except one are hearsays of a statement by one of these men who is known to be a complete liar. Here, of course, the pieces of evidence are not independent. [1.2] There is a familiar fallacy that is likely to be committed in this type of situation. A case is brought against a man consisting of a great mass of evidence. Counsel for the defence takes it piece by piece, and shows that every one is worthless evidence for the prisoner's guilt. Yet the jury cannot help feeling that, though the pieces of evidence are severally worthless, collectively there must surely be 'something in it'.

Possibly this fallacy is partly due to our tendency to confuse the preceding type of case with a third type of case in which the pieces of evidence really are severally but not collectively worthless evidence for p. This apparent paradox is illustrated by the probability of primitive inductions. We say that $f'Ag$ makes it probable that fAg. Now $f'Ag$ is of course equivalent to the conjunction $gfw \cdot gfx \cdot gfy \cdot gfz \ldots$ etc. But gfw, gfx, etc., are severally worthless evidence for $I(fAg)$; we do not judge an universal generalization to be probabilified in any degree by a single positive instance.

The solution of the paradox is to be found in the quarter in which we naturally look for it. For what these facts suggest is that the inductive probabilificatory power of a collection of observed instances resides in a property or properties that they possess collectively but not severally. And so it does; namely, in their variety and number. That these properties belong to the observed instances collectively but not severally, though obvious, may be brought out by the familiar distinction between the collective and distributive senses of 'all'. From 'All the observed instances are varied and numerous and this is one of the observed instances' we cannot of course infer 'This is varied and numerous'. These points are worth making, because philosophers often go wrong about them. Premising, correctly, that a number of positive instances make an universal generalization in some degree probable, they conclude, incorrectly, that every one of those instances logically must probabilify that generalization in some degree, however small. Consider e.g.: 'Every conjunction of characters or relations in a particular instance suggests a generalization, and seems to lend this generalization a probability. If this were not the case, induction could not claim the slightest shadow of pretence to be proof. For if the evidence of one or two exemplifications gives no probability to a generalization, the evidence of millions of exemplifications cannot do so.' [Eaton, 494]

Next, a few remarks on Locke's maxim cited above. Keynes is undoubtedly right in saying that the rule that one ought always to collect all the available evidence is an extreme over-simplification, and in urging rather that 'there is no evident principle by which to determine *how far* we ought to carry our maxim of strengthening the weight of our argument'. [Keynes, 77] Perhaps the only principle that will do duty is 'Enough is enough'. I.e., when the amount of obtainable evidence bearing on the probability of *p* is large, how much of it one ought to collect in order to determine that probability, will depend on how important it is for him to make the best possible estimate of that probability. And this, like most questions about degrees of 'importance', depends on one's purpose. The following examples illustrate the relevant considerations.

How much of the available evidence ought one to collect in order to determine the degree of (im)probability that the Channel will be smooth to-morrow? That depends on one's situation and purpose. If one is a private person who wants to know in order to decide whether or not to go sailing tomorrow, he need collect very much less than if he is a military commander who wants to know in order to decide whether or not to launch an invasion tomorrow.

Yet Locke's maxim may well be too extreme even for the latter case. For some of the obtainable evidence may be that which will become available at midnight; but it may be extremely disadvantageous for the commander to defer his decision until then. So that it may be right for him to judge the probability on incomplete, i.e. less than all the obtainable, evidence.

Again, an Intelligence officer is ordered to find out whether or not Stalin is really dead. Long before he has collected all the available evidence, he judges that the evidence that he has collected is conclusive for the affirmative. It is then in order for him to claim that it is true, and that he knows, that Stalin is dead. We should also say that he is justified in stopping his investigation at this point, that it would be unreasonable for him to make his evidence complete by collecting all the rest available. Here too, then, Locke's maxim does not fit the facts. Another point that is brought out by this example is the following. In an inquiry of this kind, the investigator collects evidence in the light of his antecedent judgements about which of the available pieces of evidence are likely to be the best, i.e. to (im)probabilify p in the highest degree. So that to pose the question solely in terms of how much evidence he ought to collect is an over-simplification. His problem is more likely to be something like this: Given that he has collected all the best pieces of evidence but one, in the form of statements by all but one of Stalin's normal entourage who were present on the day of his alleged death, and that these pieces of evidence conclusively establish in his judgement the fact of the death; should he terminate his inquiry at this point, or first collect the missing piece of best evidence and/or some of the available second-class evidence? And indeed, to speak of 'available' evidence is often to over-simplify, since the question may be precisely whether it is available. The testimony of the head of Stalin's bodyguard will be among the best pieces of evidence if it is available. But can the man be found, and if so will he talk? [Cp. on these points H. R. Trevor-Roper, *The Last Days of Hitler*, London, Pan Books, 1952, pp. 244 ff.]

When, in a case like the last, one judges that the examined evidence is conclusive that p, one is of course not claiming that the rest of the available unexamined evidence cannot make him alter that judgement. We always allow that additional evidence may make it necessary for us to revise our judgements about the probability or truth of p. Suppose, then, that another Intelligence officer collects some of the unexamined available evidence, and judges that it makes it probable that Stalin is not dead. The appropriate subtractive compositive judgement is then that the total examined evidence makes it only fairly probable that Stalin is dead.

Completeness and conclusiveness, then, are independent properties of evidence. The evidence may be conclusive but not complete, or complete but not conclusive. And making the evidence more complete, i.e. increasing its amount, will not necessarily make p more probable; though it seems to be true that making p more probable does necessarily involve making the evidence more complete. We must remember, too, that this problem about how much evidence bearing on p to collect, and in particular about the alleged obligation to make it complete, only arises when the obtainable evidence is extensive and/or the time available for collecting it is limited. But of course in many, e.g. historical, inquiries the embarrassment is, not the wealth, but the poverty of the available evidence.

In conclusion, I would emphasize that the question 'How much of the obtainable evidence ought one to collect in order to determine the degree of (im)probability of p?', though interesting, does not shed much light on probability. The only connexion lies in the truism that altering the amount of evidence usually, but not always, alters the probability of p; as we have seen earlier [1.2], this is one of the truths expressed by 'Probability is relative to evidence' and 'There is no such thing as *the* probability of p'.

For plainly, there are two distinct questions: (*a*) How ought one to estimate the probability of p given this evidence?; and (*b*) How much of the available evidence ought one to collect given that one wants to know the (im)probability of p? Locke's maxim confuses them: for he says in effect that, if one judges on incomplete evidence that, say, $\gamma P(p)$, whereas if he had judged on complete evidence he would have judged that, say, $\delta P(p)$, then he is guilty of misjudging the probability of p. But this is not so; he may have judged the probability of p on the incomplete evidence quite correctly. A man, e.g. my military commander (above), may be blamed for either or both of two different faults: for misjudging the probability of p on the evidence that he did collect; and/or for failing to collect enough of the obtainable evidence for or against p.

Of the two questions just distinguished, only (*a*) properly belongs to the Philosophy of Probability. Keynes includes some of his remarks about (*b*) under the title 'The Application of Probability to Conduct'. Seen in this view, my own observations on the question belong with my earlier observations on the effect of one's judgement of the probability of *p* on one's judgement about how one ought to act on *p*. [1.2] To be exact, however, (*b*) seems to present a converse problem; namely, the effect of one's judgement about how one ought to act in the matter of collecting evidence relevant to *p* on one's judgement of the probability of *p*. So that a more suitable title might be 'An Application of Right Conduct to Probability'. So much for amount of evidence.

Some say that a test of the probability of generalizations is that the sample be random, or fair, or unbiased. E.g.: 'The first premiss of a scientific inference is that certain things (in the case of induction) or certain characters (in the case of hypothesis) constitute a fairly chosen sample of the class of things or the run of characters from which they have been drawn.' [Peirce, 201] '. . . large and fair samples are required . . . for the establishment of laws or probability rules by induction. . . .' [Kneale, 218 f.]

The first question is, What is the meaning of 'random' (or 'fair') when predicated of a sample? The statisticians' answer is as follows: '. . . a sample of *n* individuals is random when it is chosen in such a way that, when the choice is made, all possible samples of [size] *n* have an equal chance of being selected'. [Yule, 336; Jeffreys, 48] It will be seen that 'randomness' is here defined in terms of 'equal probability'. Cp. Peirce's account: 'The rule [sc., for the validity of ampliative inference] requires that the sample should be drawn at random and independently from the whole lot sampled. That is to say, the sample must be taken according to a precept or method which, being applied over and over again indefinitely, would in the long run result in the drawing of any one set of instances as often as any other set of the same number. The needfulness of this rule is obvious; the difficulty is to know how we are to carry it out.' [Peirce, 201 f.]

Here we may mention two incorrect accounts of the meaning of the expression, which it is necessary to guard against. It may be thought that 'fair sample' means the same as 'representative sample'. Thus e.g. Black: 'To say that the wedge of a melon is a fair sample with respect to ripeness is to say that *if the wedge is ripe the whole melon will be ripe*. [Black, C, 278] But it is untrue that a sample is random or fair with respect to, say, the proportion of gf among f if and only if the composition of the sample is the same as that of the population. For the sample may be random and large yet quite unrepresentative. If the composition of the population is $f1/2g$, it is possible though most (casually) improbable for the composition of a (large) random sample from it to be $f'Ag$ or $f'A\bar{g}$. Or again, it may be thought that 'randomness' as predicated of a sample means the same as 'randomness' or 'irregularity' as predicated by von Mises of a 'collective'. [2.1, 2.2] But the concepts are quite distinct.

As the last quotation from Peirce suggests, the real difficulty lies, not in defining 'random sample', but in finding how to get one. But here too the statisticians are circumstantial enough about what to do. They distinguish two cases: that in which the population is homogeneous and that in which it is non-homogeneous. I have explained 'homogeneity' and its connexion with 'stability' earlier. [2.1] When selecting from a population known to be homogeneous, one should employ a reliable method of random sampling, which will ensure that one's sample is probably random. E.g. selection by lottery, by Tippett's Numbers, or by some other 'randomizing apparatus' are reliable methods of random sampling, whereas selection by human agency is not. [Peirce, 202; Yule, 340 f., 346 f.]

When the population is known or believed to be non-homogeneous in certain respects, one should deliberately vary the sample. If h is certainly or probably relevant to g among f, one should include both hf and $\bar{h}f$ in the sample, preferably in the proportion in which these exist in the population, if this is known. In particular, a combination of both methods called 'stratified sampling' is recommended for non-homogeneous populations. As has been mentioned earlier [2.1], this technique is employed in the Gallup polls. The population (f) is stratified in respect of attributes judged to be certainly or probably relevant to the problematic attribute (g); individuals are selected by a reliable method of random sampling, such as those mentioned above, from each stratum; and the sample is composed by including these individuals in it in the proportions in which these strata exist in the population (e.g. twice as many hf' as $\bar{h}f'$). Thus: 'Random sampling is the basis of the representative [i.e. stratified] sample . . . which is nothing more than a weighted combination of random subsamples'. A stratified sample is accordingly 'a more complex form of random sample' than that described in the preceding paragraph. [Tippett, 87 f.]

Williams maintains that there is no difficulty about obtaining a random sample, for: 'If the sample is not known to be unfair . . . it is fair'. [Williams, G, 141, 72; Wisdom, 215 ff.] But this contention is unacceptable. For Williams is suggesting that we can use the Principle of Indifference as a test of randomness or fairness, and so in effect of equal probability; for we saw above that 'randomness' is formally defined in terms of 'equal probability'. But I said earlier, in discussing 'casual probability', that I agree with the general opinion among modern philosophers that the Principle of Indifference is altogether unacceptable as a test of the equal probability of alternatives. [2.2] Moreover, the contention that we are entitled to call a sample random if we are completely ignorant about its randomness or non-randomness, can hardly be reconciled with the statisticians' doctrines just reviewed. For these evidently involve that a sample can be called certainly or probably random only if we know certain things, as that the method of selection employed is reliable. I shall revert to this matter in criticizing Williams' theory of inductive probability as a whole. [4.2]

This is the natural place to comment on Peirce's rule of predesignation as a '*conditio sine qua non* of valid induction'. [Peirce, 206 ff.] This rule states that, when generalizing, it is wrong to take a sample of, say, BU; find that some proportion, say two-thirds of them, possess a certain property, say H-ness; and then generalize that the same proportion obtains in the population as in the sample. We must rather specify before we take the sample what is the problematic property, say H-ness, in which we are interested; i.e. 'predesignate' it. The preceding remarks on varied and stratified sampling provide one strong reason in favour of Peirce's rule. For these procedures involve making up the sample in the light of our knowledge about what properties are certainly or probably relevant to the problematic one, say H-ness, among, say, BU. And this obviously entails our predesignating the problematic property before we select the sample.

But now, is it true that the randomness of the sample is a criterion of the probability of a generalization? To begin with, it cannot be the criterion (i.e. sufficient and necessary condition) of it, since it cannot vary in degree, whereas inductive probability of course does. It can therefore be at best a criterion (i.e. necessary condition) of it, the degree of inductive probability being determined by some other factor that does vary in degree. This situation obtains in casual primitive judgements. In the formula, (6′), $\gamma\mathrm{PF}(gx, f\mathrm{M}g \cdot fx \cdot \mathrm{C_1})$, the randomness condition, $\mathrm{C_1}$, is a necessary condition of gx being casually probable at all; its degree of casual probability is determined by the degree of approximation of the constituent general statement-formula $(f\mathrm{M}g)$ to universality. However, both Peirce and Kneale assert that randomness is a necessary and not a sufficient condition. Kneale, it will be noticed, says that the other necessary condition is the size of the sample, and this can of course vary in degree.

However, the contention seems to me mistaken. In my view, the degree of variety in the sample is the criterion (sufficient and necessary condition or determinant) of the degree of inductive probability of generalizations. Randomness of the sample, on the other hand, is a criterion (necessary condition) of the validity of direct or inverse casual and hypothetic probabilification-judgements about the population from the evidence of the sample, the other criterion being largeness of the sample.

Possibly belief in the thesis under examination arises from the fact that variety of the sample is normally involved in both of these two distinct types of inference from sample to population. For it is not only the case that a primitive induction is probabilified by the evidence of a varied sample. The preceding remarks on stratified sampling show that when we are dealing with non-homogeneous populations, as we normally are, we must for one thing vary the sample in respect of relevant attributes in order to obtain a random sample. But the facts that (a) the randomness of the sample is a necessary condition of the probability of the casual and hypothetic types of inference from sample to population, (b) the variety of the sample is the sufficient condition of the inductive probability of the inductive type of inference from sample to population, and (c) the variety of the sample is normally a necessary condition of the randomness of the sample, do not entail that (d) the randomness of the sample is a necessary condition of the inductive probability of the inductive type of inference from sample to population.

4.1.2 *Criteria for Functional Formulas*

Thus far on additional suggested criteria of the probability of subject-predicate inductions; I turn now to those of the probability of functional inductions, and shall begin with Johnson's views respecting the determinateness of functional generalizations. He writes: 'The degree of probability to be attached to a generalization based upon facts varies directly with the degree of accordance between the generalization and the facts. . . . With regard to determinateness, the degree of accordance is high in proportion as the generalization fits the facts closely and precisely. Thus, if a formula is comparatively indeterminate, then it cannot be said to accord closely with facts, even though it may cover a large range. E.g., the generalization that bodies falling to the ground move more and more rapidly as they descend may be confirmed by observing an actual increase of velocity, in which case a certain degree of accordance could be said to obtain between the formula and the facts. But if the formula asserts that for every second the rate of movement increases by approximately 32 feet per second, and by measuring the actual fall of bodies it is ascertained that the velocity of their descent does actually increase at this rate, the degree of accordance in this case may be said to be high—on the score of comparative determinateness.' [Johnson, III, 34 f.]

Johnson holds that the degree of accordance between the generalization and the facts is the criterion of the degree of probability of both subject-predicate and functional generalizations, and that the degree of number and variety of the observed instances as well as the degree of determinateness are criteria of the degree of accordance. But I shall consider only his view of the bearing of determinateness on the probability of functional generalizations.

At this point it will be well to clarify the terminology of 'criteria', 'tests' and 'determinants' of degrees of probability. This is best done in terms of the preciser notions of sufficient and necessary conditions. [Broad, D, I, 305 ff.; Wright, T, 66 ff.] When I say e.g. that the degree of variety of the observed instances is *the* criterion or test of the degree of probability of subject-predicate generalizations, this means that it is the sufficient and necessary condition thereof, that a subject-predicate generalization is (very, etc.) probable if and only if the sample is (very, etc.) varied. If it is said e.g. that it is *a* criterion thereof, this is ambiguous. It may mean that variety is a sufficient but not a necessary condition, another sufficient condition being e.g. number; so that the generalization is (very, etc.) probable if, but not only if, the sample is (very, etc.) varied. Alternatively, it may mean that variety is a necessary but not a sufficient condition; so that the generalization is not (very, etc.) probable unless the sample is (very, etc.) varied, though it is not necessarily the case that if the sample is varied the generalization is probable. It is e.g. in this sense that Hume holds degree of analogy to be a test of the degree of probability of derivative inductions. Again, it may be said that A, B and C are *the* criteria of degree of probability; meaning that these are the severally necessary and jointly sufficient conditions thereof. Thus, Johnson's position is that degree of accordance with the facts is the criterion (sufficient and necessary condition) of degree of primitive inductive probability, and that degree of number, variety and determinateness are the criteria (severally necessary and jointly sufficient conditions) of degree of accordance, and hence of degree of probability. Finally, it is desirable to repeat the distinction already drawn between conditions that can vary in degree, e.g. size of the sample, and those that cannot, e.g. randomness of the sample. The latter can be criteria of probability only in the sense of being necessary conditions of the presence of probability at all, whereas the former can be sufficient conditions of degree of probability. Cp. the formula, $(6')$, $\gamma PF(gx, fMg \cdot fx \cdot C_1)$. Here, gx is not casually probable at all unless the necessary condition of randomness, C_1, is satisfied; but the degree of probability is determined by another factor, namely, the degree of approximation of the constituent general formula to universality.

However, it is untrue that the 'degree of accordance' with the facts of a more determinate generalization, e.g. (*a*) 'The breadth of this leaf in cms. is equal (directly proportional) to its length in ins.', is greater than that of a corresponding less determinate generalization, e.g (*b*) 'The breadth of this leaf is a function of (covaries with) its length'. The expression 'degree of accordance (or correspondence)' strictly makes no sense: it is clear that Johnson intends 'degree of closeness of correspondence'. But the notion of degree of closeness of correspondence does not apply to the correspondence between statements and facts; the words and the world either correspond or they do not. All the same, the error of supposing that, in particular, a more determinate statement corresponds more closely with certain facts than does a corresponding less determinate one, is often committed. But, to change the example, 'Harris is at the door' does not correspond more closely with certain facts than does 'A man is at the door', any more than a large-scale map corresponds more closely with the ground than does a small-scale map of the same area.

Again, it is untrue that the facts (i.e. the observed values of the variables) make generalization (a) more probable than generalization (b). They probabilify them both, if at all, equally. What is true is the different point that it is harder to establish (a) than (b) with that degree of probability, whatever it may be. The reason for this is, as we have seen earlier, that making generalizations of type (a) prerequires discovering a formula or colligating concept that will fit the facts, whereas making generalizations of type (b) does not. [1.1]

This doctrine of Johnson's, and that of Keynes which I discussed first, may both be said to maintain that degree of inductive probability is determined by degree of specificity. But it is desirable to point out that different senses of 'specific' are involved. The specificity of statements depends, of course, on that of their constituent terms; it is therefore to the latter that we must attend. Keynes uses the word in two distinct senses accordingly as he is speaking of the specificity of the subject- or the predicate-term. In the former case, he would say e.g. that 'rational animal' is more specific than 'animal'; and generally, that a logical product is more specific than any of its components. In the latter case, he would say e.g. that 'animal' is more specific than 'animal or vegetable'; and generally, that any of its components is more specific than a logical sum. Johnson may be represented as saying that 'direct proportionality' and 'inverse proportionality' e.g. are more specific than 'functionality'; and generally, that determinates are more specific than the determinable to which they belong. Finally, on account of an example that I gave above, we should notice in passing that the sense in which 'Harris' is more specific than 'man' differs significantly from the sense involved in the last case; cp. Johnson's discussion of the resemblances and differences between the meanings of 'Red is a colour' and 'Plato is a man'. [Johnson, I, 173 ff.] It may well be that there are yet other meanings of 'specific'. But all we need to notice is that in none of the three meanings that figure in Keynes' and Johnson's doctrines does degree of specificity determine degree of inductive probability.

Finally, let us examine Johnson's suggestion that degree of simplicity is a criterion (necessary condition) of the degree of probability of functional generalizations. He writes: '. . . the criteria of simplicity and analogy, especially when conjoined, confer upon a formula of covariation that highest degree of probability which allows us to regard the induction, not as merely problematic [probable], but as virtually demonstrative [true]. E.g., the experiments that have been conducted in regard to the covariations of temperature, pressure and volume of gases have always been treated by physicists as conferring absolute demonstrative certitude upon the formulae inferred, although they have been actually confirmed from a necessarily limited number of observations'. [Johnson, II, 250] Johnson is not alone in this opinion about simplicity; v. Wright reports Cournot as holding it, and Nicod entertains it. [Wright, T, 296 f.; Nicod, 209 f.]

It will be seen that Johnson here suggests that another criterion (necessary condition) of degree of probability of functional generalizations, besides degree of simplicity, is degree of analogy. Thus, he holds that e.g. Coulomb's law of electrostatics is probabilified in part because of its resemblance to Newton's law of gravitation, both being 'inverse square of the distance' laws. This suggestion seems to me insufficiently plausible to be worth examining in detail; but we shall do well to note in passing yet another sense, distinct of course from both of those criticized above, in which degree of analogy may be held to affect degree of inductive probability.

As to the meaning of 'simple' when predicated of functional descriptions and generalizations, it will be remembered that we accepted Kneale's account, according to which degree of simplicity is determined by the number of parameters in the formula. The case in which the colligating concept is a straight line, as in my example about the values of the length and breadth of this leaf, is simpler than the case in which the colligating concept is any curve, say a circle. We also followed Kneale in distinguishing this use of 'simple' from that in which 'simple' is predicated of non-empirical hypotheses, the test of degree of which he suggests to be the number of independent concepts involved. [1.1]

Johnson's claim can be confuted by a short and familiar method; namely, by pointing out that a functional generalization may be (called) simple but not probable, or probable but not simple. So that degree of simplicity is not a criterion in the sense of being either a sufficient or a necessary condition of degree of probability.

It is true, however, that simplicity is reckoned a virtue in functional generalizations; so that, other things being equal, the simpler of two rival such generalizations is preferred. So that the mistaken view that simplicity is a test of probability originates, perhaps, in a confusion between the goodness in general of such a generalization and its goodness as an assertion (i.e. its probability); as a result of which a test of the former, namely simplicity, is mistaken for a test of the latter. I suggested at the end of my discussion of hypothetic probability [1.2] that a similar confusion may underlie the mistaken belief that simplicity in the other sense is a criterion of the probability, as opposed to goodness in general, of non-empirical hypotheses. It may be that this diagnosis applies to determinateness also; for we think a determinate functional generalization superior to a mere covariation-generalization. On the other hand, it can scarcely apply to specificity in the more important of Keynes' two senses, namely, that affecting the subject-term in a subject-predicate generalization. For we account breadth, not narrowness, of scope a virtue in such generalizations; other things being equal, the one of two rival such generalizations with the less specific subject-term is judged the better. Following Popper, Kneale adduces this truth as a major criticism of Keynes' theory. [Kneale, 233 f.]

Another general and basic criticism that affects specificity and determinateness as well as simplicity is this. I suggested [1.2] that primitive probabilification-judgements are of the doubly evaluative form: 'q (e.g. that $f'Ag$ and that f' are varied) is good evidence that p (e.g. that fAg), and so makes it probable (or right to assert that) p'. It follows that any acceptable criterion of primitive probability-judgements must relate to some feature of the evidence for them, such as the variety of the observed instances. But the alleged criteria of specificity, determinateness and simplicity fail to satisfy this condition; they refer not at all to evidence, only to features of propositions considered in themselves, or to 'the character of the generalization *a priori*', as Keynes puts it. For this reason, the suggested criteria of analogy (as presented in the traditional argument and by Hume), of amount and of randomness stand better than the other three; for they do at least all locate the source of the probability of primitive judgements in features of the evidence for them, even if they identify those features incorrectly.

In conclusion, Johnson is of course right in pointing out in the last citation that Boyle's law e.g. is judged to be true and not merely very, very probable. But the reason is not, as he suggests, the pre-eminent degree of simplicity and analogy (in his sense) possessed by this law. It is because the evidence for it is judged to be conclusive, because the conditions C_2 and C_3 are satisfied in the highest degree. Were this not so, the formula would not be called a law, since it is a necessary but not a sufficient condition of an induction's being (called) an inductive law that it should be verified and not merely probabilified by the evidence for it. [1.1]

4.2 GROUNDS AND PRINCIPLES OF INDUCTION

We have now to consider a line of argument which is very familiar and entirely different from the criteria approach. Some inductive philosophers hold that inductions can only be justified by being shown to be deducible from some ground or principle. It is supposed, then, that the sort of proof appropriate to inductions is demonstrative or deductive proof. It is held further that inductions are not deducible from the ground alone, but that some other premiss is necessary. Typically, the ground is regarded as a major premiss which is unexpressed or tacitly presupposed, and the minor premiss is taken to be a description or observation-statement, the truth of which is undisputed. Theories of this type can conveniently be divided into those which claim to demonstrate the truth of inductions (conclusions) and into those which claim to demonstrate their probability; I shall consider first two of the former sort and then three of the latter sort. Most, but not all, of the latter sort use probable deductive reasoning in Jevons' sense, i.e. reasoning in the Calculus of Probabilities. [1.1] This point is connected with another distinction between these theories, namely, between those which claim that the ground (major premiss) is true and those which claim that it is probable; but though this is significantly related to the more important distinction between true and probable inductions (conclusions), it is of course a different distinction.

The central tasks of Inductive Philosophy, on this view, are regarded as two. First, to discover and formulate a ground such that, if it is true or probable and a certain minor premiss is true, then a certain induction logically must be true or probable. Second, to prove that the ground is true or probable. Since most, but not all, such theories give as grounds contingent statements of fact, usually of very wide scope; it is thought that the ground must be empirically proved true or probable by some very general fact about the course of Nature. In fine, what is claimed by these theories is this: for any particular induction, the truth or probability of the major premiss and the truth of the minor premiss are the severally necessary and jointly sufficient conditions of the truth or probability of that induction.

4.2.1 *Theories Designed to Prove Inductions True*

This view of the problem is evidently of ancient lineage; for the Stoics, who in Greek philosophy represent the rationalist approach to induction, adopt it. Thus, we find the Epicureans objecting to their doctrine as follows: '. . . we do not need to presuppose the conclusion in our premiss, so as to say: "Since men, in whatever places they are, are similar to men in our experience even in being mortal, All men must be mortal" '. [Philodemus, 75] I.e., the Stoics contend that what really justifies the induction 'All men are mortal' is the verification-judgement: 'The fact that the truth about the mortality of observed men is also the truth about the mortality of all (i.e. unobserved and observed) men, and that the truth about the mortality of observed men is that they are all mortal, makes it true that all men are mortal'. Here, the ground is the constituent statement: 'The truth about the mortality of observed men is also the truth about the mortality of all men'.

My fundamental objection to this doctrine is as follows. In the verification-judgement just formulated, the conclusion is deduced from the two premisses. If, therefore, the conclusion is to be an induction at all, at least one of the premisses logically must be a primitive induction; if, but only if, this is so, the conclusion will be a deductive derivative induction. [1.1] But the minor premiss, 'The truth about the mortality of observed men is that they are all mortal', is a description and not a generalization; so that what must be a generalization is the ground itself. Now if it is a generalization, it logically must be the evidenced-statement of the evidential-statement: 'The fact that in all observed cases the truth about the mortality of observed men is also the truth about the mortality of all (i.e. unobserved and observed) men, is evidence that in all (i.e. unobserved and observed) cases the truth about the mortality of observed men is also the truth about the mortality of all men'. [1.1] But the evidencing-statement in this putative evidential-statement is illogical, since to speak of observed cases of something being true of unobserved men is to contradict oneself. Consequently, the evidential-statement as a whole is logically impossible, and its constituent evidenced-statement logically cannot be a primitive induction. Consequently, 'All men are mortal' cannot be a deductive derivative induction; and the claim that the truth of the proffered ground is a necessary condition of the truth of the induction 'All men are mortal', must be rejected.

It will be seen that Philodemus criticizes the Stoic doctrine on the further score that it is circular. His criticism is correct in the following sense. We cannot know that the truth (whatever it may be) about the mortality of observed men is also the truth about the mortality of all (unobserved and observed) men, except by knowing that what actually is the truth about the mortality of observed men (namely, that they are all mortal) is also the truth about all men. I say 'circular in the following sense', because 'circular' is ambiguous. An argument is called circular, either when the conclusion is included among the premises, or when the truth of at least one of the premises cannot be known unless the truth of the conclusion is known. It is the second sense that is involved here.

In the preceding argument, the major premiss permits only one induction to be deduced, namely, 'All men are mortal'. But one can easily think of a major premiss of far wider scope that will enable us to deduce, not only this induction, but all inductions. So that all inductive inferences will have the same major premiss, but of course different minor premisses. We may formulate this premiss: 'Everything that is true of observed things or events of any sort is true of all (unobserved as well as observed) things or events of that sort'. And this is much nearer to the sort of statement designated 'the ground, or principle, of induction' or 'the principle of the uniformity of Nature'. That is, it is a distinguishing mark of such grounds that they serve as major premisses for very many, even all, inductions; and consequently are of very wide scope.

The above formula undoubtedly renders correctly one common

interpretation of 'the uniformity of Nature' and/or 'the inductive principle'. Consider Hume's mention of 'that principle, *that instances, of which we have had no experience, must resemble those, of which we have had experience, and that the course of nature continues always uniformly the same*'. [Hume, T, 89] We have noticed earlier that Hume sometimes adopts the unsatisfactory, because too narrow, version, that future instances will resemble past instances; this fault also vitiates Reid's rendering of the ground, which he includes among 'the first principles of contingent truths'. [Reid, 389] Cp. now with Hume's Johnson's formulation of 'the inductive principle: "What can be predicated of all examined members of a class, can be predicated, with a higher or lower degree of probability, of all members of the class" '. [Johnson, II, 23] The important difference lies in the substitution of 'probably' for 'certainly'. We have seen earlier [2.1] that Keynes interprets the principle of the uniformity of Nature as asserting the irrelevance of position in space or time to all other properties. His version of the principle may therefore be rendered: 'Everything that is true of things or events of any sort in any part of space or time is true of things or events of that sort in all parts of space or time'. And this amounts in practice to Hume's version; for Keynes is thinking of our generalizing from the evidence of things and events in observed parts of space and time to things and events of those sorts in unobserved parts of them.

The falsity of both the Hume/Keynes and the Johnson principles is easily shown. Armed with the former principle, I observe a redhead to be lame and correctly deduce that all redheads are lame. But the next redhead I observe is not lame. Hence, at least one of my premisses is false. But the minor premiss is true by observation, so that the major premiss, the principle, is false. Alternatively, armed with the latter principle, I observe a redhead to be lame and correctly deduce that it is in some degree probable that all redheads are lame. But this is to claim that (primitive) inductions can be probabilified in some degree by a single observed instance. But this is false, since such inductions are not (judged to be) probabilified in any degree by such evidence. Johnson's principle too is therefore false.

Evidently, these principles are much too strong, and it is not surprising that other philosophers advance weaker assertions as the principle of the uniformity of Nature [Eaton, 534 ff.; Venn, P,

119 ff.; Wisdom, 118 ff.] Consider the formula: 'Some things that are true of observed things or events of some sorts are true of all (unobserved and observed) things or events of those sorts'. It should be compared with my original strong formulation, above. But of course it is too indeterminate to serve as a ground. We need to know which sorts of things and events and which facts about them. Given that this redhead is lame, I cannot deduce from this fact and the principle, that all redheads are lame, unless I know that redheads are one of the right sorts of thing and being lame is one of the right facts about them.

The answer that some thinkers give to these questions is in effect as follows: the sorts of things are those that are to be found in all regions of space and time, and the facts about them are 'important' facts. Thus, 'All matter gravitates' is the sort of conclusion that is supposed to be deducible from the weak principle, because matter is diffused throughout space and time and because gravitating is an important property. 'All ravens are black', on the other hand, is not the sort of conclusion that is supposed to be deducible from the principle, because ravens are confined to a very small region of space and time and because being black is not an important property. On this view, then, 'Nature is uniform' means that the Universe is homogeneous or all of a piece in some respects, since there are uniformities or laws, not merely in, but of Nature; i.e. universal laws which, it will be remembered, can be proportional or statistical as well as universal in the other sense of 'universal'. [2.1, end] In this way, 'the uniformity of Nature' is identified with 'the rule of universal law', and 'the inductive principle' with 'the principle of determinism'.

Two examples will suffice to illustrate this weak interpretation of the principle. The first is Mill. [Mill, 200 ff.] He declares that '. . . the proposition that the course of nature is uniform is the fundamental principle, or general axiom, of Induction'. And he tells us that the meaning of 'the course of nature is uniform' is that 'whatever is true in any one case, is true in all cases of a certain description; the only difficulty is, to find what description'. He meets this difficulty in the way sketched above, so that on his final analysis the principle means simply that there are universal laws of Nature; the uniformity of Nature, he continues, is simply a 'complex fact' compounded of these uniformities or laws. I shall return to Mill's inductive philosophy shortly.

My second example is Bondi's formulation of 'the cosmological principle', which is just another name for the principle of the uniformity of Nature. This states that '. . . we live in a world that is homogeneous at least as far as the laws of nature are concerned', though it is of course conceded that there are 'local irregularities' as well as these universal regularities. [H. Bondi, *Cosmology*, Cambridge, 1952, pp. 11 f.]

The question of the truth or falsity of this weak principle of the uniformity of Nature, i.e. the question whether there are any truly universal laws, is by no means so easy to settle as that of the truth or falsity of the strong principle. At least one eminent philosopher, Whitehead, believes it to be false, holding laws to hold true only within 'cosmic epochs'. I shall restrict myself to indicating the kind of considerations relevant to deciding between what I shall call 'universalism' and 'regionalism'.

Take first physical laws. In modern Cosmology there are both universalists and regionalists. Bondi continues: '*If* we are still able to apply our terrestrially gained knowledge in such far-flung fields (*sc.*, distant astronomical objects, the ancient geological history of the Earth etc.), then the uniformity of the cosmos must be very great. But it is not universally agreed that our knowledge can be directly used in such fields; it is, in fact, maintained by some schools of cosmology that in interpreting observations of far-distant or very ancient objects we must take account of the non-uniformity of the background in some way, to be decided by other considerations. Another view, however, rejects any such attempt to discuss the consequences of a real non-uniformity of the universe.' The universalist position is taken by Bondi and Gold in their steady-state theory. The regionalist position is taken by those theorists who hold that the constants of Nature, such as the gravitational constant, and accordingly the important class of natural laws or principles that involve these constants, vary with the age of the Universe. This is true e.g. of Milne's kinematic relativity theory. [E. Whittaker, *Eddington's Principle in the Philosophy of Science*, Cambridge, 1951, pp. 20 f., 28 ff.]

Consider next the laws of human nature, individual and social. How about the uniformity of *human* nature? Hume provides a classic statement of the universalist thesis: '. . . human nature remains still the same, in its principles and operations. . . . Would you know the sentiments, inclinations and course of life of the

Greeks and Romans? Study well the temper and actions of the French and English: You cannot be much mistaken in transferring to the former *most* of the observations which you have made with regard to the latter.' [Hume, E, 83] The operative word is 'most'. Human nature is uniform in the weak sense; there are universal laws thereof, but there are also of course local and temporal irregularities.

The opposition between universalism and regionalism in this sphere is well illustrated by the conflict of methodologies respecting economic and political science, for this has long been a major problem in the Philosophy of the Social Sciences. It will suffice to consider this issue as it arose in Economics about a century ago. The universalist position was taken by the British classical school of economists, i.e. Smith, Ricardo and their followers. They were challenged by the German historical school, i.e. Roscher, Hildebrand and others, who took the regionalist position. 'The Historians held that the greatest sin committed by Smith and his followers was the inordinate stress which they laid upon the universality of their doctrines. Hildebrand applies the term "universalism" to this feature of their teaching . . . [namely, the thesis] that the economic laws which they had formulated were operative everywhere and at all times, and that the system of political economy founded upon them was universal in its application.' [C. Gide and C. Rist, *A History of Economic Doctrines*, tr. R. Richards, London, 1915, p. 390] I.e., regionalists hold that, though there are some economic laws that are true of Britain and others that hold true of Germany, or some that apply to the economic facts between 1770 and 1870 and others that apply from 1870 to the present, there are no economic laws that hold true universally, nor consequently a single science of Economics. So similarly a physical regionalist might hold that there is no science of Physics, only terrestrial physics, etc.

The position of Mill on this issue is interesting. Characteristically, it is a compromise. He distinguishes sharply between pure and applied Economics. In the former, he remains loyal to the universalism of Ricardo and his father. But he concedes to the regionalists that, when these universal laws are applied, they need to be 'corrected for practice'. And he projects a new science to find out what the appropriate corrections are, namely, 'Political Ethology, or the theory of the causes which determine the type of character belonging to a people or to an age', which is a branch of 'Ethology, or the science of the formation of character'. The way in which he thinks that the conclusions of this study will help in the practical application of Economics is illustrated by the following passage: 'In political economy . . . empirical laws of human nature are tacitly assumed by English thinkers, which are calculated only for Great Britain and the United States. Among other things, an intensity of competition is constantly supposed, which, as a general mercantile fact, exists in no country in the world except these two'. [Mill, 562 ff., 583 ff.; J. N. Keynes, *The Scope and Method of Political Economy*, 4th ed., London, 1917, pp. 297 ff.; K. R. Popper, *The Poverty of Historicism*, Sect. 26]

The upshot of this discussion is then this. The strong uniformity principle, in both its 'true' and 'probable' forms, is false. And to the extent that there is force in the regionalist views, specimens of which have just been given, it is doubtful whether even the weak uniformity principle is true. It follows that neither principle will serve as ground from which, with suitable minor premises, we can deduce the truth or probability of extrapolations in space or time. This point is important, and I shall revert to it later. [5.2] At present, we need only note that the notion of extrapolation is wider than my discussion in 3.2 might suggest. For there I was concerned only with one sort of extrapolation, which arises only in the case of functional inductions, and which consists in asserting that the dependent variable will have value so-and-so when the independent variable has value such-and-such, when the latter value lies outside the observed range of variation of that variable. But in fact we extrapolate whenever we eliminate from an induction a possibly necessary qualifying condition which we have not varied; when, e.g., knowing only that $hf'Ag$ and not that $hf'Ag$. $hf'Ag$, we generalize that fAg and not that $hfAg$. And we extrapolate in space or time when there are substituted on h, say, 'within range of human observation' or 'present or not long past'.

These remarks on the principle of the uniformity of Nature form a natural introduction to the inductive philosophy of Mill. [Mill, III, i–x, xiv, xxi; IV, ii] He distinguishes two main types of inductions: causal laws, and empirical laws. The former he identifies with 'uniformities of succession', not with the much smaller class of generalizations that explicitly assert causation. We will consider his account of the proof of causal laws only.

According to Mill, causal laws are properly proved by the law of universal causation conjoined with the Experimental Methods. The law of causation is the proposition 'Every event has a cause'. By 'cause' Mill understands 'immediate, unconditional and invariable antecedent event'. It will be convenient to represent antecedent events by A, B, C, etc. and subsequent events by X, Y, Z, etc. To say that A is an 'unconditional' antecedent of X means that, when A occurs, then X occurs, whatever else happens; i.e. that A is a sufficient condition of X. Thus, night is not called the cause of day because day would not succeed night if, e.g., the Sun were extinguished.

Mill enumerates five Experimental Methods. In the Method of Agreement, we prove that A is the cause of X by establishing that X (say, prosperity) is always preceded by A (say, free trade). In the Method of Difference, we prove that A is the cause of X by establishing that: (i) when X (say, a man's death) did not occur, A (say, his being shot through the heart) did not precede; (ii) when X did occur, A did precede; and (iii) there was no other difference between situation (i) and situation (ii) besides the absence of X and A in (i) and the presence of X and A in (ii). In the Method of Concomitant Variations, we prove that A is the cause of X by establishing that an increase (or diminution) in X (say, prosperity) is always preceded by an increase (or diminution) in A (say, free trade). This method therefore resembles that of agreement, except that whereas the latter deals with the presence or absence of A and X, the former deals with variations in degree of A and X. It is by the former that we establish numerical laws, such as Boyle's and Ohm's. The Joint Method of Agreement and Difference is explained by its name and by what precedes; and the Method of Residues may be ignored.

The proof of causal laws by the law of causation conjoined with the Experimental Methods possesses two important features. First, the type of proof is demonstrative, not empirical, proof. Thus Mill writes: 'A general proposition inductively obtained is only then proved to be true when the instances on which it rests are such that, if they have been correctly observed, the falsity of the generalization would be *inconsistent* with the constancy of causation'. The word that I have italicized plainly indicates that Mill is thinking of deductive proof. Second, the type of induction involved is eliminative, not enumerative, induction. We prove that A is the cause of X, not by accumulating observed constant conjunctions of A with

X, but by eliminating all other possible candidates for that title, as B, C, etc. [5.1] However, Mill recognizes that only the Method of Difference possesses these two features, and he prizes it above the other methods accordingly. What impairs the probative force of the Method of Agreement is 'plurality of causes', i.e. alternative causes. E.g., death is caused by shooting through the heart, or cancer, or . . . etc. Hence, if X occurs without A's preceding, we cannot eliminate A, since it may yet be true that A causes X when it does precede it.

The principle of induction itself, the law of causation, stands on the same footing as the principles of Mathematics and Formal Logic: it is an enumerative induction which is true because, although its scope is of the maximum width (being about all events), yet no exception to it has been found. Mill concedes incidentally that enumerative inductions of less than universal scope are in various degrees probable, but not true or certain. It results that causal induction is 'scientific' and indirect, not prescientific and direct. We establish the proposition, 'A is the cause of X', not by direct induction, by accumulating evidence of a constant conjunction between A and X; but by indirect induction, by deducing it from a wider and better established induction, namely, the law of causation. This is revealing, both of Mill's indebtedness to Whewell's account of the 'consilience of inductions', and of his own conception of 'inductive logic'. For he writes: 'To test a generalization, by showing that it either follows from, or conflicts with, some stronger induction, some generalization resting on a broader foundation of experience, is the beginning and end of the logic of Induction'.

Mill includes far too much under 'causal laws'. It is wrong to equate these, for instance, with laws of succession; here, Mill is presumably following Kant. Again, it is false that the laws of functional dependence established by the Method of Concomitant Variations are laws of succession or of causation: they are non-temporal. Had he seen these points, Mill would not have exaggerated the importance of causation in induction as he does, claiming that 'the notion of Cause . . . is the root of the whole theory of Induction'.

His doctrine of the Experimental Methods is open to the following main criticism. We will take it that we are interested in establishing the causes of effects rather than the effects of causes. Now, the Method of Agreement is not an eliminative method at all for this purpose. For what it eliminates are candidates for the style of necessary condition; whereas, as we have seen, Mill means by a 'cause' a sufficient condition. (A is a sufficient condition of X if, whenever A occurs, then X occurs; and A is a necessary condition of X if, whenever A does not occur, then X does not occur.) The method does however provide enumerative evidence about sufficient conditions. The Method of Difference, on the other hand, does indeed eliminate candidates for the style of sufficient condition. It follows that Mill is right in rating the Method of Difference higher than the Method of Agreement, but wrong in the reason he gives for doing so. The reason is, not so much that the latter method is frustrated by the existence of alternative causes (though this is true), as that it is not an eliminative method of proving causation at all. Similar remarks apply to the Method of Concomitant Variations as to the Method of Agreement.

There is also a decisive objection to Mill's doctrine of the principle(s) or ground(s) of induction; namely, that it (they) will not afford a demonstrative proof when conjoined with the data yielded by the methods. It is to be observed, first, that the law of causation, though necessary, is not sufficient to make causal proofs formally valid. There is need of another premiss, which v. Wright calls the postulate of completely known instances, and formulates thus: '[first] certain categories of simple properties can be left out of consideration as being *irrelevant* to the eliminative method of induction, and . . . [second] in each single case we are able to judge whether the information about the instances, which has been taken into account, represents complete knowledge as to all the remaining relevant properties or not'. [Wright, L, IV] There are indications that Mill half saw the need for this second principle, as when he remarks that in establishing the causes of chemical phenomena we take no account of the positions of the planets, because these are judged to be irrelevant.

But even if Mill had explicitly adopted this second principle, it would have availed him nothing, because neither principle can be shown to be true or probable. In the case of 'Every event has a cause', the reason is simply that this form of words is not of the type that can be true or probable, i.e. is not a statement. That it is not a generalization, as Mill maintains, can be shown by the following consideration. Suppose I adduce what I claim to be an exception, an uncaused event, say cancer: will my claim be allowed? Patently not: I shall be told that cancer is not an uncaused event, but an event the cause or causes of which are not yet known. And so generally with any alleged exception. Genuine generalizations, however, logically must be open to disproof by exceptions. But not only is this form of words not a generalization, it is not any kind of statement. It is rather, in my view, a rule for investigators which happens to be couched in a rather misleading grammatical form. (See below.) And a rule cannot of course be true or false, probable or improbable.

As for the postulate of completely known instances, it seems clear enough that we know neither of its clauses to be true or probable. Some, indeed, argue for the first clause. Keynes, as we have seen, maintains that we know *a priori* that place and date are always inductively irrelevant, this truth being the principle of the uniformity of Nature: but for my part I am unable to see that this proposition is either true or known *a priori*. The second clause is even more plainly false. We frequently judge circumstances to be relevant when they are not, and (what is much more serious) exclude them from consideration as irrelevant when they are not. To say this is not to deny the important truth that previous judgements of (ir)relevance are essential to making inductions of all sorts, not merely causal ones. But it is to deny that these judgements are infallible.

Further, even if Mill's ground were a generalization, his claim that it is true because its scope is of the maximum width, cannot be allowed. I discussed this point earlier [4.1, beginning], when examining degree of specificity of the subject-term as a test of degree of inductive probability.

Again, if Mill were to prove all causal laws true, as he claims to do, he would thereby disprove his own theory. For we judge some and perhaps most of them to be only more or less probable; e.g. 'It is fairly probable that cigarette-smoking is a cause of lung-cancer'. Indeed, there is a general and fatal objection on this score to theories of this type, as Broad points out. [Broad, R, II, 11 f.] Since the minor premisses are all true by observation, all conclusions must have the same 'value' as the major premiss or ground, being true if it is true, very probable if it is very probable, and so on. Yet it is truistic that generalizations differ in respect of their degrees of probability.

Finally, a few words on the historical antecedents of Mill's inductive philosophy. It is evident that much of it is derived from other authors. His Experimental Methods derive from Bacon's Tables of Presence, Absence and Degrees, and from Hume's Rules by which to judge of Causes and Effects. From Hume comes too his definition of 'cause', and from Kant he takes his view of the central importance of the 'Law of Causality', that 'Everything that happens, that is, that begins to be, presupposes something upon which it follows according to a rule'. [*Critique of Pure Reason*, tr. N. Kemp Smith, London, 1933, p. 218] And to Whewell he owes his conception of 'scientific induction' and 'inductive logic' as turning on the 'consilience of inductions'.

But it is interesting to notice that these views do not originate with Whewell, since the germ at least of a similar theory of 'scientific induction' is to be found in Hume. His fourth Rule runs: 'The same cause always produces the same effect, and the same effect never arises but from the same cause. This principle we derive from experience, and is the source of most of our philosophical [i.e. scientific] reasonings. For when by any clear experiment we have discovered the causes or effects of any phenomenon, we immediately extend our observations to every phenomenon of the same kind, without waiting for that constant repetition, from which the first idea of this relation is derived.' [Hume, T, 173 f.; 104 f., 132] The similarities to Mill's theory are plain: causal laws are proved true by being deduced from the principle and minor premisses obtained by experiment; this is the scientific procedure which replaces crude induction by simple enumeration; and the principle or rule itself is a true induction by simple enumeration.

The most interesting resemblance, however, is this. Hume's, Kant's and Mill's principles are all philosophically perplexing for the same reason, namely, that their meaning, force or logical status is obscure, so that one is uncertain how to take them. Thus, are they generalizations, as Hume and Mill say; or synthetic *a priori* judgements, as Kant says of his principle; or not statements at all, despite their appearance of being so? [G. J. Warnock, 'Every Event has a Cause', in A. G. N. Flew (ed.), *Logic and Language*, 2nd Series, Oxford, 1953, pp. 95 ff.] The fact that these authors refer to these propositions, sometimes as 'principles', sometimes as 'laws' and sometimes as 'rules', suggests that they themselves are not very clear on this point.

My own view is that the force or meaning of both Kant's and Mill's principles is pretty much that which Kant ascribes to some of his 'regulative principles of reason'. It may be rendered: 'Proceed as if every sort of event has at least one other sort of event as its sufficient temporal precondition'. The reason for this particular regulative principle is, of course, the great practical advantage of discovering such sufficient temporal preconditions; for when we succeed in doing so, we are commonly thereby enabled to produce or avoid the effect-events in question at will. Unfortunately, Kant himself includes the 'law of causality' among the 'constitutive principles of understanding'; 'cause', for him, is a 'category', not an 'idea'.

It is interesting that the second of Newton's Rules of Reasoning in Philosophy bears some resemblance to the second half of Hume's fourth Rule: '. . . *to the same natural effects we must, as far as possible, assign the same causes.* As to respiration in a man and in a beast; the descent of stones in *Europe* and in *America*; the light of our culinary fire and of the sun; the reflection of light in the earth, and in the planets.' [F. Cajori (tr.), *Sir I. Newton's Mathematical Principles,* Berkeley, California, 1947, p. 398] But there are also manifest differences; in particular, whereas Hume represents his 'rule' as a true generalization, Newton clearly regards his as a maxim for scientific investigators.

4.2.2 *Theories Designed to Prove Inductions Probable*

Let us next consider briefly the views of Russell as contained in his *Problems of Philosophy.* [Russell, P, 93 ff., 109 ff.; Mace, 265 ff.] He formulates the 'principle of induction' for (universal subject-predicate) generalizations as follows: '(*a*) The greater the number of cases in which a thing of the sort A has been found associated with a thing of the sort B, the more probable it is (if no cases of failure of association are known) that A is always associated with B; (*b*) Under the same circumstances, a sufficient number of cases of the association of A with B will make it nearly certain that A is always associated with B, and will make this general law approach certainty without limit.' [Russell, P, 104 f.] It is noteworthy that, in his latest contribution to Inductive Philosophy, he again argues that generalizations can be proved to be probable only if certain postulates or presuppositions are true. [Russell, H, 439 ff.] Thus, according to Russell's earlier account, a typical inductive primitive probabilification-judgement goes: 'The fact that all generalizations are more or less probable accordingly as the observed evidential instances are more or less numerous, and that the observed BU are very numerous and all H, makes it very probable that all BU are H'. He adds that his inductive principle is a 'logical principle'; more precisely, a necessary *a priori* truth of Logic, like the principle of identity, $p \supset p$. [Russell, P, 113 ff.]

We shall do well to notice at the outset two important differences between this account and those of Mill and the Stoics. First, the inductive ground is here said to be a necessary and *a priori* truth of Logic, whereas the latter hold their grounds to be contingent and *a posteriori* truths of fact. Second, whereas the latter claim to prove inductions true from their grounds, Russell claims to prove them in various degrees probable but never true or certain. In this respect his principle resembles Johnson's, cited above.

My chief criticism is on the same lines as one that I have made of the Stoics. Namely, the sort of conclusions that Russell has in mind are not (rightly called) inductions. For by his account they are deductions from a necessary *a priori* truth of Logic conjoined with a truth of observation. Consider the argument: 'If any proposition is true then it is true; it is raining; so it is raining'. No-one would call its conclusion 'an induction': yet by Russell's account a typical inductive primitive probabilification-judgement, such as the one above about BU, is of exactly the same logical type. Of course, the reason why we are inclined to think that the argument about BU is inductive, whereas we fall into no such temptation when considering the argument about its raining, is that the former but not the latter contains such words as 'generalization', 'probable' and 'evidential instances'. But we should not let ourselves be deceived by that.

Further, the principle 'All generalizations are more or less probable accordingly as the observed evidential instances are more or less numerous' is not in fact a necessary truth, since it is not self-contradictory to say the opposite. Here the alleged parallelism with $p \supset p$ breaks down, for $p \, . \sim p$ certainly is a self-contradictory formula. Indeed, it is not even false to say so; in other words, the principle is not even contingently true. To be this, it would be necessary to replace the word 'numerous' by the word 'varied'. It was on this ground that I criticized this first half, (*a*), of Russell's principle earlier. [2.1]

In conclusion, two words on its second half, (*b*). The expression 'a sufficient number of cases' is unsatisfactory, because tautological, since it means presumably 'a number of cases sufficient to make the generalization nearly certain'. More important is the view that no amount of any kind of instantial evidence can ever make a generalization true or certain as distinct from very, very probable. This opinion is held by a large number of inductive philosophers. Yet it is surely false: it makes perfectly good sense to speak of true generalizations, and they are rightly claimed to be so when the instantial evidence for them is judged to be, not merely very, very good, but conclusive. [5.2]

It will be convenient to take next Williams' theory, which resembles Russell's in a number of important respects. [Williams, G, 77 ff.; Williams, D] He writes: 'Given a fair-sized sample, then, from any population, with no further material information, we know logically that it very probably is one of those which match the population, and hence that very probably the population has a composition similar to that which we discern in the sample. This is the logical justification of induction.' I.e., his ground of inductions is: 'Most of all the possible samples of a given large size which can be taken from any population have approximately the same composition as the population'. And by his account a typical inductive primitive probabilification-judgement goes: 'The fact that most of all the possible samples of a given large size which can be taken from any population have approximately the same composition as the population, and that this sample of BU is large and two-thirds H, makes it probable that the composition of the population BU is approximately two-thirds H'. It is understood, of course, that 'has approximately the same composition as' or 'nearly matches' is a symmetrical relation: if a sample nearly matches a population, then the population logically must nearly match it. Finally, we are told that the ground is a necessary *a priori* truth of Mathematics.

The resemblances to Russell's theory are striking. Both theories are engagingly simple. Both are concerned with subject-predicate generalizations, Russell with universal ones, Williams however with proportional ones. Both claim to prove such generalizations to be, under one condition, probable rather than true; and they agree further that the condition is that the observed instances or sample be numerous. Finally, both ground generalizations in a necessary *a priori* truth, Russell in a truth of Logic, Williams in a truth of Mathematics.

However, as he formulates it, Williams' ground is not in fact a necessary truth. To make it so, it is necessary to substitute for his 'all the possible samples of a given large size' the very different expression 'all the possible *random* samples of a given large size'. The typical judgement, above, likewise requires a corresponding amendment: for 'this sample of BU is large and two-thirds H' must be substituted 'this sample of BU is large and random and two-thirds H'. But Williams' omission of this vital qualification is quite deliberate: cp. the clause 'with no further material information' in the passage quoted above. His reason is that he holds that samples can always be assumed to be random or fair if they are not known to be unfair. However, I rejected this thesis earlier [4.1] when discussing randomness as a suggested test of the probability of generalizations, on the ground that it in effect maintains the Principle of Indifference to be an acceptable criterion of equal probability.

This amendment made, Williams' ground does in fact express a necessary truth about combinations. But three remarks must be added. Notice, first, that the qualification 'approximately' is essential: it is by no means a necessary truth that most large random samples of a given size exactly match their populations. Second, although Williams does not stress the point, it is a merit of his theory that it can account for the existence of different degrees of probability of the sort of judgements he is considering. For his doctrine involves that it is more probable that a random sample approximately matches its population, and so conversely, accordingly as it is larger. This is simply the effect of Bernoulli's Theorem. This feature makes the resemblance between his theory and Russell's even closer. But third, I must point out that the introduction of the essential randomness qualification into major and minor premiss destroys the simplicity of his doctrine. For it means that, to reason in this manner in practice, we must satisfy ourselves that the sample *is* random; and this, as we saw when discussing randomness as predicated of samples, is not without its difficulties. Indeed, it is a fairly obvious objection to both this and Russell's theory that they make out probable inferences from samples to populations to be much too easy. For anybody can tell at a glance whether a sample is large; and how can the claim that this is the sole test of probability be reconciled with the generally agreed facts that, when using the inductive mode of inference, the sample must be varied, and that, when using the direct or inverse deductive mode, the sample must be random as well as large?

My chief criticism of Williams' theory, however, is similar to that which I have made of Russell's. Namely, deductions from a necessary *a priori* truth of Mathematics, as of Logic, conjoined with a truth of observation, are not (rightly called) inductions. Consider the argument: 'All even numbers are divisible by two without remainder; the number of men in this room is even; therefore the men in this room can be divided into two equal groups'. No-one would call its conclusion 'an induction', unless he held, with Mill, that mathematical truths are inductions. Yet, by Williams' account, a typical inductive primitive probabilification-judgement is of the same logical type as this. Here again, we must not let ourselves be misled into thinking that the sort of arguments which he discusses are inductive just because they contain words which commonly feature in arguments which genuinely are inductive, such as 'sample', 'population' and 'probable'. The title of his book, *The Ground of Induction*, is a misnomer, because the sort of judgements it is about are not probable inductions. They are what Jevons calls probable deductions, only of the direct rather than the inverse type. And I emphasized earlier [1.1] that both the older inverse and the newer direct modes of probable reasoning are indeed deductive and not inductive.

There is another but related way of bringing out the fact that the sort of probability-judgements with which Williams is concerned are not inductive. For his theory logically involves that the degrees of probability of his sort of judgements are always at least in principle measurable in the strong sense of 'to measure'. But we noticed above [1.2] that only casual probabilities are thus measurable. So that Williams' judgements are, not inductive, but casual.

Finally, let us consider the views of Keynes. Those of Broad respecting natural kinds are similar, and the doctrine of Russell examined above is admittedly influenced by them. [2.1; Russell, P, v; Keynes, 217 ff., 251 ff.; Broad, P; R, II] The problem to which Keynes addresses himself is that of 'justifying' the 'methods' of making sound universal subject-predicate generalizations which he has distinguished earlier; namely, increasing the specificity of the subject-term or 'positive analogy', increasing the variety or 'negative analogy' of the observed instances, and diminishing the specificity of the predicate-term or the 'scope' of the generalization. [4.1, beginning] It is essential to an understanding of his theory to grasp that he holds the problem of 'justifying induction' to be two-fold. The first problem is to discriminate the criteria which we judge to make generalizations sound or probable; otherwise, the 'methods' of making probable generalizations. But beyond this lies the deeper problem of justifying these criteria or methods. He writes: 'What are the qualities which in ordinary discourse seem to afford strength [probability] to an inductive argument [conclusion]? I shall try to answer this question before I proceed to the more fundamental problem—What ground have we for regarding such arguments [conclusions] as rational [probable]?' He thinks that the way to deal with the latter problem is 'to elucidate what sort of assumptions, *if* we could adopt them, lie behind and are required by the methods' and finally if possible to 'justify' these assumptions. [Keynes, 217 f.]

The doctrine which he offers in carrying out this programme is not easy, and is moreover sketched rather than fully worked out, so that I shall not attempt a summary of it. But, as is well known, the chief of these assumptions is his Principle of Limited Independent Variety or Inductive Hypothesis; another is his Principle of the Uniformity of Nature, which I have discussed earlier. Concerning the former, he writes: '. . . we can justify the method of perfect analogy, and other inductive methods in so far as they can be made to approximate to this, by means of the assumption that the objects in the field, over which our generalizations extend, do not have an infinite number of independent qualities; that, in other words, their characteristics, however numerous, cohere together in groups of invariable connection, which are finite in number'. Again, he speaks of it as '. . . an underlying assumption, that if we find two sets of qualities in coexistence there is a finite probability that they belong to the same group, and a finite probability also that the first set specifies this group uniquely. Starting from this assumption, the object of the methods is to increase the finite probability and make it large'. [Keynes, 256, 253] I shall explain what he means by 'perfect analogy' shortly. In brief, the effect of

his Principle is to confer some degree of initial or antecedent probability on any universal subject-predicate generalization, and the
effect of his methods is to increase this degree. He adds that the
degree of probability of such generalizations is in principle numerical [Keynes, 259]; and that what is needful is to show the finite
antecedent probability, not the truth, of the Principle itself.

I shall restrict myself to three criticisms of this theory, the last
of them being the one which is of chief philosophical importance.
First, the theory is open to my last objection to Williams' theory;
namely, that it is not true that inductive, as opposed to casual,
probability-judgements are always at least in principle measurable
in the strong sense of 'to measure'. However, it would not be
quite correct to say that Keynes' judgements, like Williams' ones,
are casual and not inductive at all. They are rather heterogeneous,
being both casual and inductive. This is the effect of Keynes' Principle being itself (at best) inductively probable, and not true. For
it is a peculiarity of Keynes' theory that not only inductive conclusions, but also the ground itself, are probable and not true. I
say 'at best', because Keynes speaks with an uncertain voice when
discussing how we know his principle to be probable. He says on
the one hand, like Mill, that it is made (inductively) probable by
experience; but on the other hand, that he can find no reason for
judging it to be so. He arrives at the same negative conclusion
respecting the question how we know his Principle of the Uniformity of Nature to be true or probable. [Keynes, 260 ff.]

Either of these objections is fatal to his theory, but my chief
objection is directed against another point, namely, his opinion
that there is any such ulterior problem as he alleges behind the
problem of discriminating the criteria of the probability of generalizations. Yet he is not alone in supposing that there is such an
ulterior problem. For Johnson also characterizes his own treatment of inductive probability in Part III of his *Logic* as '. . . an
attempted enumeration of broadly formulated criteria for the
evaluation of the degrees of probability to be attached to the
generalizations of inductive inference. These criteria are merely
expressions of what is popularly felt, and their rational justification
can only be represented as depending upon postulates; that is,
speculations that are neither intuitively self-evident nor experien-
tially verifiable, but merely demanded by reason in order to supply
an incentive to the endeavour to systematize the world of reality

and thus give to practical action an adequate prompting motive.' [Johnson, I, xl; III, 16 ff.] There is plainly an important difference between Johnson's 'postulates' and the various grounds or principles that we have examined. For whereas the latter must be true or probable in order to prove generalizations true or probable, the question of the truth or probability of the former does not arise; they are conceived of on the analogy of Kant's regulative principles of reason, their purpose being partly theoretical, to systematize our knowledge, and partly practical. (Cp. my remarks, above, on 'Every event has a cause'.) The reader will notice that Johnson's notion of the first part of the allegedly two-fold problem of inductive probability, as expressed by the first sentence in the passage quoted, is precisely that taken of the problem as a whole in the present essay.

Yet it is plain that Keynes' and Johnson's alleged ulterior and more fundamental problem is in fact a pseudo-problem. For it makes sense to ask, When are subject-predicate generalizations (very, fairly, etc.) probable?, and to answer, say, When the observed evidential instances are (very, fairly, etc.) varied. And it also makes sense to ask further, Why is it true that subject-predicate generalizations from varied evidential instances are probable?, and to answer, Because that is what 'probable' means (descriptively) when predicated of such generalizations. What does not make sense is to answer to the latter question, say, Because the amount of independent variety in Nature is limited. For this is to commit a major type-fallacy, namely, to misconstrue a question about (the meaning of) a word as a question about (the constitution of) the world.

What is the cause of this error? I submit, misassimilating the probability of generalizations to the truth of generalizations. For the nature of things is not relevant to the former in the same way as it is relevant to the latter. To explain.

Cp. 'All subject-predicate generalizations from varied evidential instances are probable' with 'All such generalizations are true'. The former is equivalent to 'All such generalizations are rightly called "probable" '. But the latter is not equivalent to 'All such generalizations are rightly called "true" '. The former, then, is about the word 'probable'; it is a metalinguistic statement which mentions but does not use this word. The latter, however, is not about 'true', but about the world. This is connected with the fact that 'true' is primarily a descriptive word, in that it is rightly used when and only when there obtains a certain relation between a proposition and the world which is usually called 'corresponding with the facts'; whereas 'probable' is an evaluative word which is rightly used when and only when the evidence for a proposition is good. [5.2] Cp. therefore with the above pair of contrasted statements the following pair: 'All accurate watches are good' and 'All such watches are Swiss-made'. The former is equivalent to 'All such watches are called or judged "good"'. But the latter is manifestly not equivalent to 'All such watches are called "Swiss-made"', which means something quite different.

And I imagine that it is precisely through supposing that a generalization is probable when and only when there exists some relation like 'correspondence' between it and the facts, that Keynes and Johnson arrive at their erroneous belief in an ulterior problem of justification as they define it.

Consider now the statement 'All subject-predicate generalizations from varied evidential instances are true', in order to see how facts about the course of Nature may be relevant to its truth. Suppose the following case. We know that the variety in Nature is drastically limited, in that there are only the following seven attributes: being a BU, being H, being non-H, being observed, being unobserved, being large and being non-large. We also know that all observed light and non-light BU are H. Then, how does knowledge of the first fact about Nature bear on the truth of the generalization 'All BU are H'? In this way. We have seen earlier that the besetting danger in subject-predicate generalization is that of overlooking some attribute common to all the observed instances additional to the attributes connoted by the subject- and the predicate-terms; so that we generalize incorrectly from e.g. 'All observed light BU are H' to 'All BU are H' instead of to 'All light BU are H'. But in the present hypothetical case, since by supposition there are no such additional attributes, the chance of the unconditioned generalization 'All BU are H' being false is correspondingly diminished. But this applies to all generalizations; so that if we knew that there were but few attributes, the chance of the truth of 'All subject-predicate generalizations from varied evidential instances are true' would be much greater.

The effect of the above hypothesis is to ensure that we have got as close as is possible to what Keynes calls 'perfect analogy', i.e. a

situation in which every property common to the observed instances is included in either the subject- or the predicate-term of
the generalization. [Keynes, 225 ff.] But of course 'perfect analogy'
in generalization logically cannot be attained. For, by the very
meaning of 'generalization', there must be one attribute common
to the observed instances which is not included in the subject- or
predicate-term of the generalization; namely, that of being observed. For this reason, the drastic limitation of the variety in
Nature in the example does not of course demonstratively prove
the truth of the unconditioned generalization: it is perfectly possible that all observed BU are H but that some BU are non-H. The
only fact about the nature of things which will do that is some
strong uniformity principle, e.g. 'Everything that is true of observed things or events of any sort is true of all things or events
of that sort'.

In conclusion, I shall give some illustrations from the literature,
first, of other authors who misassimilate probability to truth, and
second, of authors who perceive the distinction and its relevance
to the central question of 'justifying induction'. As to Keynes himself, Wisdom supports my view in his discussion of Keynes' Principle of Limitation of Independent Variety in remarking that it
'constitutes . . . a description of what the universe is like wherever
generalizations actually hold [true]'. [Wisdom, 140]

Consider next a difference of opinion between Lewis and Black
about the powers of the anti-inductive demon. This fictitious
character, who is evidently a near relative of Descartes' evil spirit,
is a graphic device for discussing the question, Could there be a
world so irregular or chaotic as to baffle inductors?—a question
which should not be confused, incidentally, with the question,
Could there be an absolutely irregular or chaotic world? Lewis
thinks that there could not, and attempts '. . . to show that there
could not be a world of apprehensible things in which empirical
generalizations should fail of valid foundation; that if there are
things then laws of the type which empirical generalization seeks
to grasp must hold [true]; and hence that such generalizations may
be genuinely probable. . . .' [C. I. Lewis, *Mind and the World-Order*,
New York, 1929, p. 378] Black disagrees, and argues that '. . .
there can be no *a priori* guarantee of the success or, indeed, of the
reasonableness of inductive prediction'. [Black, H, 224] The point
that I want to bring out is that both authors, while disagreeing

about their problem, nevertheless agree in taking it for granted that the question of the probability of generalizations is the same as that of their truth. Black, indeed, speaks of the success and reasonableness of inductive inference rather than of the truth and probability of inductive conclusions. But we shall see shortly [4.3] that the 'successfulness' of modes of ampliative inference is explicable in terms of the truth of the conclusions thereby attained, whereas the meaning of 'reasonable' in this context must be explained in terms of probability.

On the other hand, Williams is clear about the distinction, and writes in the course of his own discussion of the anti-inductive demon hypothesis: 'The question whether a demon could or does defeat our inductions, be it noticed, is not the question whether inductions are . . . probable. Inductions are . . . probable whether there is a demon or not.' [Williams, G, 151] And it is drawn with great clarity by Strawson, who notices that '. . . the rationality of induction, unlike its "successfulness", is not a fact about the constitution of the world. It is a matter of what we mean by the word "rational" in its application to any procedure for forming opinions about what lies outside our observations. . . .' [Strawson, 261 f.] As he goes on to point out, it is through conflating successfulness and truth on the one hand with reasonableness and probability on the other that philosophers are led to ask muddled questions like Keynes', 'Given that certain inductive methods are rational, what must the nature of the universe be to make them so?'

In taking leave of Keynes' theory, I wish to add one more criticism which also seems to me fundamental. The gist of his constructive account is contained in the following places in his treatise: (a) Chh. I–III, where he discusses the meaning of probability generally; (b) Chh. XVIII—XXII, where he discusses the probability of universal subject-predicate generalizations; and (c) Chh. XXVII and XXXIII, where he discusses the probability of proportional (or 'statistical') subject-predicate generalizations. My criticism in the last few paragraphs is directed against the view he takes of the nature of the problem in (b) and, by implication, in (c). But additionally, there seems to me to be a complete lack of connexion between the doctrine of (b) and (c) on the one hand and that of (a) on the other; the essence of the latter being, it will be remembered from my discussion of it above [1.2], that 'degree of probabilification' means 'degree of partial implication'. Nor is the reason for this want of connexion far to seek. Failing to see that 'probable' is an evaluative word and that the philosophical problem of inductive probability consists primarily in discriminating the descriptive meaning or criteria of 'probable' when predicated of inductions; he naturally also fails to see that when, in (*b*) and (*c*), he applies himself to the genuine problem of discriminating these criteria and not to the bogus ulterior problem of justification, he is in fact answering in part the problem he poses himself in (*a*), in that he is elucidating the descriptive meaning of at any rate *inductive* probability.

4.3 SUCCESSFUL AND RELIABLE MODES OF AMPLIATIVE INFERENCE

Under this head, I propose first to examine Peirce's theory of inductive probability, then to examine Kneale's theory of the same subject, and last to put forward my own views on the matter. Peirce's theory is properly called pragmatic, as I shall show shortly. Kneale's is not, but shares with Peirce's the essential characteristic of representing the probability of inductive conclusions as dependent on the 'mode' or 'policy' of inference by which they are reached. This is evidently a different approach from that taken by those who search for criteria [4.1] or those who search for grounds [4.2]. It is moreover the most widely favoured approach at the present time, which makes consideration of it particularly desirable. [Ayer, 49 f., 99 ff.; Black, I, J, P; Braithwaite, 255 ff.; Nagel, 72 f.]

4.3.1 *Criticism of Two Theories*

Peirce's theory is contained in the following extracts: (*a*) 'The character of probability belongs primarily, without doubt, to certain inferences'. (*b*) '. . . in a logical mind an argument is always conceived as a member of a *genus* of arguments all constructed in the same way, and such that, when their premisses are real facts, their conclusions are so also. If the argument is demonstrative, then this is always so; if it is only probable, then it is for the most part so. As Locke says, the probable argument is "*such as* for the most part carries truth with it"'. (*c*) '. . . there is a real fact which corresponds to the idea of probability, and it is that a given mode of inference sometimes proves successful and sometimes not, and that in a ratio ultimately fixed. As we go on drawing inference after inference of the given kind, during the first ten or hundred cases the ratio of successes may be expected to show considerable fluctuations; but when we come into the thousands and millions, these fluctuations become less and less; and if we continue long enough, the ratio will approximate towards a fixed limit. We may, therefore, define the probability of a mode of argument as the proportion of cases in which it carries truth with it. The inference from the premiss, A, to the conclusion, B, depends, as we have seen, on the guiding principle, that if a fact of the class A is true, a fact of the class B is true. The probability consists of the fraction whose numerator is the number of times in which both A and B are true, and whose denominator is the total number of times in which A is true, whether B is so or not. Instead of speaking of this as the probability of the inference, there is not the slightest objection to calling it the probability that, if A happens, B happens.' (*d*) 'The conception of probability here set forth is substantially that first developed by Mr. Venn, in his *Logic of Chance*.' (*e*) '. . . in the case of synthetic [or ampliative] inferences we only know the degree of trustworthiness of our proceeding'. (*f*) 'To say . . . that a proposition has the probability ρ means that to infer it to be true would be to follow an argument such as would carry truth with it in the ratio of frequency ρ.' (*g*) 'In ampliative reasoning the ratio may be wrong, because the inference is based on but a limited number of instances; but on enlarging the sample the ratio will be changed till it becomes approximately correct.' [Peirce, 158 ff., 188, 193, 197]

My first three criticisms will be brief, because they turn on points already made. Peirce holds that what are probable are primarily particular inferences or arguments (not, as he says in extract (*c*), modes or types of argument); and secondarily propositions, or equivalently events, when they are the conclusions of probable inferences. But, as I said earlier [1.2], inferences are never in fact (called) probable, not even in a derivative sense when their conclusions are judged to be probable. Further, he claims to be giving a definition of 'probable' in terms of relative truth-frequency. But since the defining expression is descriptive whereas the word to be defined is evaluative, he thereby commits the naturalistic fallacy. I pointed out above [1.2] that most relative frequency theories of probability are open to this charge, and that Peirce's relative truth-frequency theory is of course just one type of relative frequency theory, as he himself declares in extract (*d*). Again, we saw in a preliminary discussion of Peirce's theory [2.2] that an advantage of the relative truth-frequency type over plain relative frequency theories is that it can give an account of the probability of general, as opposed to singular, propositions. But there is a corresponding disadvantage. For, when the conclusion is a generalization, Peirce's theory involves that degree of inductive probability is measurable in the strict sense and expressible by a fraction; which, however, is not so. We saw earlier [4.2] that Williams' and Keynes' theories are open to this criticism. It will also be remembered that I suggested [1.2] that, in defining 'degree of probabilification' in terms of 'degree of partial implication', Keynes is in fact embracing the relative truth-frequency theory.

To these I have to add two further criticisms, the first of which is my main one and raises the points of chief interest. Peirce's theory is, then, that $\gamma P(p)$ means 'p is the conclusion of an inference exemplifying a mode or pattern of ampliative inference that is successful'; and that 'The mode of ampliative inference, M, is (perfectly, very, etc.) successful' means 'Most (All, Nearly all, etc.) examined inferences exemplifying M have had true conclusions when they have also had true premisses (i.e. evidencing-statements)'. E.g., M might be the inference-pattern: $f'Ag . \gamma C_2 \therefore fAg$. And an exemplification of it might be: 'All observed BU are H and varied $\therefore$ All BU are H'. It will be seen that degree of successfulness is defined in terms of proportion or relative frequency of true premisses and conclusions among true premisses. And it is particularly to be noticed that the meaning of M's being successful is correctly defined in terms of most examined inferences exemplifying it having had true conclusions when they have also had true premisses. As I have just said, this seems on the whole to be Peirce's view too; but notice how he slips in extract (f) to talking of 'an argument such as would carry truth with it, etc.' as opposed to 'such as has carried truth with it, etc.', and in extract (e) to talking of the trustworthiness as opposed to the successfulness of our proceeding. The differences are in fact crucial.

As to the first difference: Peirce is trying to explain the meaning of 'p is probable' thus. It is said when we are in a position to reason as follows: 'Most conclusions of inferences exemplifying

M are true when the premisses are also true; p is the conclusion of an inference exemplifying M the premiss of which is true; therefore p is probably true (or, is probable)'. But he does not say this. For the first premiss he actually supplies is 'M is a successful mode of ampliative inference', which means not 'Most conclusions of inferences exemplifying M are true when, etc.' but 'Most examined conclusions of such inferences are (i.e. have been) true when, etc.'. And this premiss will not do the job that Peirce wants done. To call M 'successful' is simply to describe what has been the case with examined inferences exemplifying it; whereas the premiss Peirce needs is an induction. This is true of other uses of 'successful'. When I say that Maurice is a highly successful business-man, I am simply describing him, saying something about his fortunes to date.

However, suppose Peirce's first premiss to be 'M has been and always will be a successful mode of ampliative inference'. This is indeed equivalent to 'Most conclusions of inferences exemplifying M are true when, etc.'. It is a probable (or, in the limiting case, true) induction, not a description. But his definition of 'probable' is now circular. For he is defining 'p is probable' as 'p is the conclusion of an inference belonging to a class of inferences most of which are probably (or, in the limiting case, certainly) true'.

Notice also that it is implicit in Peirce's theory that 'p is probably true' means the same as 'p is probable'; i.e. in my notation that $\gamma P(p) \equiv \gamma P(T(p))$. This assumption seems to be correct. However, it does not commit one to maintaining that in general there is no distinction of meaning between saying that p and that $T(p)$. This more general thesis, called the semantic or 'no-truth' theory of truth, seems to be incorrect.

As to the second difference: the word that we actually use in this connexion is, not 'successful', but 'reliable', a synonym of which is Peirce's 'trustworthy'. What we say is: 'M is a reliable mode or pattern of ampliative inference; p is the conclusion of an inference exemplifying M the premiss of which is true; therefore p is probable'. I shall explain fully the resemblances and differences of meaning between 'reliable method' and 'successful method' below in my positive consideration of this question. It is enough for now to remark that, whereas 'successful' is a purely descriptive word, 'reliable' is evaluative and so only partly descriptive.

Here we may notice some other words which frequently recur

in this context. Common synonyms of 'is successful' are 'is effective or efficacious' or 'works'. 'The accredited, or recognized or accepted, methods of science' is a conception that is very commonly appealed to. Now it is true that we rightly say: 'M is a scientifically recognized mode of ampliative inference, and p is the conclusion of an inference exemplifying M the premiss of which is true; so that p is fairly probable'. Thus, M might be a method of inferring to the presence of water underground from certain types of evidences that is accepted by geologists. However, the argument as stated is elliptical. For first, what do geologists recognize M *as*? Plainly, as a reliable mode of ampliative inference. Analogously, if e.g. an independent school describes itself as 'recognized by the Ministry of Education', this is understood to be an ellipsis of 'recognized as efficient by the Ministry'.

Second, what do we suppose to be the connexion between M being recognized as reliable by geologists and its actually being reliable? Equally plainly, we judge that the fact that M is thus recognized as reliable is very, very good evidence that it is reliable. So that stated in full the argument goes: 'All scientifically recognized modes of ampliative inference are very, very probably reliable; M is a scientifically recognized mode of ampliative inference; therefore M is very, very probably a reliable mode of ampliative inference; p is the conclusion of an inference exemplifying M the premiss of which is true; therefore p is fairly probable'. If we do not make this judgement about M's reliability on the evidence of its being recognized as reliable by scientists, we are of course behaving unintelligently and accepting their judgement uncritically. If we attach weight to the fact that the medical profession does not recognize the techniques of osteopaths as reliable, this is or ought to be because we judge that, if the profession judges them unreliable, then they very probably are unreliable. Or, if we hold that osteopaths ought to be recognized by the medical profession, this is or ought to be because we judge their methods to be reliable notwithstanding that the profession judges otherwise.

It is the leading part played in Peirce's theory of probability by the notion of 'successfulness' that makes it right to call it a 'pragmatic' theory. I add some remarks on the relation between Peirce's pragmatic theory of probability and Pragmatism generally. Note first that Peirce's pragmatism is a theory of probability as well as of meaning, whereas James' pragmatism is a theory of truth.

Gallie is doubtless right in saying that there is no connexion between Peirce's pragmatic theory of meaning and James' pragmatic theory of truth. [W. B. Gallie, *Peirce and Pragmatism*, London, 1952, p. 26] But there is a resemblance worth noticing between the latter and Peirce's theory of probability, in that their authors define truth and probability respectively in terms of successfulness. Peirce, we have seen, holds that $\gamma P(p)$ means 'p is the conclusion of an inference exemplifying a successful mode of ampliative inference'. And James maintains that $T(p)$ means 'Belief in p is successful, or works'. However, there is also a difference, in that Peirce and James understand different things by 'successfulness', the former defining it in terms of truth, but the latter defining it in terms of expediency. For Peirce, we have also seen, holds that 'M is a successful mode of ampliative inference' means 'Most examined inferences exemplifying M have had true conclusions when they have also had true premisses'. But according to James, 'Belief in p is successful' means 'Belief in p is expedient'. His formula is: '"The true" . . . is only the expedient in the way of our thinking. . . . Expedient in almost any fashion; and expedient in the long run and on the whole of course. . . .' [W. James, *Pragmatism*, London, 1908, p. 222]

My final criticism of Peirce's theory is directed against his claim, in extracts (*c*) and (*g*), that induction is a self-correcting process; a doctrine which is also advanced by his disciple, Reichenbach. Take the following case. I draw a sample of 100 BU, observe that 40 are H, and judge that there is a very small inductive probability that the casual probability that a BU selected at random is H is 2/5. But next I increase the size of my sample to 1,000, observe that 800 are H, and judge that there is a small inductive probability that the casual probability that a BU selected at random is H is 4/5. Then, I have corrected my original estimate of the casual probability, in the sense of changing or altering it. But it does not necessarily follow that my revised estimate is correct, in the sense of being right or true. It is quite possible that my first thought was best. Nor is it necessarily the case that, the larger I make the sample, the more nearly correct or right my estimate of the casual probability will be. We judge indeed that there is a slight probability that it will be so, on account of the real if very limited inductive probabilificatory power of numerous observed instances; but there is no necessity about it. [2.1]

Peirce writes elsewhere: '. . . it is mathematically certain that the general character of a limited experience will, as that experience is prolonged, approximate to the character of what will be true in the long run, if anything is true in the long run. Now all that induction infers is what would be found true in the usual course of experience, if it were indefinitely prolonged. Since the method of induction must generally approximate to that truth, that is a sufficient justification for the use of that method. . . .' [Peirce, 222] This strongly suggests that his doctrine that induction is a self-correcting process is nothing more than the fallacious doctrine of the 'maturity of the chances'. This is the fallacy of supposing that what Poisson calls 'the law of great numbers' is both a demonstrated theorem of Mathematics (namely, Bernoulli's theorem and Poisson's own extension of it) and a law of Nature (namely, the proposition that, in all observed successions of events, a casual probability will certainly be 'realized as a relative frequency', provided only that the succession is 'long enough'). [Keynes, 332 ff.; Kneale, 139 f.] This diagnosis is supported by the fact that other patrons of the relative frequency theory of probability as well as Peirce have fallen into the same error. [See e.g. the passage of R. L. Ellis' quoted in Keynes, 341]

Let us now turn to Kneale's theory of inductive probability, which is conveyed in the following extracts: (a) 'In speaking of a result of induction as probable on its evidence we are undoubtedly saying that for a person knowing that evidence and no more it is approvable as a basis for action; but our ground for saying this cannot be any rule about chances, and there is nothing else on which we can base our approval except the simple consideration that the result has been reached from the given evidence by the method of induction. In short, the probability of the conclusions of induction depends on the justification of induction, and not vice versa. But this means that in order to justify induction we must show it to be rational without reference to the truth or even to the probability of its conclusions.' (b) '. . . induction is a rational policy not because it is certain to lead to success, but because it is the only way of trying to do what we want to do, namely, make true predictions [and true statements about the past and present unobserved]'. (c) 'Wherever we try to extrapolate beyond experience, we must rely on some supposed law or probability rule [i.e. universal or proportional generalization]; for even the attempt to make predictions without the help of science involves a kind of pseudo-science. If anyone decides to guide his life by prophecies, he must use some criterion to select those statements about the future which he will adopt as prophecies, and in so doing he shows his reliance on some supposed law or probability rule, even if it be only the assumption that whatever comes into his head first is most likely to be true.' [Kneale, 225, 234 f.]

It will be remembered that I dissented earlier [1.2] from Kneale's view that the evaluative force of $\gamma P(p)$ is to commend action on p, and suggested instead that it is to commend the assertion of p. Again, it is surely not true to say that the only reason one can give for calling an induction probable is that it has been reached by generalizing. If I say that all BU are probably H, and you ask me why, I can reply, e.g., Because I have examined a varied sample of BU and found them all to be H. Nor indeed is Kneale's reason a good reason. If I reply to your question, Because I have reached this conclusion by generalizing, you will regard my reason as quite unsatisfactory, For you know that inductive inference generally cannot be judged a reliable or reasonable mode of ampliative inference, because it is not the case that most examined inductive inferences have had true conclusions when they have had true premises and have also been varied. This claim can only be made for certain modes of inductive inference, e.g. inductive inference from varied samples. So that, although it is true and important that an acceptable reason for judging an inductive conclusion probable is that it has been reached by an inference exemplifying a reasonable or reliable mode or type of inductive inference, it is false that an acceptable reason for so judging is that the conclusion has been reached simply by inductive inference which is as such a reasonable or reliable mode of ampliative inference, *a fortiori* that this is the only acceptable reason for so judging. These points will be clarified shortly.

It is because the key concept in Kneale's theory is the rationality or reasonableness, not the successfulness, of the inductive mode of ampliative inference, that his theory is not properly called pragmatic. We shall soon see that 'reasonable' in this context means the same as 'reliable' or Peirce's 'trustworthy', also that there is an important overlap of meaning between these terms and 'successful'.

Inductive inference is of course just one species of ampliative inference. Others are inference from the first proposition that enters my mind to the truth of that proposition, from the movement of a diviner's hazel wand to the presence of water underground, or more seriously hypothetic inference. It is no more possible to maintain that hypothetic inference is simply as such a reliable mode of ampliative inference than it is to maintain that inductive inference is so. This claim can only be made for certain modes of hypothetic inference, e.g. hypothetic inference from numerous pieces of independent evidence. Indeed, the typical reliability-judgement about modes of ampliative inference is much more specific than this. The sort of thing that is actually said is: 'For psephological purposes, generalization from a sample which has been stratified in respect of sex, age, income, religion and occupation is a far more reliable mode of inference than generalization from a sample which is much larger but which has not been so stratified'.

Passing now to the grounds that Kneale gives for calling induction a reasonable policy of inference, I observe first that it is not true that induction is the only way of trying to do what we want to do, namely, make true statements about the unobserved. We can also guess, read the tea-leaves, or employ hypothetic inference. Nor is it true that one who, wishing to make true statements about the unobserved, adopts the procedure of asserting the first thought about it that enters his head, must first have made some such judgement as 'It is very probable that all thoughts that first enter my head about the unobserved are true'. Thus, one who makes this probability-judgement 'implies' that he has evidence for the generalization. Yet it is possible for a man to adopt the policy without possessing any evidence at all for the generalization. Certainly it would be unreasonable for him to do so; but that is another matter. For, given that what he wants to do is make true statements about the unobserved, the mode of inference that the reasonable man will adopt is one that conduces to that end; i.e., a mode of inference, the conclusion of any inference exemplifying which is probably or certainly true.

4.3.2 *Successfulness, Reliability and Probability*

My own view of these matters is as follows. What is true and important in Kneale's theory is that one fact that probabilifies an inductive conclusion is its having been reached by an inference exemplifying a reasonable mode of inductive inference. And to the extent that there is an overlap of meaning between 'reasonable mode of inductive inference' and 'successful mode of inductive inference', there is truth and importance in Peirce's theory too. Let us see how this is so.

What is the meaning of 'M is a reasonable mode of inductive inference'? It means that M is a mode of inductive inference which it is reasonable for us to adopt given the end that we wish to attain. This end is, as Kneale says, to make true statements about the unobserved. Hence, M will be a mode of inductive inference, the conclusion of any inference exemplifying which is probably or certainly true (i.e., probable or true). But this is also the meaning of calling M a reliable or trustworthy mode of inductive inference.

I take the expression 'mode of inference or argument' from Peirce (see extract (c), above). We can say indifferently either that generalizing from varied instances is a reliable method of or policy for making inductive inferences, or that $f'Ag \cdot \gamma C_2 \therefore fAg$ is a reliable pattern or scheme of inductive inference. By 'reliable mode of inductive inference' I mean either of these two equivalent expressions.

I said above that 'reliable', unlike 'successful', is a value-word. When I say 'M is a reliable or reasonable mode of inductive inference', the evaluative force of my judgement is to commend M's employment. Its descriptive meaning is revealed by the following pair of what it is convenient, if ugly, to call reliabilification-judgements: 'The fact that all (or most) examined inferences exemplifying M have had true conclusions when they have also had true premisses and have been varied (or very, very varied) makes M a reliable mode of inductive inference'.

The next step is to explain the relation of meaning between 'reliable' as predicated of a mode of inductive inference and 'probable' as predicated of the conclusion of an inference exemplifying that mode. It is this: 'M is a reliable mode of inductive inference' means descriptively, but not evaluatively, the same as 'The conclusion of any inference exemplifying M is inductively probable'. The difference in evaluative force is of course this: whereas to call M reliable is to commend its employment, to call p probable is to commend its assertion. Notice in this connexion an interesting asymmetry in what things are (called) probable and reliable. What are called reliable are either modes of inference or propositions; as applied to the latter, 'reliable' has the same descriptive and evaluative meaning as 'probable'. It is in fact commonly used as a synonym of 'probable', especially of 'inductively probable'. [Kneale, 236; Lewis, 292 ff.; Ryle, I, 44 ff.] But methods of inference, or of anything else, are never called probable, only reliable.

The identity of meaning resides in the more important descriptive meaning, which we have just seen to be 'All (or Most) examined inferences exemplifying M have had true conclusions when they have also had true premises and have been varied (or very, very varied)'. Set out in full, the arguments are in the two cases respectively: 'All examined inferences exemplifying M have had true conclusions when they have also had true premises and have been varied; therefore it is inductively probable that all inferences exemplifying M have true conclusions when they also have true premises; therefore the conclusion of any inference exemplifying M is inductively probable when the premiss is true'. Cp. formula $(3')$, $\gamma PF(gx, \gamma P(fAg) . fx)$. Alternatively: 'Most examined inferences exemplifying M have had true conclusions when they have also had true premises and have been very, very varied; therefore it is inductively very, very probable that most inferences exemplifying M have true conclusions when they also have true premises; therefore the conclusion of any inference exemplifying M is casually and inductively fairly probable when the premiss is true'. Cp. formula $(5')$, $\delta PF(gx, \alpha P(fMg) . fx . C_1)$.

This fact that 'reliable or reasonable mode of inductive inference' is descriptively and hence effectively equivalent to 'mode of inductive inference, the conclusion of any inference exemplifying which is inductively probable' shows why one fact that probabilifies an inductive conclusion is its having been reached by an inference exemplifying a reasonable mode of inductive inference. For take the argument: 'This inductive conclusion is the conclusion of an inference exemplifying a reliable or reasonable mode of inductive inference; therefore this inductive conclusion is inductively probable'. Substituting in the premiss we obtain: 'This inductive conclusion is the conclusion of an inference exemplifying a mode of inductive inference, the conclusion of any inference exemplifying which is inductively probable; therefore this inductive conclusion is inductively probable'. Since the latter argument is plainly valid, the equivalent former one is so too.

But it also shows that this fact cannot be the only fact that prob-abilifies an inductive conclusion. For it cannot be the way in which a judgement such as 'The conclusion of any inference exem-plifying M is inductively probable' (which is descriptively equiva-lent to 'M is a reliable mode of inductive inference') is probabilified. This must be directly probabilified by the fact that a variety of examined inferences exemplifying M have had true conclusions when they have had true premisses. To think otherwise is to fall into the error of believing that every induction is probabilified by being shown to be deducible from or consilient with some other probable induction. Indeed, these considerations bring out an im-portant point about this sort of indirect probabilification. We noticed earlier [2.2, beginning] that inductions can be probabilified (or verified) by being shown to be deducible from some wider probable (or true) induction. But one interesting type of such probabilification is the type just examined, in which we judge: 'The fact that it is inductively probable that all inferences exem-plifying M have true conclusions, and that p is the conclusion of an inference exemplifying M, makes it inductively probable that p'. I.e., this sort of indirect probabilification of inductions includes not only the exhibiting of some inductions as deducible from wider probable generalizations, but also the exhibiting of some induc-tions as conclusions of reliable modes of inductive inference. And since a good deal of effort is devoted in these days by those concerned with sampling to discovering what modes of inductive inference *are* reliable, this seems to be a methodological point of some importance.

Consider next the relation of meaning between 'reliable' and 'successful' as predicated of modes of inductive inference. The identity of meaning consists in this: both the statement 'M is a successful mode of inductive inference' and the judgement 'M is a reliable mode of inductive inference' involve that all or most examined inferences exemplifying M have had true conclusions when they have had true premisses. But the differences of meaning are these. First, the latter has the evaluative force of commending the use of inferences of M's type, whereas the former has not. Second, the latter has the additional descriptive meaning that the examined inferences are (very, etc.) varied, whereas the former has not. Hence, in short, 'M is a successful mode of inductive infer-ence' is part of the descriptive meaning of 'M is a reliable mode of inductive inference'. Notice that degree of reliability is determined by two factors. First, by degree of successfulness: cp. 'All examined inferences exemplifying M have had true conclusions when they have had true premises' with 'Most examined inferences exemplifying M have had true conclusions when they have had true premises'. Second, by the degree of variety of the examined inferences.

The resemblance and difference of meaning between calling M a successful mode of inductive inference and calling it a reliable one can also be brought out in this way. The former means that all or most examined inferences exemplifying M have had true conclusions when they have had true premises. But the latter has the same descriptive meaning as 'It is inductively probable that M is always a successful mode of inductive inference', this being equivalent to 'It is inductively probable that all or most inferences exemplifying M have true conclusions when they have true premises'. For the descriptive meaning of both the reliability- and the probability-judgement is 'All (or Most) examined inferences exemplifying M have had true conclusions when they have had true premises and are (very, very) varied'. But the following differences are also plain. The former is a descriptive statement whereas the latter is a value-judgement, and the former is about examined inferences exemplifying M whereas the latter is about all inferences exemplifying M.

It is the fact that 'successful' is included in the meaning of 'reliable' when predicated of modes of ampliative inference which has caused the confusion, and which gives pragmatic theories of probability their plausibility. As I suggested above in discussing Peirce's account, the crucial confusion occurs over the form of words 'M is a successful mode of ampliative inference', which is sometimes interpreted correctly as 'M *has been*, or has proved, a successful mode of ampliative inference', but is at other times interpreted incorrectly as 'M *probably always is* a successful mode of ampliative inference'.

From the descriptive and therefore effective synonymity between 'reliable' as predicated of methods of inference and 'inductively probable' as predicated of conclusions reached by such methods, one further important conclusion can be drawn. We have seen that probability-judgements about populations are made from the evidence of samples in two different ways, namely, by inductive reasoning on the one hand and by (casually) probable deductive reasoning on the other; that what is called the 'Theory of Sampling' is concerned almost exclusively with the latter; and that there are two species of the latter, namely, the older inverse mode of reasoning favoured by Laplace, Jevons and others on the one hand, and the modern direct mode of reasoning favoured by Fisher, Neyman and Williams on the other. We have seen further that a necessary condition of the validity of both species of the latter mode of reasoning is that the sample be random, and that the practical test of the randomness of a sample is whether it has been selected by a reliable method of random sampling. [4.1] Let us now examine the meaning of this last expression.

In the light of the preceding analysis of 'reliable method', it will be seen at once that 'M is a reliable method of random sampling' is descriptively and hence effectively equivalent to 'Any sample selected by M is probably random'. The descriptive meaning common to both the reliability- and the probability-judgement is 'All (or Most) examined samples selected by M have been random and varied (or very, very varied)'. This needs explaining.

How is it normally established that sampling by means of this lottery (M), or some other 'chance-machine', is a reliable method of random sampling? [Yule, 340, 346] We conduct a number of tests under varied conditions with different populations the properties of which are known. Each test will consist of selecting a number of large samples by M, recording the results in the form of a frequency-distribution of (say) the ratio, and comparing this observed frequency-distribution with the expected one that we ought theoretically to get if our sampling is indeed random. Then, provided that the observed distributions agree tolerably with the theoretically expected ones, we judge M to be more reliable accordingly as the variety and number of the tests is greater. Hence, it is only in the rare upper limiting case that we can judge that a method of random sampling is perfectly reliable, and equivalently that any sample selected by it is certainly random. Usually we judge that the method is (very, etc.) reliable and that any sample selected by it is (very, etc.) probably random. However, it is going too far to say that '. . . we can never be . . . certain that a method of sampling is random'. [Yule, 346] For here too the evidence is sometimes judged to be conclusive. Cp. the corresponding erroneous belief of Russell and many other philosophers, that inductions can never be (rightly judged) certain or true, but only at best very, very probable. [4.2]

An alternative or additional way of testing M's reliability is of course to inspect the mechanism of the lottery. Similarly, one can test the trueness of a die by determining experimentally whether its point of balance is at the geometrical centre of the cube, instead of or as well as by throwing it a large number of times and seeing whether each face turns up with approximately equal frequency.

Naturally, the foregoing points apply to the random selection of individuals as well as of samples. They explain why I said earlier [2.2] that in practice we commonly make, not homogeneous casual probabilification-judgements of the form, (6′), $\gamma PF(gx, fMg . fx . C_1)$, but rather heterogeneous casual and inductive ones of the form, (17′), $\delta PF(gx, fMg . fx . \alpha P(C_1))$.

The interesting conclusion to be drawn from these considerations is, I submit, as follows. There is a sense in which the inductive mode of inference from samples to populations and inductive probability has primacy over the probable deductive modes of inference from samples to populations and casual probability, so that the two modes of inference are not co-ordinate. For it is a prerequisite of the practical application of the latter modes that it be inductively probable or certain that the sample is random, or equivalently, that the mode of sampling employed be reliable or completely reliable. Since writers on statistical theory tend to give the impression that inferences from samples to populations are made exclusively by casually probable deductive reasoning, it is well worth emphasizing that these very inferences involve in practice the notion of inductive probability or reliability.

I want now to amplify what I said earlier about the relation of 'reliable' and 'successful' as predicated of methods and 'inductively probable' as predicated of propositions, by considering some examples of the grounds on which methods and techniques are adversely criticized. It will be convenient to include methods of procedures other than ampliative inference. In which connexion, we may note for a start that the descriptive meaning of a reliability- or rationality-judgement about a method naturally depends on what the method is taken to be a method *of*, i.e. on the end to which the method is used as a means. Thus, 'M is a reliable or sound method of making inductive inferences' is descriptively equivalent to 'The conclusion of any inference exemplifying M is probably true (or, is probable) when the premiss is true', because our end in employing M is to make true statements about the unobserved. But 'Method II (the so-called country house-party method) is a reasonable or sensible way of selecting candidates for the Civil Service' is descriptively equivalent to 'The candidate selected by any application of Method II is probably suitable', since the object of those who apply Method II is to select suitable candidates for the Civil Service.

The first ground of adverse criticism, then, is that M has not been successful. E.g., the technique of a certain rain-maker, whose way of making rain is to sprinkle water around with a bunch of twigs. It may be criticized as not having proved (very, completely) successful; the meaning of which is that it is not the case that most (nearly all, all) of his observed sprinklings have been followed by rain.

Another ground of criticism is that, although M has proved successful, it is nevertheless not reliable. E.g., the procedure of a certain treasure-seeker, who searches for buried gold with a divining-rod of withered mistletoe. It may be criticized as not being reliable, the descriptive meaning of which may be that, although most observed cases of the rod's moving have been cases of there being gold buried below, the cases have not been varied. E.g., the man has scored his predominance of successes within a mile of his own house.

Again, M may be adversely criticized on the score that, although it has been directly reliabilified, it has not been indirectly reliabilified; or, putting the same point another way, because the observed successfulness of M in varied conditions has not been explained. E.g., poultry-farmers made the useful empirical discovery that exposing fowls to electric light is a reliable method of stimulating their egg production in winter. But the direct evidence of the successfulness of this technique in a variety of observed cases did not make it nearly as reliable as it subsequently became when this fact was explained; namely, by the true generalization that the pituitary gland, which secretes a hormone regulating the ovary, is reflexly activated by light at the red end of the spectrum. For the effect of the explanation was that all the other evidence for this generalization indirectly reliabilified the method.

A cognate case is that in which the successfulness of M is alleged to be explained, but is not so in fact, because the explanatory generalization is not true or probable. E.g., suppose that the technique of the rain-maker or the treasure-seeker had proved completely successful in a variety of examined cases. He might claim that it was not only directly reliabilified by this fact, but indirectly reliabilified by all the other evidence for the Law of Similarity, that 'like produces like'. But his claim would have to be rejected on the ground that the alleged law is no law because it is false. By contrast, if e.g. the employment of a charged gold-leaf electroscope is judged to be a completely reliable method of finding out whether a body is positively or negatively charged, the reason is that this method is conclusively reliabilified, not so much by the direct evidence of a great variety of successful applications, as by the behaviour of the leaves in the presence of such a body being explicable by accepted electromagnetic theory. It is in this difference respecting indirect evidence that lies the superiority of the gold electroscope over the golden bough. Of course, all this rests on what has been said earlier about the indirect probabilification and verification, and the consilience, of inductions. [2.2]

The last sort of case that we need to notice is that in which M is directly reliabilified, but indirectly completely or highly unreliabilified. Suppose e.g. that we know that in most or all of a variety of examined cases gold has been found buried at the place where the diviner's rod has moved. We nevertheless also know it for a true generalization that metals do not cause wood at a distance to move by attraction, repulsion, or whatever. Hence, we make a subtractive compositive reliabilification-judgement, and conclude that, taking into account both the favourable direct evidence and the unfavourable indirect evidence, the method is unreliable. This type of case must of course be distinguished from the poultry case, above. There, M was criticized because we did not know any true or probable wider generalization or theoretical principle indirectly reliabilifying it. Here, M is criticized because we know a true generalization that completely indirectly unreliabilifies it. The former objection is not fatal, but the latter is. Naturally, compositive reliabilification-judgements correspond to the compositive probabilification-judgements which I discussed earlier [1.2]. As Mill interprets Hume, it is on the simple and familiar notion of what I call a subtractive compositive probabilification-judgement that Hume's doctrine about the (in)credibility of miracles rests. [Mill, 408 ff.] If part of the meaning of 'miracle' is 'exception to a law of Nature', and part of the meaning of 'law of Nature' is that the proposition in question is conclusively evidenced and so rightly claimed to be true; it follows that we can never rightly judge that an alleged miracle actually occurred when the evidence, which is usually testimonial, that it did occur is less than conclusive; which, however, it always is.

Finally, there is the following difference between 'reliable method' and 'probable proposition'. The former expression belongs to the vocabulary of Art or Practice, whereas the latter belongs to that of Science or Theory. But we shall be the less likely to exaggerate the importance of the distinction when we remember that to every judgement of the former type, e.g. 'Sampling by Tippett's Numbers is a reliable method of random sampling', there corresponds a descriptively and effectively equivalent judgement of the latter type, e.g. 'Any sample selected by Tippett's Numbers is probably random'.

It is instructive to relate this fact to Mill's account of the difference between the language of Art and the language of Science. He writes: '. . . the imperative mood is the characteristic of art, as distinguished from science. Whatever speaks in rules or precepts, not in assertions respecting matters of fact, is art. . . .' [Mill, 616] This seems to be true. 'Take six eggs . . . etc.!' belongs to the language of the art of cookery, whereas 'Eggs contain vitamins A and D' belongs to the language of science. But it is certainly not the whole truth. For the language of Science includes, besides statements made with indicative sentences, value-judgements about statements of the form $\gamma P(p)$. Similarly, the language of Art includes, besides rules expressed in imperative sentences, value-judgements about rules, such as 'If you want to obtain a random sample, it is a sound (or safe, good, etc.) rule to select it by Tippett's Numbers'. Notice that, as 'It is probable that it will rain to-night' is equivalent to 'The proposition "It will rain to-night" is probable (i.e. good as an assertion)'; so 'It is a sound rule to carry an umbrella in February' is equivalent to 'The rule "Carry an umbrella in February!" is sound (i.e. good as a guide to action)'.

To this it is only necessary to add that 'If you want to obtain a random sample, it is a sound rule to select it by Tippett's Numbers' has the same evaluative and descriptive force as 'Sampling by Tippett's Numbers is a reliable method of random sampling', and hence the same descriptive but not the same evaluative force as

'Any sample selected by Tippett's Numbers is probably random'. The examples typify the relation of meaning between 'sound rule', 'reliable method' and 'probable proposition'.

To conclude this discussion, I wish to touch on a philosophical problem in which the intimate connexion between the reliability of a mode of ampliative inference and the inductive probability of the conclusion of any inference in that mode, is very clear. I mean the problem of, or rather one problem about, Memory. [R. F. Harrod, 'Memory', *Mind*, 1942; E. J. Furlong, 'Memory', *Mind*, 1948; R. F. Holland, 'The Empiricist Theory of Memory', *Mind*, 1954]

As often in Philosophy, 'Memory' is the name, not of a single problem, but of a knot of problems. One to which some philosophers devote a good deal of attention is that of the reliability or trustworthiness of memory. And here we have to notice at the outset a point about the logical implications of 'to remember'. To claim to remember such-and-such an event is to claim that that event occurred; for one can no more say 'I remember such-and-such an event although it never happened' than one can say 'I see a so-and-so although there is no so-and-so there'. On the other hand, memory-claims, like perception-claims, are not irrefutable. For it not infrequently happens that, on the strength of having what may be called a 'memory-experience', i.e. thinking that one remembers such-and-such, one claims to remember such-and-such; but then has to withdraw the claim on discovering that such-and-such never in fact occurred, so that one logically cannot have remembered it. In these respects, at least, there is a significant resemblance between 'remember' and the verbs of perception, 'see', 'hear', etc. (Cp. below however.)

The question of the reliability of memory may therefore be put thus: Is inferring from the fact that one thinks one remembers an event to the conclusion that one remembers it (or, that it actually occurred) a reliable mode of ampliative inference about the past? Now, if my account of the descriptive meaning of 'reliable mode of ampliative inference', and of the relation between that expression and 'inductively probable', is correct, we shall expect two things. First, if memory is judged to be reliable, it will be on the ground that most examined 'memory-inferences', as we may call them, have had true conclusions when they have had true premisses and have been very, very varied. Second, if memory is judged to be reliable, we can at once infer to the descriptively equivalent judgement that the conclusion of any memory-inference is inductively probable.

Now, these two theses are in fact the very ones that Harrod and Furlong are most concerned to inculcate. As to the first, they point out that memory-inference is reliabilified in the following sort of way. From the fact of thinking I remember turning off the hall light last night (true premiss), I infer that I remember doing so (or that I actually did so); and I establish that this is true (true conclusion) by observing that the light is turned off this morning and satisfying myself that all other possible explanations of this fact are ruled out, i.e. that no-one else turned it off, it did not turn itself off, etc. And so similarly with a variety of other examined memory-inferences. The money that I seem to remember putting in a box is indeed there and could have got there in no other way; to the letter which you think you remember sending there comes a reply, and so on. As to the second thesis, these authors are emphatic that the upshot of this justification or validation of memory is to render the conclusions of memory-inferences probable and not certain; or, in Locke's terminology, to make memory a source, not of knowledge, but of opinion or belief.

I have two comments to add. As Furlong notes, it is doubtful whether there is a genuine problem about the reliability of memory in general. The genuine problems always relate to the reliability of the memory of an individual or of a group of individuals: the question of the reliability of the memory of a particular witness in a case at law may well be a matter of the last consequence. In this respect, there is a resemblance to the problem of other minds, touched on above. [1.2] For here too, as Thomson sees, the genuine problem is not the highly general one, How can anyone ever know anybody else's state of mind about anything?, but rather highly specific ones such as, How can I find out what my brother really thinks about this suggestion? [Thomson, 349]

Again, it results from these considerations that what may be called 'memory-experience-reports' are evidences. If a statement such as 'I seem to remember switching off the hall light last night' can be good evidence for or probabilify a statement such as 'I remember switching off, etc.' or 'I switched off, etc.', then *a fortiori* it can be evidence for it. However, some deny this. Ryle e.g. disputes that '. . . recalling what took place is using a piece of evidence from which certain or probable inferences are made to what took place . . .', and points out in support of his contention that one '. . . does not argue "I recall the collision occurring just after the thunder-clap, so probably the collision occurred just after the thunder-clap"'. [Ryle, C, 274] Now, this last statement is quite true. The reason is that, as we saw above, 'I remember the collision occurring, etc.' entails 'The collision *occurred*, etc.'; this is why it is illogical to say 'I remember the collision occurring, etc., so *probably* the collision occurred, etc.'. But Ryle's example has no tendency to show that it is wrong to say 'I *think* I remember the collision occurring, etc., so probably the collision occurred, etc.'.

It also follows that there is an interesting difference between memory-experiences and sensations in this respect. For, following Ryle, I said earlier [1.2] when speaking of phenomenalism, that sensation-reports are not evidence for observation-reports; that it is a mistake to think of the relation between 'sensation-statements' and perceptual statements as that holding between evidencing-statements and their corresponding evidenced-statements. 'I am having such-and-such a visual sensation' is not evidence for 'I see a mouse in the corner' or for 'There is a mouse in the corner'. To this extent, then, Locke and Hume are misleading when they speak in the same breath of the evidence of our senses and of our memory. For whereas one's memory-experiences are evidence that one is remembering, one's sensations are not evidence that one is perceiving. This disparity may surprise theorists who construe the concept of memory (or at any rate some kinds of memory) on the model of the concept of perception, even to the extent of using such expressions as 'perceptual memory'. But, although as we have just seen there is at least one significant resemblance between 're-member' and 'see', 'hear', etc., this perceptual analogy is in the main seriously misleading, as Holland plainly shows. [Holland, *op. cit.*; Broad, *The Mind and its Place in Nature*, Ch. V]

5 INDUCTIVE PROBABILIFICATION BY ELIMINATION

I shall first [5.1] examine various theories of induction by elimination, devoting most attention to the argument by elimination of chance, which seems to me the most interesting of them. I shall then [5.2] explain the sense in which it is right to characterize the method of inductive probabilification as eliminative, and complete the constructive account of inductive probability offered above [1.1 to 3.2, inclusive].

5.1 THEORIES OF ELIMINATIVE INDUCTION

The opposition between Induction by Simple Enumeration (or by Confirmation, or Pure Induction) and Induction by Elimination (or by Infirmation, or by Exclusion), and the claim that the latter is the true or proper form of induction, date from Bacon, who writes: '. . . the induction which proceeds by simple enumeration is childish; its conclusions are precarious, and exposed to peril from a contradictory instance; and it generally decides on too small a number of facts, and on those only which are at hand. But the induction which is to be available for the discovery and demonstration of sciences and arts, must analyse nature by proper rejections and exclusions; and then, after a sufficient number of negatives, come to a conclusion on the affirmative instances. . . .' [Bacon, 291] Some modern authors too make much of the distinction, notably Nicod, who however defends Induction by Simple Enumeration. [Kneale, 110 ff.; Nicod, 219 ff.; Wisdom, 114 ff.; Wright, T, 84 ff., 129 ff.]

What is meant by Induction by Simple Enumeration is clear enough; namely, inference in accordance with the evidential-statement-formula, (2), $E(fAg, f'Ag)$; or, more precisely, in accordance with the formula, $E(fAg, gfx . gfy . gfz$. etc.). But I shall argue that different things have been meant by 'Induction by Elimination'. In distinguishing them, it will be helpful to attend to the questions: (*a*) What is supposed to be eliminated?; (*b*) When, i.e. under what conditions, are whatever are required to be eliminated in fact eliminated?; and (*c*) How does the elimination of whatever it is that has to be eliminated bear on the probability or truth of the conclusion?

5.1.1 *The Elimination of Possible Conditions and of Possible Causes*

The first sense of 'induction by elimination' may be illustrated by two passages from Mill: 'Both [the Method of Agreement and the Method of Difference] are methods of *elimination*. This term . . . is well suited to express the operation . . . which has been understood since the time of Bacon to be the foundation of experimental inquiry, namely, the successive exclusion of the various circumstances which are found to accompany a phenomenon in a given instance, in order to ascertain what are those among them which can be absent consistently with the existence of the phenomenon.' 'The tendency of unscientific inquirers is to rely too much on number, without analysing the instances; without looking closely enough into their nature, to ascertain what circumstances are or are not eliminated by means of them. Most people hold their conclusions with a degree of assurance proportioned to the mere *mass* of the experience on which they appear to rest; not considering that by the addition of instances to instances, all of the same kind, that is, differing from one another only in points already recognized as immaterial, nothing whatever is added to the evidence of the conclusion. A single instance eliminating some antecedent which existed in all the other cases is of more value than the greatest multitude of instances which are reckoned by their number alone.' [Mill, 256, 287]

In this sense of the phrase, then, the things which are eliminated are circumstances or possibly necessary qualifying conditions. Notice, too, how on this view of the matter the opposed methods of induction are distinguished thus: Induction by Simple Enumeration regards generalizations as more reliable accordingly as the examined instances are more numerous, whereas Induction by Elimination regards generalizations as more reliable accordingly as the examined instances are more various. I shall argue shortly [5.2] that it is in this sense that inductive probabilification is indeed eliminative. However, Mill does not work out these suggestions. Nor do they represent his own main theory of induction, for this is eliminative in a different sense, in that the things which are eliminated are candidates for the style of 'cause'. The same is true of Bacon, if we may call 'causes' what he calls 'forms' or 'generating natures'. And this is the second sense of the expression 'induction by elimination'.

Take, as simplest illustration of this conception, Mill's account of his Method of Agreement. He writes: 'The validity of all the Inductive Methods depends on the assumption [rather, 'law'] that every event, or the beginning of every phenomenon, must have some cause, some antecedent, on the existence of which it is invariably and unconditionally consequent. In the Method of Agreement this is obvious; that method avowedly proceeding on the supposition that we have found the true cause as soon as we have negatived [eliminated] every other.' [Mill, 369: cp. 4.2] It is to be observed that this type of eliminative theory, which involves the elimination of causal candidates, tends to be confused with the type which I considered first, which involves the elimination of irrelevant qualifying conditions. There is no doubt a certain resemblance between the two procedures; but it is evident that they are not identical from the simple consideration that the latter is applicable to non-causal generalizations whereas the former is not.

It is instructive to consider the reasons why philosophers have thought induction to be intimately bound up with causation. I suggest that there are two main ones. The first is the confusion of the relation 'is evidence of' with the relations 'is the (or a) cause (or effect) of'. This confusion is strikingly manifest in Hume's inductive philosophy: 'All reasonings concerning matter of fact seem to be founded on the relation of *Cause and Effect*. By means of that relation alone can we go beyond the evidence of our memory and senses. If you were to ask a man, why he believes any matter of fact, which is absent; for instance, that his friend is in the country, or in France; he would give you a reason; and this reason

would be some other fact; as a letter received from him. . . .'
[Hume, E, 26] But his own example shows that this is wrong; for
what we say is that the arrival of a letter from Bob postmarked
Paris is evidence of his presence in France, not the effect of it.
Plainly, it is the former relation that Hume really has in mind. And
there is indeed a vital connexion between induction and evidence,
for I suggested at the beginning of this book that the meaning of
'a generalization' must be explained in terms of the notion of an
evidential-statement. It follows that his account of causation,
which bulks so large in Hume's inductive philosophy, is strictly
irrelevant; though to say this is not of course to deny its independent value.

The second reason is the confusion of 'cause' with 'reason' or
'because'. 'Cause' means 'invariable temporally antecedent event',
and is a word of primarily practical use. 'Reason', on the other
hand, means 'logically antecedent proposition'. Now, generalizations are very commonly given as reasons, as when I explain the
fact that this bird is black by pointing out that it is a raven and
that all ravens are black. And so, reasons being conflated with
causes, it may have been confusedly thought that there is some
essential connexion between generalization and causation. The
conflation is particularly clear in the writings of the 17th-century
Rationalists and of older writers on the Calculus of Probabilities,
who regularly speak of 'causes' where we should naturally speak of
'explanations': we shall notice shortly an important example in the
famous Sixth Principle of Laplace. [Leibniz, 222, 273 f.] Observe
too, in this connexion, the obvious parallelism between the Principle of Causation, as found in Kant and Mill, 'Every event has a
cause', and the Principle of Reason, as found in Descartes and
Leibniz, 'Every truth has a reason'. According to Couturat, the
latter means for Leibniz 'Every truth is analytic'; i.e. every truth
has a reason in the sense that in every true proposition the predicate is 'contained in' the subject and can be 'seen' to be so by a sufficiently powerful intelligence. [Leibniz, x f.] However, this familiar
distinction between 'cause' and 'reason' should not be exaggerated.
For in many uses the notions are indeed equivalent: we may say indifferently that the reason why Dick collided with the lamp-post
was that he skidded, or that a skid was the cause of his collision
with the lamp-post. To this extent Leibniz is right in saying that
'. . . "cause" in things [events] corresponds to "reason" in truths.'

This is why "cause" is often called "reason" [and conversely] . . .'
[*Further Essays concerning Human Understanding*, Paris, Flammarion,
no date, p. 425] The existence of this overlap of meaning between
the two terms has doubtless contributed largely to their confusion.

5.1.2 *The Elimination of Chance*

The third sense of the expression 'induction by elimination' is
what may conveniently be called, after Mill, the argument, or
probabilification, by elimination of chance. It will be well to begin
with a discussion of Mill's own account of it. [Mill, 286 ff., 344 ff.,
350 ff.; Lalande, 233 ff.] Take the following case. Having thrown
a certain die 600 times and observed that ace turns up in 400 of
them, I seek the explanation of this fact, and conclude that it very
probably is that the die is biased. According to Mill, my reasoning
is as follows. There are only two possible explanations of the fact:
either that the die is true and the preponderance of aces is due to
chance; or that the die is biased (either naturally or through having
been loaded). But the former explanation is very improbable; and
consequently, the latter is very probable.

He tells us that 'the question falls within Laplace's Sixth Principle', which states: 'Each of the causes to which an observed event
may be attributed is indicated with just as much likelihood as there
is probability that the event will take place, supposing the event to
be constant. The probability of the existence of any one of these
causes is then a fraction whose numerator is the probability of the
event resulting from this cause and whose denominator is the sum
of the similar probabilities relative to all the causes; if these various
causes, considered *a priori*, are unequally probable, it is necessary,
in place of the probability of the event resulting from each cause,
to employ the product of this probability by the possibility [i.e.
antecedent probability] of the cause itself.' [Laplace, 15 f.] Notice
(cp. above) how Laplace here speaks of causes where we should
speak of explanations, of the probability of the existence of a cause
where we should speak of the probability of the truth (or simply
of the probability) of an explanation, and of possibility where we
should speak of probability. As we saw earlier [2.2] in discussing
casual probability, he and others following him are particularly
prone to speak, paradoxically, of 'equal possibility' where we
should speak of 'equal probability'; I say paradoxically, because

we do not ordinarily speak of possibility as possessing degrees. [Laplace, 6 f.]

Mill holds that the case under consideration falls under the last clause in the Principle quoted, and consequently concludes: 'The probabilities . . . that the fact originated in these two modes [namely, by chance or by bias] are, as their antecedent probabilities, multiplied by the probabilities that if they existed [were true] they would produce the effect'. [Mill, 359] Thus, he represents the reasoning involved as inverse casual probable deductive reasoning, Laplace's Sixth Principle being his principle of inverse probability, 'the fundamental principle of this branch of the analysis of chances which consists in passing from events to causes'. [Laplace, 16]

This sense of 'induction by elimination' plainly differs from the two senses distinguished above, in that what are eliminated are neither possibly necessary qualifications of a generalization, nor candidates for the style of cause of some sort of event, but candidates for the style of explanation of some event.

I have pointed out earlier, in discussing hypothetic probability [1.2], how the study of ampliative inference has suffered from philosophers' inveterate tendency to misassimilate it to explicative inference, from what I there called the deductivist fallacy. Thus, hypothetic inference, it will be remembered, is misassimilated to the pattern: $p \supset q$; q; $\therefore$ p, and alleged to commit the fallacy of asserting the consequent. Similarly, the pattern of Induction by Simple Enumeration is alleged to be: fIg; $\therefore$ fAg, so that this mode of inference is also regarded as fallacious through the illicit process of the minor term. Hence, it comes as no surprise to find the form of Induction by Elimination likewise represented by a deductive inference-pattern, namely, a mixed alternative syllogism in the *modus tollendo ponens*, the simplest case of which is: $p \vee q$; $\sim q$; $\therefore$ p.

In the traditional view of Induction by Elimination, the alternatives are taken to be universal affirmative subject-predicate generalizations, which are eliminated when they are demonstratively falsified. This, of course, a single negative instance suffices to do, though a single positive instance does not suffice to demonstratively verify such a generalization. This is the meaning of Bacon's remark: '. . . in the establishment of any true axiom, the negative [as opposed to the affirmative] instance is the more forcible of the two'. [Bacon, 266] Hence, the advantages of eliminative over enumerative induction are supposed to be that, whereas in the latter many positive instances only probabilify a conclusion, in the former few (or even one) negative instance(s) demonstratively verify a conclusion. 'A favourable case increases more or less the probability of a law, whereas a contrary case annihilates it entirely. Confirmation supplies only a probability; invalidation on the contrary, creates a certainty.' [Nicod, 220] However, we shall see shortly that there are less simple cases in which elimination yields only a probable, not a true, conclusion.

It is necessary to note that this traditional doctrine takes into account only universal generalizations, not proportional ones. For its simple account does not fit the latter. $I(fMg)$ is not demonstratively falsified by $\bar{g}fx$ as $I(fAg)$ is. Nor is it demonstratively disproved (falsified) by $f'M\bar{g} . \alpha C_2 . \gamma C_6$; though it is indeed disproved by it. For here, as always, it is necessary to distinguish entailing and (dis)proving demonstratively from conclusively evidencing and (dis)proving empirically. The traditional theory of eliminative induction is essentially deductivist, and so employs the former concepts exclusively.

Induction by Elimination, then, is more fortunate than Induction by Simple Enumeration or hypothetic inference, inasmuch as the deductive inference-pattern to which it is assimilated is at least valid. But the following considerations will show that the foregoing is too simple a pattern to represent at all adequately the reasoning by which we establish one explanation by ruling out alternative ones.

First, comparison of the traditional account of eliminative induction with the argument by elimination of chance now under consideration, reveals these obvious differences. In the alternative syllogism, alternatives are eliminated when they are shown to be false, in consequence of which the conclusion is proved to be true. But here, alternatives are eliminated when they are shown to be improbable, in consequence of which the conclusion is proved to be probable. These two types of elimination, by falsification and improbabilification respectively, may conveniently be distinguished as strong and weak elimination. Thus, the pattern here is: $p \lor q$; $\gamma P(\sim q)$; $\therefore \gamma P(p)$; or, as it may alternatively be written: $\gamma PF(p, (p \lor q) . \gamma P(\sim q))$.

Another distinction of some importance between types of elimination is Nicod's distinction between complete and partial elimination. [Nicod, 222]. The latter is illustrated, for strong elimination, by the inference-pattern: $p \vee q \vee r$; $\sim q$; $\therefore p \vee r$. Practically speaking, only complete elimination matters, since what we normally want to establish is *the* true or probable explanation of the fact to be explained.

However, to point out that the traditional account of eliminative induction will not cover the argument by elimination of chance, is not of course to say that eliminative arguments conforming to it are never used. E.g., a detective may succeed in discovering, first, that only one of two persons physically could have committed the crime, and then that one of them has a perfect alibi. That the elimination be strong, however, is a necessary but not a sufficient condition of the conclusion's being true as opposed to probable; the other necessary condition is that the alternative premiss be true and not probable. I proceed to explain this point.

The preceding objection to the traditional account of eliminative induction is on the score that the minor premisses, and hence the conclusions, of our alternative syllogisms are sometimes probable and not true. But sometimes, indeed usually, the major premiss too is probable and not true. For we normally include among the suggested alternative explanations on which we practise elimination, only those which we judge probably to exhaust the possibilities. Thus, in the die example, our major premiss is likely to be: 'In all probability either this die is true and the observed preponderance of aces is due to chance, or alternatively it is biased and the observed preponderance is due to that fact'.

We thus obtain two types of case accordingly as we practise strong or weak elimination on a probable major premiss. First, $\gamma P(p \vee q)$; $\sim q$; $\therefore \gamma P(p)$; or, in the alternative writing, $\gamma PF(p, \gamma P(p \vee q) \,.\, \sim q)$. Second, $\gamma P(p \vee q)$; $\gamma P(\sim q)$; $\therefore \epsilon P(p)$; or, in the alternative writing, $\epsilon PF(p, \gamma P((p \vee q) \,.\, \sim q))$. The existence of the former type is noticed by Nicod. [Nicod, 225 f.] But that of the latter is not, since he does not recognize that there is such a thing as weak as well as strong elimination.

The following general point about the meaning of alternative probability-judgements needs to be made here: $\beta P(p \vee q) \equiv \beta P(p) \vee \beta P(q)$. When we say e.g. 'It is very probable that either Tom or Dick did it', we mean simply that these alternatives very probably exhaust the possibilities. We do not mean that each alternative is very probable and so equally probable. Again, respecting the meaning of hypothetical probability-judgements, 'It is probable that if Tom comes Dick will come' means 'If Tom comes it is probable that Dick will come', not 'If it is probable that Tom will come it is probable that Dick will come'. So generally, $\gamma P(p \supset q) \equiv p \supset \gamma P(q) \lessdot \gamma P(p) \supset \gamma P(q)$. By contrast, 'It is probable that both Tom and Dick will come' does mean 'It is probable that Tom will come and it is probable that Dick will come'; and so generally, $\gamma P(p \cdot q) \equiv \gamma P(p) \cdot \gamma P(q)$.

All this is relevant to what I said earlier [2.2] about probable deduction and the logic of probability. It will be remembered that I there suggested that the latter name might well be used for the systematic study of the entailments of probability-judgements, and that a natural way to start such a study would be to take the inference-patterns discussed in the standard deductive logic of truth (or statement-logic), replace true premisses by premisses that are in various degrees probable, and formulate rules about how the degrees of probability of conclusions are affected. For the preceding remarks evidently relate to probable alternative syllogisms. They also show that study of this particular inference-pattern is not purely academic, since it expresses the form of argument that we often employ when establishing explanations by ruling out alternative ones.

It is often said that there are indefinitely many, or at any rate a very large number, of possible explanations of any fact. This seems on the face of it to constitute a serious objection to establishing explanations by elimination. For it involves that, in order to make a complete strong or weak elimination, we must falsify or improbabilify indefinitely many, or at any rate very many, alternative explanations; and this is impracticable. However, the foregoing discussion shows that there is an answer to this objection. Namely, that we practise elimination, not upon the very numerous alternative possible explanations at least one of which we hold to be certainly true, but upon the manageably small number of alternative possible explanations of which we hold at least one to be probably true. Mill's argument about the die illustrates the point. He says, we have seen, that there are only two possible explanations of the observed preponderance of aces over chance expectation: either that the die is true and the observed fact is fortuitous, or that the die is biased and the observed fact is caused by this. Now, it might be objected that there are actually other possible explanations, as that the die is true and the preponderance of aces is due to a peculiarity in the manner of throwing it. In fact, however, we should not take this into consideration as an alternative possible explanation, because we have very, very good inductive evidence that dice-falls are not thus affected by peculiarities of throwing. Mill is therefore right, though he ought strictly to say that in all probability there are only the two possible explanations of this fact that he instances.

He is also right in saying that we must take account of the antecedent or initial probabilities of the alternatives on which we practise elimination. Suppose that I had thrown 600 times, not a die, but a small cube-shaped stone that I had found on the beach, and that one side turned up 400 of these times. In this case, we should not judge the possible explanation, that the stone is true (i.e. a homogeneous cube) and the observed fact fortuitous, antecedently probable enough to be worth including in the 'field' of alternative possible explanations. The reason why we judge otherwise in the case of the die is, of course, that we know the true generalization, Most dice are true; so that it is antecedently probable (i.e. probable before I throw it) that this (random) die is true too.

Cp. the following observation of Laplace: 'On a table we see letters arranged in this order, C o n s t a n t i n o p l e, and we judge that this arrangement is not the result of chance, not because it is less possible [probable] than the others, for if this word were not employed in any language we should not suspect it came from any particular cause, but this word being in use among us, it is incomparably more probable that some person has thus arranged the aforesaid letters than that this arrangement is due to chance'. [Laplace, 16] This passage is the earliest discussion that I have discovered of the argument by elimination of chance. There is however a difference between this case and the die or stone cases in that, whereas the reasoning in the latter turns on the concept of a combination, that in the former turns on the concept of an arrangement; and these must of course be distinguished. We form combinations by forming groups of *n* objects (e.g. samples of BU) taken out of a total number of *m* objects (e.g. the population of BU) without regard to the order of objects in the group. But we form arrangements by forming groups of *n* objects (e.g. groups of 14 letters) taken out of a total number of *m* objects (e.g. the 26 letters of the alphabet) with regard to the order of the objects in the group. [J. V. Uspensky, *Introduction to Mathematical Probability*,

New York, 1937, pp. 17 f.] It is the former concept which is the fundamental one in probable deductive reasoning from samples to populations.

I suggest, then, that the argument by elimination of chance in the case of the die actually goes, when made fully explicit, as follows. 'Required to explain the fact that 400 out of 600 throws with this die have turned up ace (the *explanandum*). It is antecedently very, very probable that only one of only the two following alternative explanations is true: either (*a*) the die is true and the *explanandum* is fortuitous; or (*b*) the die is not true (i.e. is biased) and the *explanandum* is explained by this. But (*a*) and (*b*) are not antecedently equally probable; for the facts that we know it for a true generalization that most dice are true, and that this is a random die, make (*a*) antecedently probable and consequently (*b*) antecedently improbable. However, if (*a*) were true the *explanandum* would be very, very improbable; the truth of the latter therefore makes (*a*) very, very improbable. Hence, compounding its antecedent probability with its consequent very great improbability (i.e. the very great improbability conferred on it by the truth of the *explananuum*), (*a*) is on balance improbable. Therefore, (*a*) should be eliminated as improbable and (*b*) accepted as fairly probable.' The argument accordingly exemplifies the formula: $\delta PF(p, \alpha P(q \lor p) \cdot \gamma P(\sim q))$.

Two points in this proposed analysis call for comment. The improbability of (*a*) is a 'net' improbability arrived at by 'subtracting' from its consequent very great improbability its antecedent probability. Finally, it is possible to assign a degree of antecedent improbability to (*b*) because it is a matter of observable fact whether a die is true or biased. It is this which enables us to generalize that most dice are true, and so judge that (*a*) is antecedently probable and (*b*) correspondingly improbable. However, this is not always the case. Cp. in this respect the possible explanations 'This die is biased' or 'These letters were deliberately arranged in this order by a human being' with the possible explanation of Jones' statistically significant degree of success in guessing cards, 'Jones has a capacity for extra-sensory perception'. Since it is not a matter of observation whether or not men possess this capacity, no analogous generalization can be made and no antecedent probability be assigned to this hypothesis. For it is not as if, e.g., some men possessed special organs, from the existence of which it might be inferred that they perceived what other men do not. The only evidence for or against the hypothesis is the consequent evidence of the *explanandum* itself. In considering probabilification by elimination of chance, therefore, we must recognize that there is a significant distinction between cases in which the explanations we are dealing with are empirical hypotheses and cases in which they are non-empirical ones. [Keynes, 298 ff.]

Although restricting the alternative explanations for elimination in the manner described is practically inevitable, it involves the risk of our assuming that there are fewer alternatives worthy of consideration than there actually are. Thus, Lalande writes of 'telepathy': '. . . the hypothesis of thought-communication is strongly recommended by the fact that the only other possible hypothesis is fortuitous coincidence, and that the probability of this coincidence is . . . low. . . .' [Lalande, 238] Yet this is perhaps to claim too much. To be sure, there is general agreement among the experts that all possible normal explanations of the occurrence of ψ-correlations—as that the subject can see through the backs of the cards about which he is guessing, or the like—have been excluded by due arrangement of the experimental conditions; and this is presumably what Lalande has in mind. But we must also take account of abnormal explanatory hypotheses, such as telepathy itself; and when the latter is virtually the only abnormal explanation that has as yet been invented, it is surely premature to regard it as the only possible one. It is worth observing, in this connexion, that at the present time philosophers study probabilification by elimination of chance almost exclusively as part of the Philosophy of Parapsychology; although in fact the argument is frequently encountered in other and less difficult fields, as the die example shows. [A. Flew, *A New Approach to Psychical Research*, London, 1953, pp. 84 ff., 111 ff.] According to Keynes, the first person to apply this mode of argumentation to parapsychological phenomena was the economist and statistician, F. Y. Edgeworth. [Keynes, 298]

Finally, we must recognize that, chance being just one possible explanation among others, the weak elimination of chance does not of itself effect a complete elimination, and hence the probabilification of an alternative explanation, unless there is (probably) only one other possible explanation. This is true in the case of the die, but it is by no means usually true. And when it is not true, the weak elimination of chance effects only a partial elimination, so that the work of ruling out all but one of the other possible explanations has still to be done.

Thus far by way of elucidation of the argument by elimination of chance. It remains to be seen whether Mill's account of it is true. This need not detain us long, since it is clearly open to two decisive objections. First, Mill explicitly claims that some probable inductive reasoning is of this type, that in discussing this mode of argumentation he is elucidating inductive reasoning. [Mill, 344 f.] Yet, by his own account, the type of reasoning involved is inverse casual probable deductive reasoning. And, as I have insisted more than once, the former is not ('really') identical with the latter. Cp. my comments on Jevons' and Williams' theories. [1.1, 4.2]

But further, it is not true that the reasoning involved in probabilification by elimination of chance is inverse casual probable deductive reasoning. If the analysis that I gave above of the die case is correct, more than one type of probabilification-judgement is in fact involved. Thus, the judgement that explanation (a) is antecedently probable is casual and inductive. The judgement that the truth of the *explanandum* highly improbabilifies (a) goes, when made fully explicit: 'If this die is true and the outcomes of throws with it are determined by chance, it is (casually) very, very probable that in 600 throws with it ace will turn up about 100 times; but ace has not turned up about 100 times in 600 throws with it; therefore this hypothesis is (hypothetically) very, very improbable'. This judgement is casual and hypothetic, and exemplifies the formula: $\alpha PF(\sim p, (p \supset \alpha P(q)) . \sim q)$. Its constituent hypothetical-judgement-formula is obtained by casual probable deduction. The formula should be contrasted with the inference-pattern of mixed hypothetical syllogisms in the *modus tollendo tollens* which is treated of in the ordinary logic of truth, namely: $p \supset q$; $\sim q$; $\therefore \sim p$.

So much for Mill on the argument by elimination of chance. I propose to discuss next Kneale's account of the probabilification of proportional generalizations, which he calls 'probability-rules'. [Kneale, 214, 230 ff., 240 f., 243; Kneale II, 315; Ryle, I, 60 f.; Whiteley, 69 f.] He argues as follows. I observe e.g. that $f'm/ng$ and that f' are numerous [and random] and the proportion stable. I frame the explanatory hypothesis that fm/ng approximately, and judge it to be inductively probable on the following ground: 'How [casually] unlikely it would be that we should find what we do in a [random] sample as large as this [in which the proportion is stable], if the hypothesis were not true'. The judgement thus exemplifies the formula $\gamma PF(p, (\sim p \supset \gamma P(\sim q)) . q)$; which is just a special case of the immediately preceding judgement-formula, and which should be contrasted with the inference-pattern; $\sim p \supset \sim q$; q; $\therefore p$. (In both of the last two formulas given there is of course an employment of the double negation rule: $\sim \sim p \equiv p$.) He continues: 'Although there is a fallacy in the attempts which have been made to exhibit this method of estimating acceptability [i.e. inductive probability] as an argument in the calculus of chances, depending on the use of the inversion formula, the method itself is essentially sound'. [Kneale, 240 f.] Casual probabilification-judgements thus enter into these allegedly inductive probabilification-judgements. But this is not to say that proportional generalizations are casually probable. For the essential difference between the argument that tries to prove generalizations probable by using the principle of inverse probability (as found in Laplace and Jevons) and the present argument, is that the former attributes to the hypothesis a casual probability, whereas the latter does not. And this is precisely the fatal objection to the former. For degrees of casual probability are always in principle, if not always in practice, measurable in the strict sense and expressible by a fraction. But degrees of inductive probability (otherwise called acceptability or reliability) are not strictly measurable. In the present type of argument, on the other hand, inductive is distinguished from casual probability, and the relation between them resembles that between 'likelihood' and casual probability in Fisher's Method of Maximum Likelihood.

Since this distinction between casual and inductive probability is crucial to the theory, we may notice how it is expressed by Ryle in a paper in which he too attempts to explain inductive probability in terms of the elimination of chance: 'In such an argument [namely, an inductive argument] the numerical odds-fraction [i.e. casual probability] is not a premiss in our inductions, such that from it plus our empirical data we deduce our law-propositions. Rather it is the measure we use, the yard-stick against which our empirical evidence makes it relatively [inductively] "probable" or "improbable" that a causal law obtains. The arithmetic of chances yields us no more information about the world than geometry gives us information about the dimensions of St. Paul's. But we use the arithmetic of chances in our inductions just as we use geometry in fixing the dimensions of St. Paul's.' [Ryle, I, 61]

I observe for a start that, although Kneale applies this theory of inductive probabilification to proportional generalizations (or what he calls 'probability-rules') only, it can equally well be applied to universal ones (or what he calls 'laws'). Given that $f'Ag$ (the *explanandum*) and that f' are numerous and random, we may frame the explanatory hypothesis that fAg and judge it to be inductively probable on the same ground, that it is casually improbable that the *explanandum* should be true if the hypothesis is false. Such an extension of the theory to cover the probabilification of subject-predicate generalizations generally seems to me not only possible but desirable, since universal affirmative and negative generalizations are after all only limiting cases of proportional ones, as Kneale himself admits. [Kneale, 237]

Notice next that these arguments are arguments by elimination of chance just as much as is Mill's argument about the die. For the possible explanation that is weakly eliminated on the score of its improbability is, that the composition of the population is (widely) different from that of the sample and that the fact of the composition of the sample being what it is is purely fortuitous. Similarly in the case of the die: the explanatory hypothesis that is weakly eliminated is, that the die is true and that the preponderance of aces in the sample is fortuitous. Mill's name for this type of argument, 'the elimination of chance', is therefore slightly misleading to the extent that it suggests that the hypothesis to be eliminated is simpler than it actually is. For the hypothesis is in fact conjunctive; and indeed, in these cases, it is the suppositions respectively that the die is true, and that the composition of the population is widely different from that of the sample, which are the main conjuncts in the hypotheses, and which express *the* hypotheses that are eliminated.

My basic criticism of Kneale's account is that it sheds no light on inductive probability, as he claims, because the sort of reasoning he is discussing is not inductive. It is concerned rather, as he himself explicitly states in the passage quoted, with one way of probabilifying proportional or statistical hypotheses, and so falls to be discussed in an examination of hypothetic rather than inductive probability. For the form of a proportional primitive inductive probabilification-judgement is given by the formula, $(11')$,

$\gamma\mathrm{PF}(fm/ng, f'm/ng . \gamma C_2 . \gamma C_6)$; and this is evidently quite a different formula from $\gamma\mathrm{PF}(p, (\sim p \supset \gamma\mathrm{P}(\sim q)) . q)$. I shall have more to say about the distinction between inductive and hypothetic inference shortly. [5.2]

It will be remembered that I touched earlier [1.2] on the probabilification of proportional hypotheses when discussing hypothetic probability. The interesting feature of the type of judgement that Kneale is discussing is that it probabilifies p by weakly eliminating the only other logically possible alternative, $\sim p$. It effects this result by deductively elaborating $\sim p$ (conjoined with the understood conditions that the sample is large and random and the proportion in it stable) by the Calculus of Probabilities, and showing that its (casually) probable consequence is in conflict with the observed facts. But it would also be possible to argue on the following lines when probabilifying proportional hypotheses. One might suppose that p; mathematically deduce from it and the same conditions that $\gamma\mathrm{P}(q)$; show that this (casually) probable consequence is in agreement with the observed facts; and conclude that p is (hypothetically) probable. The relevant formula in this case would be: $\gamma\mathrm{PF}(p,(p \supset \gamma\mathrm{P}(q)) . q)$. It should be contrasted both with the last formula quoted, and with the evidential-statement-formula which gives the form of normal hypothetic inference, $\mathrm{E}(p, (p \supset q) . q)$. It will be seen that the difference between it and the latter is that the latter turns on the existence of an agreement between a true consequence of the hypothesis and the observed facts: consider e.g. the special case of the last formula, $\mathrm{E}(fAg, (fAg \supset f'Ag) . f'Ag)$. This method of hypothetic probabilification too seems to be substantially sound. But the essential point for us is that none of all this bears on inductive probability.

In taking leave of Kneale's theory of inductive probability, I have a final criticism to add. It seems to me that his account of the probability of proportional inductions (or rather hypotheses), just reviewed, does not square with his account of the probability of inductions generally in terms of the reasonableness of inductive inference as such. [4.3] He attempts, indeed, to connect the two lines of argument; but in my judgement without success. And of the two, it is clearly the latter which is the leading idea in his theory.

5.2 RESTATEMENT OF THE THEORY OF INDUCTIVE PROBABILIFICATION BY ELIMINATION

Here, I shall first give a constructive account of inductive probabilification by elimination, treating in order subject-predicate generalizations, functional generalizations, and difficulties affecting the probabilification of both types. I shall then discuss connected questions, namely: probability and truth, probability and meaning, and the relations between inductive and hypothetic inference.

5.2.1 *Completion of the Constructive Account of Inductive Probability*

First, then, subject-predicate generalizations. The essentials of my very simple view are best presented in the form of an answer to the three questions which I suggested earlier [5.1] are central to all eliminative theories of induction. What are eliminated are conditions, as h and $\bar{h}$. They are eliminated when they are judged to be eliminable, and they are judged to be so when the sample has been varied with respect to them, so that its description is of the form e.g. $\bar{h}hf'Ag$. And the unconditioned generalization e.g. $I(fAg)$ is more probabilified (and in the limiting case verified) as more possibly non-eliminable conditions, or possibly necessary qualifications, are eliminated. Thus, when the description of the sample is of the form, $\bar{u}hhf'Ag$, this probabilifies the unconditioned generalization $I(fAg)$ in a higher degree than when its description is of the form $hhf'Ag$. But these remarks need expansion.

The notion of condition (not, as Mill alleges, of cause) being the root of the whole theory of induction, it is desirable to clarify its meaning. This is, protasis of an hypothetical or conditional statement, as when we say that all f are g on condition that, i.e. if or when, they are h. The notion is also expressed in a variety of other familiar ways. We say that all f are g in certain circumstances, or under a proviso; namely, when they are all h. Or we say that all hf are g; and then we speak of the subject-term and/or the generalization as qualified, modified, or restricted in scope. Conditions are expressed, sometimes by qualifying adjectives, as in 'Most rich electors vote Conservative', and sometimes by qualifying phrases such as 'at sea-level' or 'over the range of pressures 50–150 lbs.

per sq. in.'. The term 'eliminable' is again an evaluative, not a purely descriptive, one. For when the description of the sample is of the form, say, $hhf'Ag$, we hold that the conditions h and h not so much can be as may be eliminated from the corresponding generalization, i.e. that their elimination is justified.

The description of the sample is better symbolized as $hhf'Ag$ than as $hf'Ag . hf'Ag$. The latter indeed is not wrong, and I have used it earlier [2.1]; for the two formulas are of course equivalent. But the equivalence holds only for universals. Thus, $hhf'Mg$ is equivalent to $hf'Mg . hf'Mg$ only when h is irrelevant to g among f'. And normally this is precisely not the case, for the reason that we vary the instances in respect of conditions antecedently judged to be probably relevant. I shall revert to this point in due course. It is the formulas $hhf'Ag$, $hhf'Mg$, etc., which correctly give the form of our sample-descriptions; for what we do is simply put in a class e.g. old and young electors and record the proportion of it that votes Conservative. The only reason why we concern ourselves at all with the proportions in the subsamples hf', hf', etc., is to ensure, in the case of generalizations that are not universal, that the condition of proportional stability (C_6) is satisfied, so that we can significantly speak of *the* proportion of f' that are g. [2.1] In these two formulas, 'all' must naturally be interpreted collectively and not distributively. 'All examined male and female children like chocolate' does not mean 'Every examined male and female child likes chocolate', for this is self-contradictory. If we wish to use 'every' in this context, we must use 'or' instead of 'and', and say 'Every examined child, whether male or female, likes chocolate'. Similarly with proportional generalizations, which, as we saw earlier [1.1], are about all of a class just as much as universal ones are. Thus, 'The majority of examined male and female children like chocolate' means 'The majority of all examined male and female children like chocolate'. But this must not be interpreted as 'The majority of every examined male and female child likes chocolate', for this is doubly absurd. To put the point another way: although the formula $hhgfx$ is illogical, the formulas $hhf'Ag$ and $hhf'Mg$ are not.

It is evident from the foregoing account of elimination that saying that generalizations are more probabilified as more conditions are eliminated is equivalent to saying that they are more probabilified as the observed instances are more varied. Consequently, what is said here respecting elimination and inductive probabilification is an amplification of what is said above [2.1–3.2] respecting variety and inductive probabilification. Consequently, too, the traditional view, expressed in the second quotation from Mill in 5.1, that there is an essential connexion between Induction by Elimination (in the pertinent one of the three senses of that name) and the variety as opposed to the mere number of the observed instances, is seen to be correct.

It is a small point, yet one worth making, that sound induction requires that the instances be varied, not merely various. For what it brings out is the fact that sound induction is a technique of experiment rather than of simple observation. We do not wait until, in the ordinary course of Nature, a class of rich and poor, old and young, etc., electors happen to fall under our observation; we deliberately produce or collect such a class. Conditions are varied in different ways according to their type. Attribute-conditions, such as colours, are made to be present or absent, as when we include in the sample red and non-red BU, or red, white and blue BU. Variable-conditions, such as pressure, are made to vary in degree, as when we produce high and low pressures under which to observe the phenomenon we are interested in.

Why, then, are subject-predicate generalizations judged to be more probable as more possibly non-eliminable conditions are eliminated, or in other words, as the observed instances are more varied? Essentially for the following reason. The inductive fallacy *par excellence* consists in making a generalization the scope of which is too wide relatively to the evidence for it. We tend to commit this fallacy on account of an ingrained propensity to hasty generalization, concerning which Bacon remarks: 'The understanding must not therefore be supplied with wings, but rather hung with weights, to keep it from leaping and flying'. [Bacon, 290] Thus, it may be that a sample is properly described by a statement of the form $hf'Mg$, h being a common property of all the observed instances, in which case the generalization ought to be of the conditioned form $I(hfMg)$, not of the unconditioned form $I(fMg)$.

The reason why it ought to be of the conditioned form is this. It is possible that h would have been relevant to g among f', in the following sense. Although the description of the sample that I have actually taken is of the form $hf'Mg$, the description of the sample that I would have taken had I varied it in respect of h

would have been of the form, say, $hhf'M\bar{g}$. Hence, one way in which I may go wrong in primitive induction is, if I gener..lize from a description of the former form to $I(fMg)$ rather than from a description of the latter form to $I(fM\bar{g})$. Notice, however, that I shall not necessarily go wrong unless h is relevant to g among f (i.e. in the population) in the same way as it would have been among f' (i.e. in the sample). And this may not be the case, since it is possible that h would have been relevant to g among f' while yet being irrelevant to g among f.

It may be objected that it is equally possible that h would have been irrelevant to g among f', in which case I have not gone wrong in generalizing to $I(fMg)$ from $hf'Mg$. This is true, but beside the point. For the thought that we convey when we say that a generalization to $I(fMg)$ from $hf'Mg$ is not probable, whereas a generalization to it from $hhf'Mg$ is so (in at any rate some slight degree), is precisely that one who generalizes in the former manner has not taken proper steps to deal with the possibility that h would have been relevant to g among f'. For it can do no harm to include hf as well as hf in the sample. For if h would in fact have been irrelevant to g among f', I should not have gone wrong on account of generalizing from the proportion of g among hhf' as opposed to among hf', since these proportions must be the same by virtue of the meaning of 'irrelevant'. Since, then, one (but not the unique) way in which I can go wrong is in generalizing to $I(fMg)$ from $hf'Mg$ rather than from $hhf'Mg$, whereas there is no corresponding one (but not unique) way in which I can go wrong in generalizing to $I(fMg)$ from $hhf'Mg$ rather than from $hf'Mg$, the latter is the reasonable course to take. And we do but express the same simple thought in an alternative way when we say that $I(fMg)$ is (in some slight degree) probable when it is inferred from $hhf'Mg$, but is not (in any degree) probable when it is inferred from $hf'Mg$.

It is a practical impossibility to ensure that there are no properties common to f' beyond those of being f and observed. Keynes' 'perfect analogy' represents an unattainable ideal. For the members of a sample that has been varied in the highest degree practicable will still have an indefinite number of common properties: the examined BU will yet share such positive properties as having been drawn on a Friday or such negative ones as not having been made in Peru. But more, it is a false ideal, since there is no point in trying to attain it. For a generalization can be, not merely highly probabilified, but verified, without eliminating all possibly common properties. My rules of probabilification stipulate merely that probabilification and verification are achieved by eliminating a (very) good number of such properties or conditions. In judging inductive evidence to be good or conclusive, we go by the maxim that enough is enough.

The following division of conditions is necessary for an analysis of inductive procedure: (*a*) known conditions, and (*b*) unknown conditions. The former subdivide as follows. (i) Conditions antecedently judged to be inductively probably (or certainly) relevant. E.g. weight among BU when the investigation is into what proportion of them are H. We ensure that lightness and non-lightness are eliminated, or vary in respect of weight, when we judge lightness likely to be favourably relevant to H-ness in this population. In such a case we also call weight an important or material property in respect of which to vary the sample. (ii) Conditions antecedently judged to be inductively probably (or certainly) irrelevant. E.g., in the same context, the colour of BU. (iii) Conditions respecting which no antecedent judgements of probable relevance or irrelevance can be made. E.g., in the same context, the size of BU.

In sound induction, priority is naturally given to the elimination of (i). What is done about (ii) and (iii) depends on the practical exigencies of the situation, such as the available time and money. Ideally, at any rate, there should be variation in respect of some of (iii), and also of some of (ii), since antecedent judgements of irrelevance may well be mistaken. I defer consideration of class (*b*) for the moment, and shall discuss it in connexion with invariable conditions.

There is an important consequence of the existence of these classes of conditions which bears on inductive probability. Namely, a generalization is more probabilified by the elimination of *h* and *ĥ* when they are antecedently judged probably relevant than when they are antecedently judged probably irrelevant or when no antecedent judgement about their probable (ir)relevance is possible; and it is more probabilified as the antecedent judgement is more probable. The rules of probabilification for generalizations given in 2.1 and 3.1 need modification accordingly; for since not all variations of conditions affect the degree of probability equally, it does not depend solely on the number of conditions in respect of which the observed instances are varied. A generalization from the evidence of observed instances that have been varied in respect of a smaller number of conditions antecedently judged to be very probably important is more probable than another generalization from the evidence of observed instances that have been varied in respect of a larger number of conditions antecedently judged to be fairly probably important, or probably unimportant, or concerning which no judgement of probable importance or unimportance is possible.

Judgements of probable (ir)relevance are normally inductive, so that their existence and importance in the making of inductive probabilification-judgements indicates another interesting aspect of what Nicod calls the 'snowball' character of the process, i.e. the way in which the making of probable inductions contributes to the making of further probable inductions. Other aspects, it will be remembered, are to be seen in the deductive systematization of probable inductions, traditionally called the 'consilience' of inductions [2.2]; and in the employment of reliable methods of sampling. [4.3] Naturally, any inquiry may present more than one of these aspects. Thus, in sampling, the first and third are often both visible. The stratification of the population in certain respects is based on antecedent judgements of (inductively) probable relevance, and the choice of a method of selecting individuals at random from within each stratum is made in the light of judgements of reliability which are approximately equivalent to judgements of inductive probability. [4.3]

I turn now to functional generalizations. I pointed out earlier [3.1] that degree of variety of conditions is one, but not the only, determinant of the degree of probability of functional as well as of subject-predicate generalizations. In these too we vary in order to eliminate. For we want to exclude otherwise necessary qualifications, so as not to have to say, as it might be: 'At sea-level, or over the range of lengths so-and-so to such-and-such, the periods of the vibrations of pendulums vary directly as the square root of their lengths'.

There is nevertheless a difference of some interest between the two types of generalization in this respect, which arises out of a certain difference in our purposes when making these two types of inference. In subject-predicate generalization, what we normally want to do is to discover and prove a fact about all f, namely, the proportion of them that are g. Suppose that we vary a sample of electors in respect of wealth, and that richness and poorness are respectively favourably and unfavourably relevant to voting Conservative among these examined electors. If we are interested simply in the proportion of electors that votes Conservative, this relevance will not interest us, and we shall make the unconditioned generalization that (say) 52% of the electors vote Conservative. But if we are interested, as we sometimes are, in a different question, namely, the support that the Conservative Party receives from different sections of the community, this relevance will interest us, and we shall generalize from the same evidence to the conditioned generalizations that (say) 81% of rich electors but 34% of poor electors vote Conservative.

In functional generalization, we tend to proceed in the latter manner rather than in the former. For our purpose is to fit a reasonably simple mathematical description to the sample of observed values of variables, which we can then generalize. If we can do this for all the values observed under the varied conditions, so that we can make an unconditioned generalization, so much the better. But if, as commonly happens, we cannot do this, we content ourselves with making conditioned generalizations about subclasses of the observed values. Thus, suppose it is found on varying with respect to it that the variable-condition, amplitude of vibration, is relevant to the functional relationship between period of vibration and length of pendulum in the sample. What is then done is to formulate two generalizations of restricted scope, as follows: 'When the amplitude of the vibration is small, period and length are related by the formula $T = 2\pi\sqrt{l/g}$, where T is the period, l the length and g the acceleration of a freely falling body'; and 'When the amplitude of the vibration is not small, period and length are related by the formula $T = 2\pi\sqrt{l/g} \cdot (1 + 1/4 \sin^2 \theta/2 + 9/64 \sin^4 \theta/2)$, where θ is the angular amplitude'.

Generally speaking, however, the same considerations apply to variety or elimination in both functional and subject-predicate generalizations. In both, the fallacy to be guarded against is asserting unconditionally what ought to be asserted conditionally on account of the presence of some common circumstance. In both, we rely heavily on antecedent judgements of (ir)relevance or (un)importance and so on the available background of knowledge. One versed in Mechanics might well judge in advance that amplitude of vibration would be an important circumstance in the pendulum inquiry, whereas the material of which the pendulum is made would not, and vary the conditions accordingly. As Jevons says: 'As natural science progresses, physicists gain a kind of insight and tact in judging what qualities of a substance are likely to be concerned in any class of phenomena'. [Jevons, II, 30] Finally, in making both subject-predicate and functional primitive probabilification-judgements, we encounter difficulties arising out of the complexity and invariability of conditions, and out of the rule that conditions should be varied one at a time. I shall now discuss these three difficulties.

First, then, the difficulty about complex conditions. A simple example of a generalization under a complex condition is 'All blue-eyed white cats are deaf'. The generalization may be, and in fact is, true when the corresponding generalizations under simple conditions, 'All blue-eyed cats are deaf' and 'All white cats are deaf', are false. If our purpose is, not to discover and prove the proportion of all cats that are deaf, but to make a true or probable universal generalization about what sorts of cats are all deaf—as it may be if we are investigating, say, the cause(s) of deafness in cats —then this is the sort of generalization that we shall want to discover and establish. But reflection will readily convince the reader that it is much more difficult to discover and prove a generalization under a complex condition than one under a simple condition, such as 'Most black cats are not deaf'. Indeed, the difficulty will be greater as the condition is more complex; for a complex condition may be a conjunction of any number of simple conditions greater than one.

I touched on this same point earlier [2.1] when discussing the replacement of unconditional preponderant subject-predicate generalizations by corresponding conditioned universal ones. I remarked then that one of the obstacles in the way of doing this was the difficulty of identifying the requisite qualifying conditions, and instanced the impossibility in the present state of our knowledge of replacing 'Most persons are right-handed' by a corresponding universal. We can now see that the difficulty of the replacement is greater as the requisite condition is more complex. But the complexity of the requisite conditions is not the only difficulty. Another arises from the recondite or unexpected nature of some necessary qualifications; and these are of course characteristics that simple conditions may well possess.

Next, the difficulty about invariable conditions. Confining attention, as usual, to the simplest case, namely that involving attribute-conditions and contradictories only, the meaning of 'invariable condition' is as follows. f are invariable with respect to the conditions h and $\bar{h}$ if it is not possible to produce at will for observation hf and $\bar{h}f$. I propose to consider two important cases of invariability in conditions: first, invariability in respect of space and time; and second, invariability in respect of unknown conditions.

The former case has received a fair amount of attention from inductive philosophers. [Broad, R, I, 395 f.; Eaton, 535 f.; Keynes, 255 f.] The point is this. Human observation is confined to a certain region of space and time: we cannot now observe things or events that are in the future, in the past, or very remote in space. Hence, all observed things and events share the common property of occurring in this region. It may be asked, Is the impossibility logical or physical? I should say, logical, on the ground that (*pace* all seers) the proposition 'No-one can observe what is in the future or the past or out of the range of our senses' is 'analytic'.

Keynes uses a short method with this difficulty. He alleges that we know *a priori* that differences of place and date are inductively irrelevant, so that the problem does not arise: 'The Principle of the Uniformity of Nature, as I interpret it, supplies the answer, if it is correct, to the criticism that the instances, on which generalizations are based, are all alike in being past, and that any generalization, which is applicable to the future, must be based, for this reason, upon imperfect analogy. We judge directly that the resemblance between instances, which consists in their being past, is in itself irrelevant, and does not supply a valid ground for impugning a generalization'. [Keynes, 256; 4.2]

I agree that, if this were true, there would be no difficulty. For if we know e.g. that $hf'Ag$ but that h is irrelevant to g among f, then we may eliminate h from the generalization and conclude to $I(fAg)$ rather than to $I(hfAg)$. But, as I said earlier [2.1], it is not true; and indeed Keynes himself seems to be rather dubious about his Principle. I also drew attention earlier [4.2] to the fact that a number of natural philosophers, whom I called regionalists, entertain grave misgivings about the uniformity of Nature, and are accordingly uneasy about the large-scale spatio-temporal extrapolations made in Cosmology and Cosmogony. Bridgman e.g. expresses his doubts as follows: 'To me the most striking thing about cosmogony is the perfectly hair-raising extrapolations which it is necessary to make. We have to extend to times of the order of 10^{13} years and distances of the order of 10^9 light years laws which have been checked in a range of not more than 3×10^2 years, and certainly in distances not greater than the distance which the solar system has travelled in that time, or about 4×10^{-2} light years. It seems to me that one cannot take such extrapolations seriously unless one subscribes to a metaphysics that claims that laws of the necessary mathematical precision *really* control the actual physical universe. For such a metaphysical claim I can find no operational meaning that would give one the slightest confidence in applying it to any concrete situation.' [P. W. Bridgman, *The Nature of Physical Theory*, New York, Dover Publications, no date, pp. 109 f.]

Another solution goes thus. We must simply accept the fact that all our observations are confined to a certain spatio-temporal region, and limit the scope of our generalizations accordingly. In particular, we must renounce any hope of making with any degree of probability truly universal generalizations which shall apply to all times and all places. This is approximately the sort of thing that Whitehead has in mind when he claims that the maximum scope of generalizations is restricted to certain 'cosmic epochs'.

My own view on this matter, which inclines more to the regionalist than to the universalist position, is as follows. What we do when we make assertions about e.g. the future is to extrapolate. Earlier [3.2], I discussed a particular sort of extrapolation, namely, that in which we go outside the observed range of covariation of variables. In fact, the term 'extrapolation', and its correlative 'interpolation', are usually employed in this restricted sense. But in the wide sense of the term, we extrapolate whenever we eliminate a condition of any kind that has not been varied, as when we infer from $hf'Ag$ to fAg. But the probabilification of extrapolations of all types is subject to the same rule as was given earlier for the probabilification of the special type of extrapolation there considered. Namely, that they only possess any degree of probability at all when the degree of extrapolation is small, the former sinking rapidly to nothing as the latter increases; and that their degree of probability is always less than that of inductions in which there is no extrapolation. Viewing the same fact from a different aspect, the degree of probability of statements about the unobserved is partly determined by the nature of the population that they are about; any statement about a population comprising, say, future things or events being, so far as that goes, less probable than a statement about a population comprising only present things or events.

However, this thesis may be disputed. For some inductive philosophers and statisticians hold it possible to make probable assertions about infinite populations or open classes (e.g. the population of pressures at different points in the atmosphere) as well as about finite populations or closed classes (e.g. the population at present in London), and about hypothetical finite or infinite populations as well as about existent ones. (An example of an hypothetical infinite population is the population of possible throws with this die.) [Braithwaite, 126 ff.; Kneale, 173 ff.; Yule, 332 ff.] Indeed, are there not also inductive laws, a law of Nature being necessarily, not merely probable, but true as well as universal, in the sense of holding in all times, places and circumstances? [1.1]

I suggest that the proper reply to this objection is on the following lines. Sometimes we do indeed judge place or date to be certainly or probably inductively irrelevant, and generalize accordingly. But when we do so, we are just making a normal antecedent judgement of probable or certain irrelevance (cp. above). The objection to Keynes' uniformity principle is that he goes much too far in saying that we can always, as opposed to sometimes, disregard differences of place and date; and that he is mistaken in saying that we can do so *a priori* as opposed to from previous knowledge or belief. It seems to me, however, that we can never make such judgements of irrelevance in the case of future, as opposed to past or distant, things and events; and that this accounts for the commonsense conviction that assertions about the future are peculiarly precarious. On the view that I am now advancing, this conviction is grounded in the fact that such assertions are always extrapolations, and hence have no probability at all if the degree of extrapolation is at all large.

Again, the opinion that we really do make generalizations about infinite classes and things or events in all times, places and conditions, arises perhaps from too exclusive attention to the literal form of the statements. For if one attends to the way in which they actually work, paying especial attention to what count as exceptions to and confutations of the particular generalization in question, one commonly uncovers tacit qualifications to it.

One sort of tacit qualification affects the quantity of the generalization. Take the example, 'Man has ten toes'. A single freak born with more or less than ten toes is not held to constitute an exception to or demonstrative disproof of the generalization, because 'Man' really means, not 'All men', but something like 'All, or nearly enough all, men'.

Another sort of tacit qualification affects the scope of the generalization; in other words, another sort of conditions are tacit conditions. Thus, one who should adduce a number of men with amputated toes as exceptions to and disproof of the generalization would be thought to be, if not joking, absurdly literally-minded. For it contains of course the tacit condition 'naturally', in that sense of this ambiguous word which means 'originally', i.e. at birth. In this matter of universality, there is an interesting parallelism between generalizations and moral rules or principles. The question, Are there truly universal generalizations or inductive laws which hold good unconditionally? is in some respects significantly like the question, Are there truly universal moral rules or moral laws which do likewise?—as it might be, 'Never say what is false!' [Hare, 50 ff.; Strawson, 195 ff.]

One important consequence of the view here advocated about the probability of extrapolations, as opposed to inductions proper, is this. The degree of probability of some of our judgements about the unobserved depends, not only on the nature of the population that they are about, but also on our range of observation, particularly under experimental conditions. Thus, until recently, inferences about processes on the Sun involved a great degree of extrapolation, since the temperatures, pressures, etc., obtaining there far exceeded anything that men had ever observed. But now that Nuclear Physics and Engineering have brought within range of observation temperatures and pressures approaching those found on the Sun, these inferences have become inductions proper, not extrapolations, and are to that extent more probable. This illustrates another way in which the ability to make probable inductions increases as the boundaries of human knowledge and skill are expanded.

Next, invariability in respect of unknown conditions. All unknown conditions are strictly speaking invariable. One who was

attempting the impossible task of ensuring that there are no properties common to all the observed things or events, would have
to show that the pendulum formula e.g. holds true both when the
pendulums are electrically charged and when they are not. But
plainly, this elimination could not be deliberately contrived by an
investigator who was generalizing at a period when the concept
of electric charge had not yet been formed. Which illustrates yet
another way in which the capacity to make probable inductions
increases with the growth of human knowledge. For the more
possibly non-eliminable conditions we know, especially probably
relevant ones, the more we can deliberately eliminate.

The only way open to us of varying unknown conditions, on
the other hand, is simply to repeat the observations, or rather
experiments, a number of times. For we may at least *hope* that an
unknown condition which was present on some occasion will be
absent on some other, so that by this repetition we shall have acci-
dentally eliminated some condition, we know not what. But we
cannot rate the effectiveness of this resource more highly, and
claim that by making a number of experiments we *probably* eliminate unknown conditions, for reasons that I gave when criticizing
Keynes' moderated defence of Induction by Simple Enumeration.
[2.1] For it is no more true to say that a number of experiments on
the relation of periods of vibration to lengths of pendulums are
probably varied in respect of unknown conditions, than it is to
say that a number of observed BU are probably varied in respect of
unknown properties.

Finally, the difficulty about varying the conditions one at a
time. This rule has been called the fundamental rule of experimental method, and is consequently discussed in the literature in
connexion with the nature of experiment and its difference from
simple observation.

The point of the rule, as it affects induction, can be seen from
a consideration of the results of varying more than one condition
at a time. If the variation makes a difference, there is no telling
how properly to condition the generalization. Suppose (contrary
to fact) that it is found on varying the temperature that, at low
temperatures, the first of the two formulas for T quoted above, to
be called F, rightly describes the functional relationship between
period of vibration and length of pendulum; whereas at high temperatures the latter of the two formulas, to be called F', does so.

Now if, when the temperature has been increased, the length of the pendulum has also been increased, there is no telling whether the generalizations should rightly be: 'When the temperature is low (or high), then period and length are related by F (or F′)'; or 'When the pendulum is short (or long), then period and length are related by F (or F′)'; or 'When the temperature is low (or high) and the pendulum is short (or long), then period and length are related by F (or F′)'. On the other hand, if the variation makes no difference, it cannot be concluded that the generalization should be unconditioned. If (again contrary of course to fact), when the temperature has been high, the length of pendulum has been short, it cannot be concluded that the generalization should be unconditioned in these two respects. For it may be that variation of the one has counteracted and masked the relevance of variation of the other, so that the generalizations should properly be the conditioned ones: 'When the temperature is low (or high), then period and length are related by F (or F′)'; and 'When the pendulum is long (or short), then period and length are related by F (or F′)'.

As for the causes of failure to obey the rule, two are of present interest. The first is the existence of conditions which are not independently variable. The meaning of this is as follows: in the special and simplest case of attribute-conditions and contradictories, the conditions h and i are independently variable with respect to f when we can produce at will for observation the four possible combinations, ihf, $\bar{i}hf$, $i\bar{h}f$ and $\bar{i}\bar{h}f$. Independent variability of conditions must naturally be distinguished from plain variability of conditions. The chief reason why some conditions are not independently variable is that a change in one causes in another a change which can be neither prevented nor counteracted. Thus, at a primitive stage of technology, temperature and length of (metal) pendulums may not be independently variable because no way is known of preventing or counteracting their expansion when the temperature rises. Actually, this effect can either be (at least in principle) prevented by insulating the pendulum or, as is in fact done, counteracted by various devices, of which that embodied in the mercury compensated pendulum affords a familiar example.

The second cause is the practical impossibility of holding constant all conditions except the one being deliberately varied. That this is an unrealizable counsel of perfection can be simply illustrated from the existence of unknown conditions. For just as, strictly speaking, all unknown conditions are invariable conditions since their variation cannot be deliberately contrived, so they are also conditions which cannot be kept unvaried or constant, since this too cannot be deliberately contrived. Thus, in the pendulum experiment, one of the innumerable sets of conditions which ought in principle to be kept constant when the amplitude of vibration, say, is varied, is electromagnetic conditions. But manifestly this could not be done by, say, the early investigators of vibratory motion, whose knowledge of electromagnetic phenomena was restricted to a few generalizations about the properties of certain natural iron ores and of pieces of rubbed amber. Moreover, there is no rough and ready device for keeping all unknown conditions constant, corresponding to repetition as a device for varying them.

5.2.2 *Probability and Truth*

My next topic is the relations between probability and truth, and I shall begin by considering truth as the upper limit of probability. In discussing Russell's theory of inductive probability [4.2], we noticed that he holds that generalizations can only be in varying degrees probable and approach asymptotically to truth or certainty. This opinion is widely held, and Kneale e.g. writes: 'I have freely assumed . . . that the results of ampliative induction are only probable'. [Kneale, 113; Johnson, II, 240; Wisdom, 130 f.] Nevertheless, it is surely mistaken. For we do often call generalizations true or certain. As Hume says: 'One would appear ridiculous who would say, that it is only probable . . . that all men [must] die'. [Hume, T, 124]

The next question is, therefore, When are generalizations true? The answer is, I submit, that, like other contingent or synthetic propositions, generalizations are (properly called) true when and only when they correspond with the facts. It would be out of place to delve here into the exact meaning of 'correspondence with the facts': it is enough for now to say that it seems to me that it must be explained in terms of the basic notions of the correct use of words and arrangements of words for the purposes of referring to things and events and describing them. [J. L. Austin, 'Truth', *Aristotelian Society Sup. Vol. XXIV*, 1950] Correspondence with the facts, then, is the sufficient and necessary condition of a contingent proposition's truth.

But as well as the question, When is a generalization properly called true? there is the question, When is a generalization properly or justifiably claimed to be true? Here it is necessary to distinguish two cases. A generalization (G) is properly and not mistakenly claimed to be true when and only when the evidence for it is judged to be, and is, conclusive. On the other hand, G is properly but mistakenly claimed to be true when and only when the evidence for it is judged to be, but is not, conclusive. (Improper, as opposed to mistaken, claims do not concern us.)

It is in these answers to the second question that lies the connexion between truth and probability. For conclusive evidence, which is linked in the way described with truth, is the upper limit of (fairly, very, etc.) good evidence, which is similarly linked with probability. The essential resemblances and differences in these respects between truth and probability are apparent from the following summary: (a) The condition of truth: G is (properly called) true when and only when it corresponds with the facts. (b) Conditions of proper claims to truth: (i) G is properly and not mistakenly claimed to be true when and only when the evidence for it is judged to be, and is, conclusive; (ii) G is properly but mistakenly claimed to be true when and only when the evidence for it is judged to be, but is not, conclusive. (c) The condition of probability: G is (properly judged) probable when and only when the evidence for it is good. (d) Conditions of proper claims to probability: (i) G is properly and not mistakenly claimed to be probable when and only when the evidence for it is judged to be, and is, good; (ii) G is properly but mistakenly claimed to be probable when and only when the evidence for it is judged to be, but is not, good.

Thus, as, when we judge q to be good evidence for p, we properly claim that it probabilifies p; so when we judge it to be conclusive evidence for p, we properly claim that it verifies p. Hence, by analogy with the formula, $(2')$, $\gamma PF(fAg, f'Ag . \gamma C_2)$, we may write: $VF(fAg, f'Ag . \alpha C_2)$, where VF is read 'verifies'. As Woozley says: 'We do have conclusive evidence for a vast number of empirical propositions, singular, particular, and general, and when we have conclusive evidence for a proposition we know it to be true'. [Woozley, 192] Similarly, when we judge q to be conclusive evidence against p, i.e. for $\sim p$, we properly claim that it falsifies p. Verification and falsification are thus respectively the upper limits of the scales of probabilification and improbabilification, and both require conclusive evidence. The lower limit of the scale of probabilification, on the other hand, requires worthless evidence. When q is judged to be worthless evidence for p we say that it does not make p (in any degree) probable; and the not probable, it will be remembered, is different from the improbable. Accordingly, I write 'It is not (the case that it is) probable that p' as $\sim(\gamma P(p))$, but 'It is improbable that p' as $\gamma P(\sim p)$. There is a point about the meaning of 'not improbable' that deserves notice in passing. Namely, that there is one not uncommon use of it in which it means 'not not probable', i.e. 'probable'. Thus, 'It is not improbable that it will rain this afternoon' is often used to mean 'It is probable that it will rain this afternoon'. I think that it is the existence of this use which is partly responsible for the fairly frequent failure to distinguish between the improbable and the not probable.

The quotation from Woozley draws attention to the further undoubted fact that, when a generalization is judged to be conclusively evidenced and so true, we may properly claim to know it. But, I add, only then; when it is judged to be inconclusively though well evidenced and so probable, we say we believe it. This fits in with the view I advanced earlier [1.2], that 'believe', in its primary use, is the word we use for the manner in which we entertain propositions that we judge to be probable; as 'know', in the primary use of 'know that', is the word we use for the manner in which we entertain propositions that we take to be true. However, since there is no clearly defined border-line between very good evidence and the very probable on the one hand and conclusive evidence and the true on the other, neither is there one between the conditions in which we may claim to know a generalization and those in which we may rightly say only that we believe it.

Leibniz alleges the existence of '. . . two sorts of *knowledge* as there are two sorts of *proof*, one of which yields *certainty*, whereas the other only leads to *probability*'. [Leibniz, *Further Essays*, etc., p. 321] Lewis also speaks of 'probable knowledge'. [Lewis, 315 ff.] But the preceding discussion shows that this is an illogical expression: the 'objects of knowledge' are true propositions, not probable ones. I am further inclined to disagree with Leibniz about 'probable proof'. For we generally claim the fact that q empirically proves that p when q is judged to be conclusive evidence for, and so to verify, p. When q is judged to be inconclusive though good evidence for, and so to probabilify, p, we usually claim only that it tends to prove that p. But the qualification 'generally' is essential, since some legal systems recognize degrees of proof, and distinguish e.g. 'proof beyond reasonable doubt', where the evidence is conclusive, from 'proof by preponderance of evidence', where the evidence is inconclusive though good. I imagine that it is legal distinctions like this that Leibniz has in mind. In the same connexion, notice Hume's distinction between knowledge, proofs and probabilities: '. . . it would perhaps be more convenient, in order at once to preserve the common signification of words, and mark the several degrees of evidence, to distinguish human reason into three kinds, viz. *that from knowledge, from proofs and from probabilities.* By knowledge, I mean the assurance arising from the comparison of ideas. By proofs, those arguments which are derived from the relation of cause and effect [rather, 'of evidencing-statement and evidenced-statement'], and which are entirely free from doubt and uncertainty. By probability, that evidence which is still attended with uncertainty.' [Hume, T, 124] It will be seen that he is right about probability and proof, but wrong in confining knowledge to knowledge of necessary truths as opposed to truths without qualification. [1.2] It is of course understood that I am speaking of empirical proof and not of demonstrative proof as employed in Mathematics and Formal Logic.

I have spoken so far only of conclusive inductive evidence and inductive truth. But there are also conclusive casual and hypothetic evidence, and casual and hypothetic truth. Thus, the upper limit of the scale of casual probabilification is represented by the equivalent formulas $VF(gx, fAg . fx) \equiv 1PF(gx, fAg . fx)$, which should be compared with the formula $m/nPF(gx, f\ m/ng . fx . C_1)$. Two points in this call for comment. First, that the concept of casual truth is identical with that of casual probability in the degree 1. Second, that the condition of random selection, C_1, is superfluous in the case of casual primitive verification-judgements though not in the case of casual primitive probabilification-judgements.

As for hypothetic truths, 'historical facts' afford a familiar illustration. For, as Gardiner says, '. . . we should recognize that there are historical statements which have attained a status so strongly supported by evidence, and which are so necessary to account for the occurrence of other historical events, that to deny them would be equivalent to making nonsense of large portions of history. We can imagine what would be the effect of denying the existence of the Roman Empire. And there are other statements that are sufficiently well attested to make the denial of their truth an unwarrantable, though less catastrophic, undertaking. [E.g. 'Hitler is dead']. Common to both is the dependence of "the objectivity of historical facts" upon evidence.' [P. Gardiner, *The Nature of Historical Explanation*, Oxford, 1952, p. 80] Historical truths are normally, though not always, hypothetic truths, rather than, say, inductive truths. When they are inductive truths, they tend to be derivative rather than primitive. For they tend to be singular statements, whereas primitive inductions or generalizations logically must be general. [1.1] Thus Peirce: '. . . generally speaking, the conclusions of Hypothetic Inference cannot be arrived at inductively, because their truth is not susceptible of direct observation in single cases. . . . For instance, any historical fact, as that Napoleon Bonaparte once lived, is a hypothesis; we believe the fact, because its effects—I mean current tradition, the histories, the monuments, etc.—are observed. But no mere generalization of observed facts could ever teach us that Napoleon lived.' [Peirce, 199]

When we know contingent or empirical truths about matters which are not observed by means of the recognized senses, it is by inference, be it deductive, inductive, casual or hypothetic. Keynes calls such knowledge indirect, to distinguish it from that obtained by observation, which he calls direct. [Keynes, 12 ff.; Mill, 3] Earlier [1.2], I criticized the attempts of phenomenalists to assimilate direct knowledge to indirect by claiming that (true) observation-statements are (inconclusively) evidenced by 'sensation-reports'. But there is a converse fallacy which consists in mis-assimilating indirect knowledge to direct. It is involved in all claims to know the future, past, remote or hidden unobserved by pretended powers of foresight, hindsight, farsight or insight. A typical example is the thesis that we know others' inward states by 'extraspection'. [1.2]

The last is a philosophical thesis; but similar claims are made by e.g. seers and crystal-gazers. It is necessary to distinguish the

claims of these, who pretend to have direct knowledge of the unobserved, from those of professors of the pseudo-sciences of the
occult, e.g. augurs and diviners, who pretend to have indirect
knowledge of it; for they are sometimes confused. Kneale e.g.
writes: 'Even . . . crystal-gazers . . . and people who claim second
sight take laws for granted when they make their predictions.
Thus people who claim second sight assume some such law as that
all involuntary images occurring to a seventh child of a seventh
child of Highland ancestry are followed by similar percepts. If
there were direct perception of future events this would, indeed,
require no law as a premiss, but only because clairvoyance in this
sense (if there is such a sense) would be a kind of observation,
not a method of making inferences beyond the limits of observation. . . .' [Kneale, 45] Yet, for all its absurdity, the claim of the
seer and the crystal-gazer surely is precisely that he observes
future events now, even if only in a glass darkly. The augur or
diviner is an intellectually more respectable figure. He recognizes
that there is no way of acquiring direct knowledge about to-
morrow's battle, and that it can only be obtained indirectly from
evidences or signs and knowledge of generalizations. Where he
goes wrong is over his generalizations and what is evidence for
what; he is mistaken in thinking that thunder on the left is evidence at all, let alone good evidence, of an unfavourable issue to to-
morrow's fight. Therefore, he is a perverted or pseudo-scientist
rather than a scientist. But it is better to be a pseudo-scientist than
to be no sort of scientist at all, which is the case with the seer.

It is in Arts as in Sciences: the applied magician is a more respectable figure than the man who claims ability to work wonders
through the possession of supernatural powers. There is much
more to be said for the man who claims to be able to add a cubit to
his stature by eating spinach than for the man who claims to be
able to do the same by taking thought. The former may overrate
the nutritive powers of spinach; but at least he understands that
the only way to bring about this sort of desired event ('effect')
which cannot be directly induced is by inducing another sort of
event ('cause') which can be directly induced, and which is related
to the desired sort of event by a causal law. He has grasped that
'Nature to be commanded must be obeyed'. [Bacon, 259] Therefore, he is at least a pseudo-technician, whereas the other man is
no sort of artist at all.

Among the relations of probability to truth, truth as upper limit of the scale of degrees of probability is of most interest for the purposes of this inquiry. But the following further relations call for briefer notice. For a start, there are these fairly obvious and important resemblances. Both truth and probability are properties of propositions; true or probable are what propositions ought to be as false or improbable are what they ought not to be; and probability is regarded as being a good substitute or second-best for truth. I imagine that it is these basic similarities that Austin has in mind when he writes of 'It is true that . . .' and 'It is probable that . . .' being 'in the same line of business'. [Austin, *op. cit.*, p. 127] Those who, like Peirce and Keynes, hold probability to be primarily a property of inferences or implications, take a similar sort of view of the resemblances of probability to validity. I.e., they see 'probable inference' as a good substitute for valid inference, and 'probable implication' as the next best thing to plain implication.

Another important point of resemblance is one noticed earlier [1.2]. A synonym of 'probable' is 'verisimilar', and I suggested that the respect in which probable propositions are like true ones is that the assertion of both is justified or warranted. The expression 'warranted assertibility' is Dewey's, who employs it in connexion with his version of the Pragmatic Theory of Truth. [B. Russell, *Inquiry into Meaning and Truth*, pp. 318 ff.; 4.3] It is incidentally, pleonastic, since to call a proposition assertible is just to say that its assertion is warranted.

On the other hand, there are the following main differences between probability and truth. 'Probable' is always both descriptive and evaluative. It is descriptive solely in that to say $\gamma P(p)$ is to 'imply' that criteria are satisfied which probabilify p. 'True' is always descriptive; but it is also sometimes evaluative as well, namely, when p is claimed to be true because the evidence for p is judged to be conclusive. Hence, 'true' is always and primarily descriptive in that to say $T(p)$ is correct when and only when p corresponds with the facts. But 'true' is also sometimes and secondarily descriptive as well in that to say $T(p)$ is to 'imply' that criteria are satisfied which verify p. It will be remembered that, when criticizing Keynes and Johnson [4.2, end], I suggested that their erroneous belief in an ulterior problem of justifying inductions arises from their wrongly supposing 'probable' to be descriptive in the same sort of way that 'true' is primarily descriptive.

'Valid', to which as we have seen some misassimilate 'probable', resembles the latter at least in being evaluative. It may be asked: If 'valid' is evaluative and 'true' and 'false' are descriptive, is it not fallacious to define the former in terms of the latter, as we do when we say that an argument is valid if and only if the conclusion is true when the premiss is? But the reply to this objection is that this formula gives the descriptive part, not the whole, of the meaning of 'valid'. What is left out is of course the commendatory effect of calling a piece of reasoning valid.

Again, there are degrees of probability but not of truth, notwithstanding the contrary opinion of the Coherence Theorists. [H. H. Joachim, *The Nature of Truth*, Oxford, 1906, pp. 85 ff.] It is of some interest to speculate what sort of considerations may have led them to this opinion. One is, perhaps, that we do indeed say 'Very true'. But this locution does not serve to indicate a degree in the way that 'very probable' does. Its typical use is rather to indicate emphatic agreement with what another has said. I suspect that another cause is a confusion between: on the one hand, 'partly (not quite) true' as opposed to 'wholly (quite) true', and even (what is different) 'part of the truth' as opposed to 'the whole truth'; and on the other hand, 'fairly true' and 'in the highest degree true'. To illustrate these familiar distinctions. We ordinarily say that 'Jack and Jill went up the hill' is wholly true if both went up the hill, but partly true or a half-truth if one but not both did. To be sure, Formal Logic disagrees. In a well-known text we read: '. . . if either one of the conjuncts is false, the conjunctive proposition must itself be false. The conjunctive proposition must be regarded as a *single* proposition, and not as an *enumeration* of several propositions.' [M. Cohen and E. Nagel, *An Introduction to Logic and Scientific Method*, New York, 1934, p. 46] Nor is there any harm in this, provided it is clearly understood that the purposes for which all conjunctive propositions 'must' be so regarded are simply those of Formal Logic. Cp. Strawson's remarks on the differences, and resemblances, between 'colloquial conjunction' and the 'simple conjunction' of Formal Logic. [Strawson, 79 ff.] Again, we say that 'Tom took Dick's umbrella' is only part of the truth when the whole truth of the matter is expressed by the sentence 'Tom took Dick's umbrella in mistake for his own'.

Another difference relates to tense. We can say that it was, but is not, probable that p, and conversely. But we cannot say that it was, but is not, true that p; we have to say rather that it seemed to be, but actually was not and is not, true that p. Similarly, we can say that it was probable, but is true, that p; but not conversely. Cases in which we might say the former are: either when there was good evidence for p but now p can be observed to correspond with the facts; or when the evidence for p was good but is now conclusive. As we should expect, the expressions which go with 'true', namely 'conclusive evidence' and 'know', work in the same way in this respect. I cannot correctly say that the evidence for p was conclusive but is now inconclusive, or that I did know that p but now only believe it. I have to say rather 'seemed conclusive' and 'thought I knew'. [Woozley, 185 f.]

Yet another distinction turns on the different relations of probability and truth to possibility. We can say that it is probable that p yet possible that $\sim p$; but we cannot say that it is true that p yet possible that $\sim p$. Cp. Hume: '. . . there is no probability so great as not to allow of a contrary possibility; because otherwise it would cease to be a probability and become a certainty [truth]'. [Hume, T, 135] Again, we say that it is possible but not probable that p, but not that it is possible but false that p.

So much for the leading resemblances and differences between probability and truth: I turn now to other relations between them. First, the relation of being about: here, the possibilities are evidently probability-judgements about truth-judgements and truth-judgements about probability-judgements. I have discussed the former already [4.3], and pointed out that we do say $\gamma P(T(p))$ and that $\gamma P(T(p)) \equiv \gamma P(p)$. Russell concurs in this view: 'It seems to me that ""p" is probable" is strictly equivalent to ""p is true"" is probable". . . .' [Russell, *Inquiry*, p. 318] It will be remembered that I also said that, though I agreed about this equivalence, I did not agree with the Semantic Theorists that in general $T(p) \equiv p$, that to say 'It is true that p' is to say neither more nor less than 'p'. We can also say $T(\gamma P(p))$. Are we then to say analogously that $T(\gamma P(p)) \equiv \gamma P(p)$? I think not, since it seems to me that in this case the 'It is true that . . .' has a definite function or meaning, namely, the 'concessive' one noted by Strawson, in which it is equivalent to 'Admittedly' or 'To be sure'. E.g. 'It is true that he is in all probability a liar and a thief, but we cannot afford to be too selective about whom we employ nowadays'. [P. F. Strawson, 'Truth', *Arist. Soc. Sup. Vol. XXIV*, 1950]

Next, truth and probability are incompatible in the sense that they cannot both be predicated of the same proposition at the same time. I.e., it is illogical to say 'It is both true and probable that p'. But that they can sometimes be predicated of the same proposition at different times has just been noticed, as when we say that it was probable but is true that p. In the light of the foregoing discussion, the reasons for this incompatibility will be pretty clear. Thus, suppose first that my ground for saying p is true is that I can see that it corresponds with the facts. Then, in saying that p is both true and probable, I am 'implying' both that I can see that p is true and that I have good evidence that p is true. But if I can see that p is true, I have no need to bother with evidence for it, so that in this case the 'It is probable that . . .' is superfluous. Alternatively, suppose that my ground for saying p is true is that I judge the evidence for it to be conclusive. Then, in saying that p is both true and probable, I am 'implying' that the evidence for p is at the same time conclusive and inconclusive though good; which is to contradict myself.

Probability prerequires truth, and in this sense the latter is the more fundamental concept. Human information could consist of true propositions without any probable ones, but it could not consist of probable propositions without any true ones. Here again, the reasons are plain enough in view of what has been said before. In primitive probabilification-judgements, the probabilifying-proposition is a fact, i.e. a truth. The categorical type goes: 'The fact that q (i.e., the truth of q) makes it probable that p'. And the hypothetical type goes: 'If q (i.e., if q is true), that makes it probable that p'. Admittedly, in derivative judgements, the probabilifying-proposition must by definition contain at least one probability-judgement. But then, that judgement must be the probabilified-proposition of a primitive judgement the probabilifying-proposition in which is a fact or truth. This is a leading objection to the thesis, advanced by Reichenbach and some phenomenalists, that all contingent propositions are only in varying degrees probable and never true. The other and more obvious objection is that their theory is highly paradoxical, since we do in fact call a great many contingent propositions true.

Finally, if certain recent accounts of the meanings of 'true' and 'probable' are correct, there is an important resemblance between them in that they are both modal words. We have just noticed that Strawson distinguishes a use of 'true' in which 'It is true that *p*' means 'Admittedly *p*'; in which its function is to enable one to assert *p* concessively, i.e. in the mode or manner of one granting a point. Somewhat similarly, Toulmin argues that the use of 'probably' is to enable one to assert *p* guardedly, i.e. in the mode or manner of one wishing to avoid committing himself. As for Strawson's account, I agree that the use he distinguishes is one correct use of 'true', though I do not think it either the only or the primary use, as will be plain from what I have said above. I defer criticism of Toulmin's theory to 6.1. But it is desirable to state here that, since I disagree with it and do not accept that 'probable' is a modal word, I also do not accept that probability and truth are alike in being modal expressions.

5.2.3 *Probabilification, Verification and Significance*

It is a short step from truth to verification and verifiability, and some say that there is an important connexion between a statement's being verifiable and its being meaningful. I shall now consider very briefly what, if any, are the relations between the probabilifiability and verifiability of statements and their significance. A convenient point of departure is afforded by some remarks of Ayer's about 'strong and weak verifiability'. [Ayer, 9 ff.; M. Lazerowitz, 'Strong and Weak Verification', II, *Mind*, July 1950]

Ayer contends that a statement is literally meaningful if and only if it is either analytic or empirically verifiable. He adds that a statement is empirically verifiable when it is either strongly verifiable, meaning when its truth can be conclusively established in experience; or weakly verifiable, meaning when experience can probabilify it.

My criticisms of this thesis are as follows. It would be better to say that a statement is meaningful if and only if it is analytic or verifiable or probabilifiable than that it is meaningful if and only if it is analytic or strongly verifiable or weakly verifiable. For to speak of strong and weak verifiability is to abuse language. Our notion of verifiability is that a statement either can be verified or it cannot; there is no strongly, weakly, etc., about it. I suspect that the illogical notions of strong and weak verifiability were arrived at by confusing verifiability with evidencability. For it makes sense to speak of a statement as strongly or weakly evidencable or confirmable.

It would be better still to say that a statement is meaningful if and only if it is analytic or verifiable or evidencable. For 'probabilifiable', meaning 'well evidencable', is too narrow, and I think Ayer would wish to say that a statement is meaningful if it is evidencable at all, however poorly.

But it would be best of all, in my submission, to say that a statement (as opposed to a value-judgement, a command, a performative utterance, etc.) is otiose unless it is analytic or verifiable or evidencable. For a vital question in all this is, What is 'analytic or verifiable or evidencable' the test of? Not, in my view, of significance, because there are statements which are not analytic nor verifiable nor evidencable, but which are yet significant and intelligible in the normal senses of those terms. Consider e.g. the statement 'All lengths are contracting in the same ratio' made in circumstances in which it is neither verifiable nor evidencable. Certainly, there is something wrong with the statement; but what is wrong is not that it is meaningless. It is perfectly intelligible, and one can even 'imagine what it would be like for it to be true'.

J. L. Evans, whose main criticism of the Verifiability Principle is directed towards this point, suggests that what 'verifiable or evidencable' is really the test of is, not the meaningfulness, but the empiricalness of a statement. I.e., that a statement is an empirical statement if and only if it is verifiable or evidencable. His actual words are: '. . . its content should be verifiable . . . by the senses, or . . . some sense observations [should] be relevant to determining its truth or falsity'. [J. L. Evans, 'On Meaning and Verification', *Mind*, January 1953, p. 16] But this is equivalent to my 'verifiable or evidencable', since in this context '*q* is relevant to the truth or falsity of *p*', means '*q* is evidence for or against (the truth of) *p*'.

However, this will not do either, because there is an important class of evidencable statements which are non-empirical, namely, those which express non-empirical theories or transcendent hypotheses. What 'analytic or verifiable or evidencable' is the test of is, to repeat it, whether or not a statement has a point. The specimen statement above about contracting lengths is, in the circumstances stated, neither meaningless nor non-empirical; it is futile or functionless. Similarly with transcendent hypotheses. The essential difference between e.g. the atomic theory of Democritus and Leucippus and the atomic theory of Chemistry of Dalton and Avogadro is that the latter is evidencable or testable whereas the former is not. But we do not on this account say either that the latter is significant whereas the former is not, or that the latter is empirical whereas the former is not: both are intelligible and non-empirical. What we do say is that the latter is a working hypothesis whereas the former is an idle speculation. The sort of statements that the Logical Positivists wish to exorcize by means of the Verifiability Principle are surely those which are normally called, not metaphysical, but pointless.

It is impossible for primitive inductions to be idle in this sense. For a generalization logically must be a generalization from its corresponding description, i.e. must be (inductively) evidenced and so evidencable. If I assert that fAg without having observed a single instance that is both f and g, my general statement is not a generalization. Generalizations are exposed to the danger of being rash or wild, but not of being idle. But it is otherwise with hypotheses. For it is perfectly possible for a man to frame an hypothesis, whether empirical or non-empirical, before he has any evidence for or against it, and only look for evidence for or against it afterwards. This is why hypothetic inference is sometimes called anticipation or presumption of fact. Hence, it is possible to invent an unevidencable and hence otiose theory. Even so, I think that very often and usually one possesses evidence for it before making a supposition. It is most unusual for detectives, e.g., to start their inquiries with a theory: it sometimes happens indeed that they hit upon a theory very early in the investigation; but it is surely truistic that there is some looking at the facts first. When this is so, these facts serve simultaneously both the psychological purpose of suggesting the hypothesis and the epistemological purpose of evidencing or confirming it. Now in induction the observed facts always serve simultaneously the dual purpose of suggesting and supporting the generalization. When I take a sample of varied BU, observe its composition, and judge that the population probably has the same composition, I simultaneously discover what the composition of the population is and prove that it has that composition. So that the resemblances and differences between inductive and hypothetic inference in this respect are these: both are methods of discovery as well as of proof; but whereas in induction the two processes are simultaneous, in hypothetic inference they are not. For some of the evidence for or against the hypothesis is always sought after the making of the supposition, irrespective of whether or not evidence has also been considered before making it.

5.2.4 *Inductive* vs. *Hypothetic Inference and Probability*

This brings me to my final topic, the relations between inductive inference and probability on the one hand and hypothetic inference and probability on the other. It will be remembered that, in earlier discussions [1.1, 1.2], I argued two main theses. First and constructively, that inductive and hypothetic probability have distinct descriptive meanings, because primitive inductive and primitive hypothetic probabilification-judgements are of quite different types. Second and critically, that it is false that there is no difference between inductive and hypothetic inference, as is claimed both by inductivists who represent hypothetic inference as 'hypothetic induction', and by hypothetists who represent inductive inference as being 'really' hypothetic inference. I now subjoin some additional remarks to complete my account of this matter.

The theses to be criticized are four. (*a*) There is no induction and consequently no inductive probability; (*b*) There is no induction in science; (*c*) Inductive inference is (really) hypothetic inference; and (*d*) Hypothetic inference is (a sort of) inductive inference. We will take them in order.

As to (*a*): 'Induction', Mill writes, 'may be summarily defined as Generalisation from Experience'. [Mill, 200] I said at the beginning of this book that this seems to me an acceptable account of the meaning of primitive induction. But now, coolly considered, it is surely not only false but highly paradoxical to deny the very existence of so familiar an operation as generalization from experience? If there is no such thing, why does our language contain the word 'generalization'? Cp. my objection, above, to those who say that there is no (contingent) truth, only degrees of probability. Similarly with the second half of the thesis: there is surely nothing more familiar and incontrovertible than that some generalizations are (called) probable.

When philosophers propound theses that are clearly paradoxical, it is generally instructive to look for the reasons or causes of their doing so. In this case, I believe the paradoxes just mentioned to derive from the dogma that there is one, unique method of discovery and empirical proof; namely, the method of hypothesis. Thus, Dewey canonizes the pattern of all thinking or inquiry and of all empirical proof in the following 'five logically distinct steps: (i) a felt difficulty; (ii) its location and definition; (iii) suggestion of possible solution (i.e. hypothesis); (iv) development by reasoning of the bearings of the suggestion; (v) further observation and experiment leading to its acceptance or rejection. . . .' [J. Dewey, *How We Think*, Boston, 1910, p. 72] A surprising number of philosophers seem to agree with him on this point. But if one does take this view, it is easy to see that one will naturally conclude to thesis (*c*) and thence in turn to thesis (*a*). However, the underlying dogma about there being a unique method of discovery and proof is simply untrue. Indeed, even on the face of it, it would be surprising if human ingenuity were restricted to this single resource. And the contention in (*c*), that generalization is really hypothetic inference, reminds one of the thesis that there is no such thing as description, what appears to be such being really the more sophisticated operation of interpretation.

Turning now to (*b*), the first point to notice is that the thesis rests on what is taken to be the meaning of 'science'. Braithwaite e.g. writes: '. . . it is this hypothetico-deductive method applied to empirical material which is the essential feature of a science; and if psychology or economics can produce empirically testable hypotheses, *ipso facto* they are sciences. . . .' [Braithwaite, 9] I.e., the employment of this method is the sufficient and necessary condition of an inquiry's (being said to) form part of a science. I fancy that other philosophers would restrict themselves to saying that it is a necessary condition of it.

But this thesis too is untenable. The employment of hypothetic inference is not a sufficient condition for an inquiry forming part of a science, because historians e.g. regularly use it, and History is not Science. True, it has long been fashionable to call the sort of history written in the West in modern times 'scientific'; but even so 'scientific history' is still History and not Science.

It is not a necessary condition either; for there are studies which employ predominantly inductive rather than hypothetic inference, but which are yet called sciences. The expression, 'the inductive sciences', is neither illogical nor inapplicable. A case in point is biological science, on which Woodger writes as follows. After distinguishing 'two primary kinds of explanation which we can call (1) Perceptual, in which the relata are perceived entities; and (2) Conceptual, in which the relata are not perceived entities', he continues: 'Now in biology in the strict sense (i.e. where we are dealing with entities above the chemical level of organization) most of our explanations belong to the first type in the form of so-called empirical laws. And it is worth while mentioning in passing that it is a mistake to despise empirical laws of this kind, and to regard them as something inferior as compared with the so-called exact laws of physics which involve hypothetical imperceptibles'. [J. H. Woodger, *Biological Principles*, London, 1929, p. 454] By 'empirical laws' he means of course 'generalizations'.

The contentions that the presence of hypothetic inference is a necessary, or the sufficient and necessary, condition of the presence of a science, only proves that there is no induction in science if the presence of hypothetic inference is incompatible with the presence of inductive inference. And I think that hypothetists do in fact take this for granted. But their assumption is false, since some sciences contain both hypotheses and generalizations. E.g., all sciences which contain non-empirical theories not merely do but logically must contain generalizations and inductive laws as well, since the *raison d'être* of the former is precisely to explain the latter.

Here again, then, it may prove illuminating to inquire into the reasons why men hold thesis (*b*). The first presumably corresponds to the first reason noted in the case of thesis (*a*); namely, the dogma that there is in science one, unique method of discovery and proof, the method of hypothesis. But the belief in *the* scientific method is as false and implausible as the belief in *the* method of inquiry or thinking.

Another reason probably is overlooking the fact that the sciences have a history, and consequently forming one's view of the nature of science from considering them in the highest stage of their development, when abstract theory admittedly predominates. This point is well put by Eaton: 'In studying the logic of the natural sciences, we tend to forget that they have a history. The cruder phases of this history are discarded as superstition or error.

In a highly integrated science, like modern physics, a single observation or experiment—a shift in the spectral lines of the light from a remote star—may establish an important result. The scientist does not seriously consider that sheer repetition of experiments, beyond two, three, or a dozen trials to eliminate possible errors, contributes much to the solidity of the theory tested by them. The corroborating weight of numbers of instances becomes less relevant as science passes beyond the elementary stages. . . . Behind this later, secondary phase of induction lies an earlier one. This is the phase of simple generalization from experience. Having observed that many particulars presenting some character C also present another character C', we conclude that all particulars of the type C are of the type C'; all swallows fly northward in summer and southward in winter. Such a generalization is a small fragment of natural science; and all natural sciences, even the most complex and closely knit, begin in this simple way'. [Eaton, 484 f.]

To this I would add that another reason, besides overlooking the early stages of the sciences, is overlooking the less advanced sciences. All too many philosophers of science form their view of the nature of science generally from an examination of modern Physics. In which connexion, I suggest that, though the presence of theory, or to be exact, of non-empirical theory, is not the or a test of the presence of science, it is *a* test or necessary condition of a science's being called 'advanced'. Not *the* test, however, because some sciences which employ non-empirical theory are nevertheless not called advanced. Freud's theory of the mind is a case in point. The essential feature of advancedness that it lacks is, perhaps, the employment of measurement and calculation.

Again, it may well be that, in advancing thesis (*b*), philosophers are in effect giving stipulated or persuasive definitions of 'science'. But persuasive definitions are never in order. And stipulated definitions are not in order here. For 'science' is a non-specialist word, not a philosophical term of art. In other words, what is or is not science is for the public, not for the philosopher, to decide; the philosopher's task is to describe systematically what the public does decide. As for the possibility of a persuasive definition of 'science', the question which presents itself is, Why should philosophers want to persuade us to this view of the nature of science? I imagine the underlying thought is something like this.

Science is a great and good thing, and non-empirical theorizing is a great and good thing too; whereas generalizing from experience is rather Earth-bound and unexciting. So that the abstract theoretical phase of science is the only part of science that is *real* science, the inductive and descriptive phases being 'pre-scientific' or 'mere natural history'.

I suppose that most agree, more or less, with the preceding judgements on the value of science and of abstract theory. But I am unable to agree with the depreciation of empirical generalization. And it is worth while pointing out one not unimportant respect in which induction is more important than theory. Namely, that whereas the former is essential to any degree of civilization, the latter is not. The proof of which is, that though all known civilized societies have had their stocks of generalizations, non-empirical scientific theories are a novelty that have been possessed by only one civilization, the Western, and that only in the last 300 odd years of its existence. Cp. the ground on which Bacon values empirical generalizations or 'middle axioms' as opposed to descriptions on the one hand and abstract theoretical principles on the other: 'For the lowest axioms differ but slightly from bare experience, while the highest and most general (which we now have) are notional and abstract and without solidity. But the middle are the true and solid and living axioms, on which depend the affairs and fortunes of men. . . .' [Bacon, 290] And so they are.

Finally, theses (*c*) and (*d*). That these are false I have tried to show in the earlier discussions, and shall accordingly proceed to consider what may have induced men to believe them. For a start, I imagine, the simple fact that both inductions and hypotheses are (called) probable. More exactly, the position is that some, but not all, inductions are in some degree probable or improbable, others being true, or false, or neither probable nor improbable; and that some, but not all, probable propositions are inductions, others being casual propositions, or hypotheses. But from the facts that some inductions and some hypotheses are probable propositions, it follows neither that all inductions are (really) hypotheses, nor conversely.

Again, I suspect that the misassimilation of hypothetic to inductive inference is related as effect, or cause, to the practice of speaking of the former as 'secondary induction'. Thus, in

T   273

discussing the relation between induction and the hypothetical method, Kneale writes: 'The best convention is perhaps to extend the use of the word "induction" to cover the hypothetical method but at the same time to distinguish this new application of the term by adding the adjective "secondary" '. [Kneale, 104, 246 ff.; Eaton, 501] The same applies to other locutions, such as Peirce's 'hypothetic induction' as opposed to plain 'induction', and Whewell's 'induction of laws of causes' as opposed to 'induction of laws of phenomena'. [Whewell, 95 ff., 431 ff.]

This use of 'secondary induction' is distinct from Nicod's, which I discussed earlier. [1.1] For Nicod means by a secondary induction an induction the evidencing-statement of which contains an induction, i.e. what I call a derivative induction. But Kneale's secondary inductions are avowedly hypotheses, i.e. not inductions at all.

Contrary to the convention which Kneale recommends, it seems to me desirable to distinguish sharply between empirical generalization and theory in science. Indeed, many and perhaps most philosophers do so distinguish the two phases, stages or levels of scientific explanation. For it is to be understood that we are here concerned more especially with non-empirical theories. And that a non-empirical theory, such as Dalton's atomic theory, logically cannot be a thing of the same sort as an empirical generalization, such as the chemical law of definite proportions, which is a typical inductive or empirical law, is evident. But apart from this, any supposition, empirical or non-empirical, is *ipso facto* very different from any generalization, empirical or non-empirical. It will be remembered that the existence of non-empirical generalizations was noticed earlier in connexion with the part played by generalization in Pure Mathematics. [1.1]

Finally, I suggest that the temptation to assimilate hypothetic to inductive inference or conversely arises from a feature of scientific explanation already commented on. [2.2, 4.2] Namely, that generalizations are explained, sometimes by wider generalizations, and sometimes by theories. The explanation of the generalization that all whales are vertebrates by the generalization that all mammals are vertebrates illustrates the former mode of explanation: the explanation of the law of definite proportions by the atomic theory illustrates the latter. What is traditionally called, after Whewell and Mill, 'the consilience of inductions', embraces both modes. [Kneale, 106 ff.] But it is plausible to suppose that, men having noticed that generalizations and theories have in common the supremely important function of explaining other generalizations, they erroneously concluded that there is no difference between them.

The quarrel between the inductivists and the hypothetists has a fairly long history, which is clearly traced by Lalande. [Lalande, esp. 83 ff., 146 ff.] In the inductivist camp are ranged Bacon, Newton, Hume, Comte, Mill and Mach; in the hypothetist camp, Leibniz, Huyghens, Whewell, Jevons, Poincaré and Popper. Inductivism, or the inductive interpretation of science, is associated with empiricism and positivism. We saw earlier [1.1] that the inductive interpretation of science tends to be misleadingly called the descriptive interpretation. Hypothetism, or the hypothetic interpretation of science, on the other hand, is associated with rationalism and transcendentalism. The views of the arch-rationalist Leibniz and of the Kantian Whewell are revealing in this regard. [Leibniz, 261 ff.; Whewell, 36 ff.] In the last forty years, Hypothetism has been in the ascendant. I think that this is due to the facts that Inductivism has had no first-rate exponents since Mach and Pearson, and that leading philosophers of science in recent years, e.g. Poincaré and Popper, have been hypothetists; sometimes indeed, as in the case of the latter, extravagantly so.

Two arguments additional to those reviewed earlier, which are used by inductivists and hypothetists respectively, are these. Some inductivists object to non-empirical hypotheses on the ground that theoretical terms are meaningless. It is on this ground that Comte, e.g., disallows the hypothesis of a luminiferous ether. But the objection rests on the relational theory of meaning, i.e. the theory that the meaning of a word is the thing it stands for. So that if there is no (observable) thing that 'luminiferous ether' stands for, the expression is meaningless. But since the theory does not, and is nowadays generally agreed not to, provide an acceptable account of the meaning of words, this objection to transcendent hypotheses fails.

For their part, hypothetists are fond of quoting a remark of Darwin's: 'How odd it is that anyone should not see that all observation must be for or against some view if it is to be of any service!' [C. Darwin, *Letters*, Vol. I, p. 195] I.e., any description or observation-statement that is not evidence for or against a theory ('view') is useless. But this is quite plainly false. For one thing, a description may be useful when it constitutes evidence for an induction. If I want to know what proportion of BU are H, my observation that one fifth of this handful are, is useful as evidence that one fifth of the population are. For another, an observation may be useful, not because it is either hypothetic or inductive evidence for or against some proposition, but in itself. If I want to know the time, my observation that Big Ben is striking noon is useful. Possibly there is an elementary confusion here between being evidence for or against some theory and being an answer to some question or a solution of some problem. Naturally, my observation of Big Ben is useful only if I am interested in the question what time it is. But being interested in the question what time it is is quite a different thing from entertaining some supposition about what the time is.

In truth, the whole controversy has generated more heat than light through the tendency of both parties to adopt extreme positions. The inductivists began it by advancing the extreme thesis that inductive inference is *the* method of scientific discovery and proof, so that 'Inductive Logic' (better, Inductive Philosophy) is coextensive with Philosophy of Science. The hypothetists retorted with the equally extreme antithesis that hypothetic inference is *the* method of scientific discovery (better, invention) and proof, so that there is no inductive inference in science and Inductive Philosophy is excluded from Philosophy of Science. The true account of the matter is more moderate. Inductive inference is employed in the early phase of science, and hypothetic inference is employed predominantly in the later phase. Hence, there is a partial overlap between Inductive Philosophy and Philosophy of Science: the common ground might be called 'the philosophy of the inductive phase of the sciences'. The part of Philosophy of Science excluded from Inductive Philosophy is everything relating to scientific observation and description on the one hand and to scientific theory on the other. And the part of Inductive Philosophy excluded from Philosophy of Science is everything relating to induction when performed by non-scientists. For men of science, after all, have no monopoly of generalization from experience: it is, as Hume emphasizes, a thing that we are all constantly doing.

Since inductive and hypothetic inference afford alternative

methods of explanation, discovery or invention, and proof, it may be asked, When do we employ the one and when the other? I will conclude by making two points about this. First, when the object is to give a non-empirical explanation, as in the advanced stage of scientific investigation, the method of hypothesis logically must be employed. For a theoretical principle, such as 'All matter has an atomic structure', logically cannot be a generalization, since it is by definition about unobservable theoretical entities, e.g. atoms. Hence, there can be no description to serve as evidencing-statement for the corresponding generalization, as it might be 'All observed matter has an atomic structure'.

Second, if the object is to discover and establish an empirical proposition, hypothetic inference is inappropriate unless there are known to be certainly or probably only a small number of possible alternative explanations. [5.1] When the detective has succeeded in narrowing down the field of possibly guilty men to a few suspects, it may be reasonable for him to proceed by supposing that each suspect committed the crime, working out the implications of each hypothesis, and seeing whether observation squares with these implications. But it will not be a sensible course for him to take when there is still all the world for him to choose from. Consider from this point of view my stock illustrations of the composition of BU and the functional relationship between period of vibration and length of pendulum. If BU are numerous, there are a very large number of possible compositions of that population. And the number of possible functional relationships between T and l is indefinitely large. Now, it would admittedly be possible to proceed by supposing that the composition is 76% H, or the relationship $T = \sqrt[3]{l/g}$; and then, if the evidence turns out to be unfavourable to these suppositions, making other ones . . . and so on, until we hit on an hypothesis that the facts do support. But in view of the number of the possible hypotheses, it obviously would not be a sensible course to pursue. We must rather employ subject-predicate and functional generalization respectively. It is just this sort of case which shows up most clearly the extravagance of the hypothetist position and the impracticability of the precept, 'Always begin with a theory, never with the facts!'

6 INDUCTIVE REASONING
AND INDUCTIVE LOGIC

6.1 INDUCTIVE PROBABILIFICATION-JUDGEMENT AND REASONING

6.1.1 *Positive Consideration of the Question*

What are the relations of inductive probabilification-judgement to reasoning? It must be recognized for a start that, since 'reasoning' and judgements of the form 'The fact that q makes (or would make) it probable that p' are expressions in ordinary use, the question is about what we rightly say: it is not to be settled by stipulated or persuasive definitions of 'reasoning'. And inductive probabilification-judgement is undoubtedly (called) reasoning. I pointed out earlier [1.2] that 'The fact that q makes it probable that p' is equivalent to 'Since q it is probable that p', and that 'q makes it probable that p' (e.g. 'The presence of dark clouds makes it probable that it will rain shortly') is equivalent to 'If q it is probable that p'. And I shall argue shortly that this is why categorical and hypothetical probabilification-judgements are called reasoning.

Induction too is (called) reasoning, and for a similar reason. For I also pointed out earlier [1.2] that 'Since q, p' sometimes means 'The fact that q is evidence that p', and that 'If q, p' sometimes means 'If q that is evidence that p'. And I shall argue shortly that this is why categorical and hypothetical evidential-statements are called reasoning.

When philosophers speak of 'inductive reasoning (or inference)', it is often unclear whether they mean induction or inductive probabilification-judgement; I mean by it the former, never the latter. The name indeed appears to be a semi-technical term of Philosophy. Its first appearance, so far as I can discover, is in Aristotle, who uses ὁ ἐξ ἐπαγωγῆς συλλογισμὸς as a synonym of ἐπαγωγή. [Aristotle, 512] The Epicureans' corresponding technical term is ἐπιλογισμος. [Philodemus, 154] Naturally, induction and inductive probabilification-judgement are not the only sorts of reasoning; there are also deduction, casual and hypothetic inference, and casual and hypothetic probabilification-judgement.

The feature common to all these modes of inference, and that which gives the essential meaning of 'reasoning', is simply this. Very roughly speaking, we have a piece of reasoning, inference or argument when and only when some proposition is given as actual or possible reason for some proposition called the conclusion. 'Reason' and 'conclusion' are correlative terms. 'p for the reason that q' is expressed in a variety of equivalent ways using familiar connectives, such as 'p because q', 'q, therefore p' and 'Since q, p'; and since we often reason from possible rather than actual reasons, there must be added 'If q, p'. This feature is common to all these modes of inference, and it is on this account that they are all called reasoning.

More interesting than this resemblance are the differences, and I shall now indicate the essential distinctions between inductive inference and probabilification-judgement on the one hand and deductive inference on the other. First, as to reasons. In deduction, the reason is a premiss, whereas in induction it is an evidencing-statement and in inductive probabilification-judgement it is a probabilifying-proposition. And these all differ in obvious ways. Thus, a premiss logically must entail, or at least purport to entail, the conclusion; and a probabilifying-proposition logically must probabilify, or at least purport to probabilify, the conclusion. But an evidencing-statement does not do or purport to do either of these things; they are moreover quite different things. Yet the fact that all three are called 'reasons' has caused them to be confused, and I shall discuss later the important confusion implicit in speaking of a premiss as 'demonstrative evidence' for its conclusion. [6.2]

Again, I pointed out earlier [1.2] that probabilification-judgements are elliptical, in that they tacitly involve evidential-evaluations. 'The fact that q makes it probable that p' goes when made fully explicit 'The fact that q is good evidence that p makes it probable that p'. Now, 'good evidence' is commonly spoken of as 'good reason'. But a premiss is not (rightly called) a good reason, or for that matter a bad reason either. It is simply a reason.

Second, as to conclusions. In deduction, the conclusion is a logical consequence, whereas in induction it is an evidenced-statement and in inductive probabilification-judgement it is a probabilified-proposition. And these again are all quite different. But the differences between the three modes of inference most clearly appear from a contrast of the relations between reason and conclusion in the three cases.

Thus, in deduction this relation is implication, in virtue of which the argument primarily, and the conclusion secondarily, are called valid. In induction, on the other hand, the relation is evidencing; and in inductive probabilification-judgement it is probabilification, in virtue of which the conclusion is called probable. Once again, these are all different. Nevertheless, I have pointed out the existence of misassimilations between some of them that are highly significant for the Philosophy of Probability. Notably, Peirce and Keynes, in contending that 'probabilification' means 'partial implication', patently misassimilate probabilification to implication. Consequently, too, they misassimilate 'probable' to 'valid'. For it is a natural consequence of their type of theory that, as when q implies p, p is valid; so when q 'partially implies' (i.e. probabilifies) p, p is 'partially valid' (i.e. probable). So that the essence of this view may be rendered: 'probability' means 'partial validity'. But as against such views, it will be enough to indicate and/or recapitulate two vital differences between probabilification and probability on the one hand and implication and validity on the other.

First, probabilification and implication are different types of relation. As we saw earlier [1.2], probabilification is of the type which holds between a value-judgement and the factual statement that is given as a reason for it; but in implication both of the related terms are of the same sort, i.e. both factual statements, or both value-judgements, etc. It may be objected, however, that both probabilification and implication are actually of the former type. For it may be urged that, just as a categorical inductive probabilification-judgement may be rendered e.g. 'All observed BU are H and varied ∴ "All BU are H" is probable'; so a categorical deductive argument may be rendered e.g. 'All BU are

H ∴ "Some H are BU" is valid'. So that in the latter case too the conclusion is after all a value-judgement, since a validity-judgement is every bit as evaluative as is a probability-judgement. But there is a reply to this objection. Namely, that this proposed rendering of a typical categorical deductive argument will not do. The argument must rather be rendered: '"Some H are BU" is a valid conclusion from "All BU are H"'. And this brings out the essential point, that the conclusion is not a validity-judgement, although the whole utterance is.

Second, the tests of validity and inductive probability are different. A (deductive) argument is valid when the conjunction of the premiss with the contradictory of the conclusion is inconsistent: the specimen deductive argument just mentioned is valid because (*a*) 'All BU are H but no H are BU' is inconsistent. Hume first pointed out that inductive arguments do not meet this test. 'All observed BU are H ∴ all BU are H' is not valid because (*b*) 'All observed BU are H but some BU are not H' is not inconsistent. [Hume, E, 33 ff.] But what is of greater interest to us is the fact that inductive probabilification-judgements do not meet this test either. Consider the conjunction (*c*) 'All observed BU are H and varied but it is not probable that all BU are H'. This is like (*a*) and unlike (*b*) in being illogical, so that one may jump to the conclusion that the tests of validity and inductive probability are the same. But closer scrutiny reveals a crucial difference between the illogicalities involved in (*a*) and (*c*) respectively, which may be brought out in this way. Of a man who asserted (*a*), it might truly be said that he did not know the meanings of the 'logical words' involved, namely 'all' and 'no'. But of a man who asserted (*c*) it might truly be said, not that he did not know the meaning of 'all', but that he did not know the meaning of 'probable' as applied to generalizations.

Conversely, and more obviously, the tests of the probability of generalizations are not the tests of the validity of deductions. The conditions C_2 and C_3 have no application to deduction at all. Connected with this is another evident difference. 'All BU are H' can alone serve as (deductive) reason for 'Some H are BU'. But 'All observed BU are H' cannot alone serve as reason for 'All BU are probably H'; the reason must rather be 'All observed BU are H and varied'.

6.1.2 *Criticism of some Other Views*

I pass now to some critical comments on Hume, Mill, Price and Toulmin, which are directed towards what these authors say about inductive probability and reasoning.

The following remarks on Hume's philosophy of probability supplement those which I made earlier. [1.2, 4.2] They are addressed particularly to what he says about 'probable reasoning' and feeling, and to the connected topics of probabilification-judgement and meaning. The gist of my criticism of his theory is that it is anti-rational.

We have seen that Hume explains the meaning of 'degree of probability' as 'degree of belief', and explains the meaning of the latter in turn as 'degree of intensity of feeling of conviction'. It results that he explains the meaning of 'probable' without reference to probabilification-judgement and reasoning at all. For on Hume's view the meaning of 'probable', as of any other word, is the 'idea' that it stands for, and to explain its meaning is primarily to locate and identify the idea that it does stand for. [Hume, E, 21 f.; Locke, 225 ff.] In the case of probability, he locates its meaning in the 'inward idea' or feeling of conviction or expectation. His programme of hunting for the idea or meaning is actually more evident in his inquiry into necessity than in that into probability. It is here that he makes the point that the idea or meaning exists only 'in the mind', or is an 'inward idea', there being no necessary connexion between events in 'the external world'. But all this applies equally well to his view of probability; indeed, he holds that the only difference between the meanings of probability and necessity resides in the greater degree of intensity of the idea of the latter. In fine, Hume maintains that the meaning of $\gamma P(p)$ is 'I (the speaker) feel sure that p'; and no consideration of the reasons why, or what brings it about that, p is probable enters into his account. But here I differ from him fundamentally. For the essence of my view is that the (descriptive) meaning of 'probable' must be explained in terms of reasons or criteria, or in other words, that the meaning of 'probable' can only be explained by a consideration of probabilification-judgements.

It may be said, however, that Hume's and Locke's notion of explaining the meaning of a word goes beyond just identifying the idea that it stands for, and includes a consideration of how we get or come by the idea. This is true, and most of Hume's discussion of probability and necessity is in fact concerned with just this question. As I said earlier [1.2], it is in this way that he distinguishes different kinds of probability. The distinction between e.g. his 'probability of chances' and his 'probability of causes' resides in the different ways in which the feeling of conviction originates. But this does not save his theory from the charge of anti-rationalism. For saying what are the causes that make me feel sure that p is not the same thing as saying what are the reasons that make it probable that p. Consequently, Hume's way of distinguishing different kinds of probability in terms of difference in origin of the meaning or idea, is different from my way of distinguishing different (descriptive) meanings of 'probable' in terms of difference in criteria of probability-judgements.

Nevertheless, certain circumstances which are causes of the feeling of conviction happen also to be criteria of the probability of propositions. This is why Hume's account of the former matter reads like a plausible account of the latter matter. The circumstances in question are the number and proportion of the observed instances. We have seen [2.1] that the number of the observed instances has a definite, if very limited, probabilificatory power in respect of subject-predicate generalizations. But the same circumstance is also a cause of expectation. Thus, Mace contrasts the psychological 'principle of associative belief' with the logical 'principle of induction' formulated by Russell in his *Problems of Philosophy*, in the following terms: 'In the case of associative belief, the more frequent the co-presentation [of f and g] the more confident is the expectation [that the next f will be g]. In the case of the principle of induction, as formulated by Russell, the more frequent the co-presentation, the more probable the conclusion [that the next f will be g].' [Mace, 266; 4.2] Similarly with the proportion of f' that are g. We have seen [2.2] that this is a determinant, in the sense of a test, of the probability that the next f will be g; but it is also a determinant, in the sense of a cause, of the degree of confidence with which the next f is expected to be g.

Hume's doctrine involves the following accounts of the meanings of 'to evidence' and 'to make probable', of 'evidence' and 'good evidence'. He holds in effect that $E(p, q)$ means 'The fact that q suggests to me (the speaker), or leads me to believe, that p'; and that $\gamma PF(p, q)$ means 'The fact that q strongly suggests to me (the speaker), or leads me firmly to believe, that p'. Analogously, he holds that 'Since q, necessarily p' means 'The fact that q irresistibly suggests to me (the speaker), or leads me unshakeably to believe, that p'. He consequently holds 'an evidence' to mean 'that which suggests something to somebody, or makes somebody believe something'. This is clear from his second definition of 'a cause'; for it will be remembered that he regularly talks of cause and effect when he means sign and significate: 'A *cause* is an object precedent and contiguous to another, and so united with it that the idea of the one determines the mind to form the idea of the other, and the impression of the one to form a more lively idea of the other'. [Hume, T, 170] Consequently, too, he holds that 'a good (piece of) evidence' means 'that which strongly suggests something to somebody, or leads someone firmly to believe something'. Similarly he takes 'a thing evidenced' to mean 'that which is suggested to somebody by something, or a belief'; as witness his definition of 'a belief': 'An opinion, therefore, or belief, may be most accurately defined, *a lively idea related to or associated with a present impression*'. [Hume, T, 96] Finally, in Hume's view 'a well-evidenced or probabilified thing' means 'that which is strongly suggested to somebody by something, or a firm belief'.

But none of this will do. Take first the alleged equivalence between 'evidences' and 'suggests'. One essential difference between the two concepts is this: 'suggests', in its primary use, is a subjective expression, whereas 'is evidence that' is an objective one. If, in my experience, all who are red-haired have been hot-tempered, then the fact that Tom is red-haired will suggest to me that he is hot-tempered; but if your experience has been different, this fact will suggest to you no such thing. Hence, if I say in this use 'The fact that Tom is red-haired suggests that he is hot-tempered' and you reply 'No, it does not', we are not disagreeing, for I am saying elliptically what this fact suggests to me and you are saying that this is not what this fact suggests to you, and these statements are not incompatible. But if I say 'The fact that Tom is red-haired is evidence that he is hot-tempered', and you reply 'No, it is not', we are disagreeing and our statements are incompatible. 'Suggests to me' makes sense, but 'is evidence to me' does not. Again, it is logically possible to say both 'The fact that q suggests (to me) that p although it is not evidence that p' and 'The fact that q is evidence that p although it does not suggest (to me) that p'. For these reasons, Hume's definitions, not only of 'to evidence', but also of 'an evidence' and 'a thing evidenced', must be rejected.

However, the divergence between the two families of concepts should not be exaggerated. For, while it is true that 'evidences' and 'suggests' are logically independent, they often in fact go together, since when the fact that q is evidence that p it commonly also suggests that p. Moreover, there is a secondary use of 'suggests' in which it does mean 'evidences' and not something psychological. This is the use in which the detective says 'The fact that he withdrew all his money from the bank the previous day suggests that he was planning to flee the country'. Here, 'suggests that' means 'is evidence that', and is not relative to the speaker, i.e. does not mean 'suggests to me (the speaker) that'.

Again, the alleged equivalence between 'makes it probable that' and 'strongly suggests that' is unacceptable, at any rate in the primary use of the latter expression. The simplest way to see this is to reflect that the former is an evaluative expression whereas the latter is not. Furthermore, Hume's account entails that the only difference between evidencing and probabilifying lies in the relative intensities of the feelings of expectation raised in the mind; whereas in fact the vital difference is that the latter involves evaluation whereas the former does not. Yet here too we must notice a corresponding secondary use of 'strongly suggests' in which it does mean 'probabilifies' and is not subjective. 'I expect him to do well in his oral examination' means, not something psychological, but 'I believe that he will do well', in that primary use of 'believe' which is found when the 'object of belief' is judged to be probable. [1.2]

Consider now what Hume says about 'probable reasoning'. In a notorious passage he writes: '. . . all probable reasoning is nothing but a species of sensation. It is not solely in poetry and music we must follow our taste and sentiment, but likewise in philosophy [i.e. science]. When I am convinced of any principle, it is only an idea which strikes more strongly upon me. When I give the preference to one set of arguments above another, I do nothing but decide from my feeling concerning the superiority of their influence.' [Hume, T, 103] But this, like so much of what the great psychological radical says, is paradoxical to the point of perversity. For whatever reasoning may be, one thing that it certainly is not is feeling or sensation. The two concepts are quite distinct and indeed opposed; the Man of Feeling and the Reasonable Man are popularly regarded as contrasted types. Again, if this is all that 'probable reasoning' means, there is not much substance in Hume's assertion that 'no truth appears to me more evident, than that the beasts are endowed with thought and reason as well as men'. [Hume, T, 176] For by 'reason' he here means what is ordinarily called judgement, this being the name we give to the faculty employed in making probabilification-judgements. But it is plain from the passage cited that all he is saying when he asserts that beasts as well as men possess the power of judging evidence, is that both have feelings of expectation.

Let us now inquire more closely into this feeling of confidence on which Hume's theory rests. For, to repeat it, that theory consists in equating $\gamma P(p)$, 'I believe that p' and 'I feel sure that p'. And for a start we may ask, Is there really any such feeling at all? Kneale denies that there is; and if he is right, that disposes summarily of Hume's theory. [Kneale, 14 ff., 194] However, it seems to me that there is in fact a feeling of expectation or anticipation; the sort of feeling that one has, for instance, when awaiting the thunder-clap after seeing the lightning-flash. It can be classified to the extent of pointing out that 'sure' and 'confident' are what Ryle calls 'adjectives of general condition'; in this respect 'I feel sure (or confident)' is like 'I feel depressed' and unlike 'I feel a tickle'.

The next question is, Does the locution 'I feel sure, expect that p' report the presence of the feeling just described in the speaker? This question is connected with the last one in that, if there were no such feeling, then of course this locution could never be used for this purpose. On the other hand, even though there is such a feeling, it may yet be true that this form of words is not always used to report its presence in the mind (or heart) of the speaker. And this in fact appears to be the situation. The primary and literal use of the locution is to report the presence of the feeling, but its secondary use is not. The latter is the use in which I say e.g. 'I feel sure, expect that he will do well in his oral examination'; here, 'feel sure' and 'expect' have the same force as 'believe'.

This leads naturally to the further question, Does 'I feel sure, expect that p' mean the same thing as 'I believe that p'? To answer it, we must first recall that I distinguished earlier [1.2] two uses or senses of 'believe': the primary, where the sufficient and necessary condition of my rightly saying that I believe that p is my judging

p to be probable; and the secondary, where the sufficient and necessary condition is my having a feeling of confidence or expectation that p. Accordingly, the answer to this further question is: the primary use of 'I feel sure, expect that p' is equivalent to the secondary use of 'I believe that p'; and the secondary use of the former locution is equivalent to the primary use of the latter locution. But the primary use of the former is not equivalent to the primary use of the latter. For I may rightly say that I believe that p but have no feeling of expectation of p, and conversely. The most that can be claimed is that this feeling often in fact accompanies belief in the primary sense.

Finally, does 'I believe that p' mean the same thing as 'It is probable that p'? In the primary use of 'believe', yes, for the reason just given; namely that the sufficient and necessary condition of my rightly saying that I believe that p is my judging p to be probable. But in the secondary use of 'believe', no, because I can rightly say that it is probable that p but that I have no feeling of expectation of p, and conversely. The most that can be claimed is that the feeling often in fact accompanies judgements of probability. This is the simplest objection to Hume's theory of probability. The non-equivalence of the two expressions is also plain from the following additional considerations. Since feelings are private, Hume's theory involves that probability-judgements are relative, not to the evidence, but to the speaker. Thus, if I say 'Rain is probable' and you reply 'No, it is not', you are, on this theory, no more contradicting or disagreeing with me than if I say 'I feel depressed' and you say 'Well, I do not'. But we in fact hold that in the former case you are contradicting or disagreeing with me. Since, then, probability-judgements are objective whereas Hume's theory involves that they are subjective, Hume's theory must be wrong. [Kneale, 6 ff.] Again, if it were true that $\gamma P(p)$ means 'I believe that p' in the sense of 'I (literally) feel sure that p', it would follow that the proper course for me to take if my judgement was challenged would be to examine my feelings more carefully to make sure that what I felt really was confidence. But in fact we hold that the right way to respond to such a challenge is, not this, but to adduce the evidence which we judge to make p probable. A similar criticism can be made of the thesis that 'I know that p' means 'I (literally) feel sure that p'. [Woozley, 186 f.]

But we must go further. Not only is $\gamma P(p)$ not equivalent to 'I (literally) feel sure that p'; we should regard the feeling, if it is present, with great caution when making probability-judgements. For its presence is only too likely to be due to our wishes, hopes and fears; whereas what we ought to be doing in probabilification-judgement is deciding on the evidence alone. The feeling of obligation in Moral Philosophy is a parallel case to the feeling of conviction in Philosophy of Probability. As Hare points out, not only is 'I feel obliged to do X' not equivalent to 'I ought to do X'; but the presence of the feeling will in all likelihood be due merely to the way in which I have been brought up. [Hare, 165 f.] There is another parallel case in Aesthetics. And in general, philosophies of probability which are based on the feeling of expectation, philosophies of morals which are based on the feeling of obligation, and philosophies of fine art which are based on the (alleged) aesthetic emotion, are of the same type and open to the same basic objection. Namely, that 'I feel sure that p' (in the primary sense), 'I feel obliged to do X' and 'I feel aesthetically (whatever that may mean) towards Y' are respectively neither sufficient nor necessary conditions of $\gamma P(p)$, 'I ought to do X' and 'Y is a good work of art'. Thus Hume, in the passage on 'probable reasoning' cited above, is as far out about poetry and music as he is about 'philosophy'; in none must we 'follow our sentiment'. And his attempt to lay the foundation of morals in the feelings of approval and disapproval is misguided for the same sort of reasons.

We will next examine the opinions of Mill and H. H. Price on these matters. The gist of Mill's view about reasoning, deductive and inductive, is as follows. [Mill, 153 ff.; Venn, P, 372 ff.] First, 'all inference is from particulars to particulars'. [Mill, 126] I.e., the pattern is $f'Ag . fx \therefore gx$, an exemplification of which is 'All examined men are mortal, Palmerston is a man, therefore he is mortal'. But every such inference *may* be regarded as a (primitive) induction followed by a deduction. I.e., the above inference-pattern may be analysed into: (*a*) $f'Ag \therefore I(fAg)$; and (*b*) $I(fAg) . fx \therefore gx$. However, (*b*) is not a pattern of reasoning or inference; it is a pattern of interpretation. Moving from 'All men are mortal and Palmerston is a man' to 'Palmerston is mortal' is just interpreting the generalization 'All men are mortal'. (*a*), on the other hand, is inference, 'real inference', since 'the conclusion . . . embraces more than is contained in the premises'. [Mill,

108] For 'a process of inference' is 'a process from the known to the unknown: a means of coming to a knowledge of something which we did not know before'. [Mill, 120]

It is further necessary to take account of his views on reasoning and language. [Mill, 123, 433 ff.] He contends that there is also inarticulate inference from particulars to a particular. This is the sort of reasoning performed by infants and animals, and is typified by the child who refrains from putting his finger in the candle-flame. On the other hand, they do not make generalizations or inductive probabilification-judgements. For consider the deductive derivative inductive probabilification-judgement-formula, $(3')$: $\gamma PF(gx, \gamma P(fAg) . fx)$. Making such a judgement involves, first, making the constituent probable generalization, $\gamma P(fAg)$; and second, making a deduction from it. But this is essentially different from inferring from particulars to particulars: for in the latter we reason *according to* a generalization such as 'All men are mortal'; whereas in the former we reason *from* it. But animals and infants cannot do the latter. For, since they have no language, they can neither formulate nor remember the constituent generalization. And the constituent generalization can only be judged probable, or in the limiting case true, if the observed instances have been varied; if, in effect, the conditions have been analysed and deliberately altered. But this animals not only evidently do not do, but cannot do without the aid of language.

My comments on these theses are as follows. The sort of reasoning Mill is referring to is more accurately called 'inference from particulars to a particular' than 'inference from particulars to particulars', since it is an essential feature of it that the conclusion is a singular proposition. And he is wrong in asserting that all reasoning is of this type. Notably, and contrary to what he says, moving from $I(fAg) . fx$ to gx is correctly called reasoning. It is doubtless also called interpreting the generalization, applying it to a particular case, subsuming an individual instance under the generalization, and so forth; but this is in no way incompatible with its being called reasoning. On the other hand, he is right in saying that some reasoning is of this type, and it is worth noticing that Hume anticipated him in drawing attention to the fact that '. . . the understanding or imagination can draw inferences from past experience, without reflecting on it; much more without forming any principle concerning it, or reasoning upon that principle'. [Hume, T, 104] And as I indicated earlier [1.1], Mill seems to me to be also right in saying that the type of inference he is discussing may be regarded as an induction followed by a deduction.

In withholding the name 'reasoning' from the deductive move (b) (above) and assigning it exclusively to the inductive move (a), Mill commits what may be called the inductivist fallacy. It is the opposite of what I earlier [1.2] called the deductivist fallacy. As the latter equates 'reasoning' with 'deductive reasoning', so the former equates 'reasoning' with 'inductive reasoning'. Now plainly, what leads Mill into the inductivist fallacy is his criterion or definition of 'reasoning'; namely, his thesis that we have ('real') reasoning or inference when and only when there is more in the conclusion than in the premiss, or a process from the known to the unknown. For to accept this thesis is to equate reasoning with ampliative reasoning; the objection to which is that explicative reasoning is also (called) reasoning. If it be asked what then the test or definition of reasoning is, I refer the inquirer back to the simple account that I offered at the beginning of this discussion. Finally, it is by no means evident that Mill's definition of reasoning does in fact exclude deductive reasoning. It is hard to say with certainty whether it does or does not, owing to the vagueness of such expressions as 'the conclusion contains more than the premiss'. But if, as seems likely, this is a psychological criterion, it is relevant to point out that mathematical theorems e.g. are sometimes news and indeed surprising news. Nor, finally, is it acceptable to define 'reasoning' in psychological terms anyway.

In this connexion, there is another fallacy about reasoning to be noticed, which leads to the deductivist fallacy. It is sometimes said that (primitive) inductive reasoning is not reasoning because, as Hume observes, the conjunction of the evidencing-statement of a generalization with the contradictory of that generalization is not inconsistent. Thus, $f'Ag . f\bar{Ig}$ is not an inconsistent formula. But what this actually shows is that generalizations are not (deductively) valid reasonings: it only shows that they are not reasonings at all if 'reasoning' means the same thing as 'valid reasoning'. And those who argue in this way tacitly make this equation. But 'reasoning' is not synonymous with 'valid reasoning' any more than it is with 'deductive reasoning', or 'inductive reasoning', or 'ampliative reasoning'. For if it were, the expression 'invalid reasoning' would be illogical; which, however, it is not.

I agree with Mill that infants and animals do not reason in the sense of making either generalizations or inductive probabilification-judgements, and that this is because both operations pre-require possession of a language. It should be noticed, however, that Price disagrees, and attributes to animals the ability to make evidential-evaluations and probability-judgements: 'Even animals can learn to distinguish strong signs [good evidences] from weak ones [poor evidences] in matters which are biologically important for them. It may seem odd to suggest that cats or rats can distinguish different degrees of inductive probability. But to judge from their behaviour they undoubtedly do. They can distinguish dangerous situations from safe ones. And "danger" is a conception which has to be analysed in terms of inductive probability. A dangerous situation is one in which there is a probability of death or injury or some other biological evil. Animals appear to recognize quite small probabilities of this kind.' [Price, 108] For he holds that such judgements can be made without using language, and indeed are made not only by animals but by creatures who are capable of using language. He instances a skilled marksman shooting at a snipe: 'The visible course of the bird's flight during a certain half second is an inductive sign of what its course will be in the next half second. And the signified movement is highly specified as to direction and velocity. The marksman shows his excellent "judgement", as we say, in directing his gun in just this direction and pressing the trigger at just this moment. But his good judgement does not manifest itself by what philosophers call an "act of judging", that is by asserting a proposition in words, not even in private and imaged words. His "act of judging", if we must call it by that name, is wholly pre-verbal. It is manifested to other people by what he does, and to himself by muscular sensations.' [Price, 101]

On the other hand, I disagree with Mill's contention that there is inarticulate inference from particulars to a particular. Price, however, is of Mill's mind on this score, and instances a cat who infers that there will be milk for her now because tea is served and because in her experience whenever tea has been served there has been milk for her. [Price, 42] Yet there is surely an important and fairly obvious difference between my simply expecting x to be g

because it is f and because in my experience $f'Ag$, and on the other hand my inferring or reasoning in the pattern $f'Ag \cdot fx \therefore gx$. The latter prerequires language whereas the former does not. This follows from the very meaning of 'reasoning'; for, as I said above, we have reasoning when and only when some proposition is advanced as actual or possible reason for some proposition called the conclusion. And one cannot have propositions without a language, in some sense, however elastic, of that word. This is the opinion of Leibniz in his discussion of reasoning. After observing that 'the *reason* is the known truth whose connexion with another less well known one makes us assent to the latter', he continues: '. . . the faculty which perceives this connexion of truths is also called *reason*. Now, this faculty actually belongs only to Man here below and is not found in other animals. For I have previously shown that that shadow of reason which is found in beasts is nothing but the expectation of a similar event in a case which seems like a past one, without knowing whether the same reason holds good. Men themselves act likewise when they are mere *empirics*. But they are superior to the beasts insofar as they perceive the connexions of truths . . .' [*Further Essays, etc.*, p. 425; Locke, 344 ff.]

In considering these questions, it makes a good deal of difference just which word one is talking about. So far as 'reason' and 'infer' are concerned, it does not seem to me that we actually do say, or are even tempted to say, that the cat looking for milk at tea-time, the rat avoiding a trap, or the marksman shooting snipe, are reasoning or inferring. We certainly sometimes call animals clever and intelligent; but I cannot assent to Price's remark: 'Whether animal intelligence deserves the honorific title of "reason" is a question the reader must decide for himself'. [Price, 44] The question surely is rather whether we in fact do speak of (intelligent) animals as reasoning.

Are animals said to 'think' either when they do these things? Again, it seems to me that we neither say so nor are tempted to say so. Price, however, is of the opposite opinion. For he holds that 'thinking' should be defined to include 'sign-cognition', and understands by the latter expression not only ordinary voiced evidential-statements and probabilification-judgements, but also the alleged unvoiced inductions and probability-judgements made by animals and minds at the animal level. [Price, 93 ff.] Yet he seems not altogether convinced by his own thesis, as witness his enigmatic remark that '. . . though we must not deny that animals think, we hesitate to call them thinkers'. [Price, 200]

'Judgement', however, is a different matter. We do not, I believe, attribute it to the cat or the rat; but we certainly do attribute it to the marksman. Good shots, batsmen, racing motorists and others are all said to possess good or nice judgement, meaning judgement of evidence. But since, in my view, they do not really evaluate evidence since they do not use language, the problem is to explain why we say this. In dealing with it, I hope also to reveal the temptations that lure some theorists, at any rate, into attributing judgement, thought and reason to beasts.

First, then, one thing that the gun does is to expect (in the literal sense) the snipe to be there then. But as we noticed earlier, expectation is connected with probabilification-judgement, in that when I judge p to be probable I commonly also expect that p. So that it is natural, if wrong, to think that whenever we have expectation we have judgement. The error is essentially the same as that which I suggested above to underlie the equation of $\gamma P(p)$ with 'I feel sure that p'. The same considerations apply to animals as well.

Another thing that the cat, the rat and the gun all do is behave in the same sort of way as do, or would do, beings who really have reasoned to the certain arrival of milk or the probable future position of the snipe. So that to attribute reason, judgement, etc., to them is to speak metaphorically, is to say that they are behaving as if they had evaluated the evidence for tea being served or for the snipe being here now.

Lastly, I suggest that the ambiguity of 'expect' may bear on the question. One thing that the cat, the rat and the gun all do is expect, in the primary and literal sense, x, which is f, to be also g. But it may be mistakenly thought that what the cat e.g. does when she does expect (in the primary sense) milk, is the same sort of thing as the tutor does when he says he expects (in the secondary sense) Ann to do well in her oral examination. So that simply having a feeling of expectation is mistaken for making a probability-judgement.

A word in conclusion about 'judgement'. In non-technical contexts, the word has many uses. One convenient way of distinguishing them is according to the matter that judgement is exercised on. A man may be a good or bad judge of opportunity, furniture, horses, teas, etc. But here, as already indicated, we are only concerned with the judgement of evidence. The term also figures in technical contexts, notably, philosophical ones. Some of these are peculiar; the idealist logicians, Bradley and Bosanquet, seem to mean by 'to judge' simply 'to assert'. The only philosophical use of interest here is Locke's. His 'judgement' plainly means 'judgement of evidence', and he accordingly and rightly connects judgement in his sense with belief and probability. [Locke, 333 ff.]

The last theory that I propose to criticize is Toulmin's. [Toulmin, Pr; J. N. Findlay, 'Probability without Nonsense', *Philosophical Quarterly*, July 1952; Kneale, 3 f.; Venn, L, 295 ff.] According to this theory, 'He said that it will probably rain tonight' means or has the force of 'He said non-committally that it will rain tonight'. 'Probably', on this account, is an assertive device that enables us to make statements in a particular mode or manner, namely, guardedly, and to avoid committing ourselves in the way that we do if we say simply 'It will rain tonight'.

My chief criticism of this theory is the same as my chief criticism of Hume's theory; namely, that it is anti-rational. For it involves that it is possible to explain the meaning of 'probable' without any reference to probabilification-judgement, i.e. to the reasons why p is probable or to what makes p probable. And this is quite opposed to the view of the meaning of 'probable' that I advance in this essay.

The theory is also open to other objections. The opposite of to assert non-committally is presumably to assert absolutely or roundly; for we do not in fact use the adverb 'committally'. Consider therefore the statement: 'He said absolutely (roundly) that it will probably rain tonight'. On Toulmin's theory, the statement is self-contradictory, since it means: 'He said "committally" and non-committally that it will rain tonight'. But the statement is not in fact self-contradictory or in any way illogical.

The theory further resembles Hume's in involving subjectivism. Suppose that A says 'It is very probable that p', and B replies 'On the contrary, it is barely probable that p'. We should certainly say that A and B disagree. But on Toulmin's theory the situation is that B has said very non-committally that p, whereas A has said barely non-committally (or almost 'committally') that p. And this no more involves that A and B disagree than if A has said loudly or in French that *p* whereas B has said softly or in English that *p*. The doctrine of modality is somewhat obscure. The traditional modal adverbs, i.e. the ones in which Aristotle and Kant interest themselves, are 'necessarily', 'possibly' and (perhaps) 'actually'. And some philosophers allege a resemblance between these adverbs and 'probably'. Venn, for instance, claims that they properly belong in the province of Probability. [Venn, L, 295 ff.] His reason is that the function of them all is to describe or express different degrees of intensity of belief or conviction in the mind of the speaker, and that this can better be done in terms of degrees of probability. Thus, whereas Toulmin in effect includes Probability in Modality, Venn includes Modality in Probability. However, I have just rejected this contention of Venn's, so far as 'probably' and 'necessarily' are concerned, when criticizing Hume's theory. And the same criticism goes for 'actually' and 'possibly'. It is an unacceptable contention that 'Actually *p*' means 'I (the speaker) feel quite sure (in the literal sense) that *p*', and that 'Possibly *p*' means 'I (the speaker) feel uncertain (in the literal sense) whether or not *p*'.

Finally, there is a resemblance of some interest between Toulmin's theory of Probability and Strawson's theory of Truth, noticed above. [5.2] For both are modal theories. As Toulmin maintains that the force or use of 'probably' or 'it is probable that' is to make assertions guardedly, so Strawson maintains that the force or use of 'certainly' or 'it is true that' is to make assertions concessively.

6.2 INDUCTIVE PHILOSOPHY AND LOGIC

My final topic is the question, Does the investigation pursued in this book properly fall within the province of Logic, more particularly, within a sub province of it called Inductive Logic? This may appear to be a purely professional and trivial question which cannot possibly interest the general reader: what can it matter, it may be asked, what names philosophers give to the different branches of their discipline? I shall hope to show, however, that this is not so, and that, lying behind the various views that have been taken of this matter, there are points of genuine significance for the present inquiry. I shall first give my own answer to the question, and then discuss some other opinions.

6.2.1 *Positive Consideration of the Question*

It will be remembered that, in an earlier discussion [2.2], I advocated the following usages. It seems to me that the best name for the present investigation as a whole is Philosophy of Inductive Probability; or, since we must take account of inductive verification- as well as of probabilification-judgements, Inductive Philosophy. The name, Logic of Inductive Probability, I proposed to restrict to the study of deductive derivative inductive probabilification-judgements; and similarly, the name Logic of Inductive Truth to the study of deductive derivative inductive verification-judgements. I also suggested that the Logic of Inductive Probability and the Logic of Inductive Truth are conveniently referred to collectively as Inductive Logic. The effect of these recommendations is to make Inductive Logic only a small part of Inductive Philosophy, since deductive derivative ones are only a small subclass of inductive probabilification- and verification-judgements.

In making these proposals, I am not laying down stipulative definitions arbitrarily, but paying regard to the traditional and generally accepted uses of the names 'Logic' and 'Philosophy'. For the sphere of Logic is traditionally regarded as entailment or logical implication, validity and consistency: 'Logic', in fact, is synonymous with 'Deductive (or Formal) Logic'. So that to call the study of all inductive probabilification-judgements 'Logic' is to encourage the erroneous belief that all such judgements, including primitive ones, involve logical implication, or at any rate something closely akin to it. But it seems to me that this belief, as expressed for instance in Keynes' theory of probabilification as partial implication, is not only false but seriously misleading. The sphere of Philosophy, on the other hand, is not thus narrowly confined, and certainly includes the study of primitive and non-deductive derivative judgements. Specifically, I contended above that the branch of Philosophy in which Inductive Philosophy as a whole belongs is Axiology or the philosophical study of value-judgements.

However, this is a minority opinion. Most philosophers regard the study of induction as part of Logic, as witness the plan of the majority of Logic texts, which contain a book or part called Inductive Logic corresponding to that called Deductive Logic. This practice seems to date from Mill, who was the first to write a popular text called *A System of Logic Ratiocinative and Inductive* which included an extended discussion of induction. I shall comment shortly on the reason why he includes the philosophical study of induction in Logic, and also on the views that some other authors take of this question. Kneale, it is to be noticed, does not subscribe to the common opinion, and holds that '. . . the philosophical theory of probability is part of epistemology, that is to say, of the philosophical discipline in which we study the different kinds of knowledge and related topics such as the nature of belief'. [Kneale, 3]

Before embarking on criticism, however, I wish to compare Inductive Philosophy with Logic. We shall see that, though there are essential differences between them, there are also interesting resemblances, which have doubtless encouraged the belief that the former study is identical with, or at any rate the same kind of thing as, the latter one.

First, as to subject-matter. Inductive Philosophy is about inductive probabilification- and verification-judgements, whereas Logic, as has just been said, is about some, but not all, valid deductive inferences and entailments. Logicians are not interested in e.g. the valid inference 'Bob is a father ∴ Bob is a male', but they are interested in the valid inference 'All fathers are males ∴ Some males are fathers'. They are interested, in short, in valid inferences which hinge on what Russell calls the 'logical words', 'all', 'some', 'not', 'and', etc. [*Inquiry into Meaning and Truth*, pp. 78 ff.] At the same time, there is an overlap between Inductive Philosophy and Logic, in that one type of inductive probabilification-judgement that needs to be studied is the deductive derivative type. Using the names in the senses I favour, the existence of this overlap is indicated by the observation that Inductive Logic forms part of Inductive Philosophy.

It is not, however, a very important part; the most interesting judgements are the primitive, not the derivative ones. Moreover, as I pointed out earlier [2.2], the entailments of probability-judgements have not in fact received much attention from logicians, who have concentrated on the entailments of propositions that are true or false, i.e. statements, rather than on those of judgements that are probable. On the latter, there is not much beyond some remarks by Aristotle and certain scholastic logicians about probable syllogisms. In this connexion, there should be noted a misleading tendency to represent as deductive judgements judgements which are not so. Consider e.g. the formula, (6'), $\gamma PF(gx, fMg . fx . C_1)$. It is a primitive, not a derivative formula, let alone a deductive derivative one. Yet Peirce calls this inference-pattern 'simple probable deduction', and Williams calls it the 'proportional (or statistical) syllogism'. They give the following patterns respectively: 'The proportion ρ of the Ms are Ps; S is an M; It follows, with probability ρ, that S is a P'. [Peirce, 191] 'Since m/n of M is P and a is M, therefore there is a probability (of m/n) that a is P'. [Williams, G, 12]

It is true to say that the subject-matters of Logic and Inductive Philosophy are alike in that they are both about the meanings of words. But behind this resemblance lie two important differences: the two disciplines explain the meanings of different words; and they explain them by attending to different conceptual relations. To elucidate. One way of describing what Logic does is to say that it explains the meanings of logical words. Syllogistic, e.g., explains in part the meanings of 'all', 'no', 'some' and 'not' by formulating rules specifying what propositions of the A, E, I or O types do or do not validly follow from two premises of these types. Inductive Philosophy, on the other hand, explains the meanings of 'probable' and 'true' when applied to inductions. As we saw earlier [6.1], one who should say 'All BU are H but some observed BU are not H' would be said to be ignorant of the meanings of the logical words 'all', 'some', 'and' and 'not'. But one who should say 'All observed BU are H and varied but it is not probable that all BU are H' would be said to be ignorant of the meaning of 'probable' when predicated of a generalization.

As to the second difference, Logic is concerned solely with the relation of entailment. In short, logicians provide partial explanations of the meanings of the logical words by exhibiting systematically what statements containing these words entail or are entailed by one another. Inductive Logic does this too; for the logical powers of 'probable' are partly revealed by showing how the probability of the conclusion is affected by the probability of the premises from which it is deduced, i.e. by formulating the rules governing probable-syllogisms, etc. But inductive philosophers do not confine themselves to studying these relations of entailment. Notably, when explaining the (descriptive) meaning of 'probable' as it occurs in primitive judgements, they are studying the relation between a value-judgement and the statement which informs us that the criterion of that value-judgement is satisfied. This second difference involves an important point about philosophical method in general. For, as Strawson notes, there is a mistaken tendency to think that explaining the meaning of a sentence, and hence of the words that that sentence contains, consists wholly in saying what other sentences entail and are entailed by it. In fact, however, the operation involves much more than this. [Strawson, 211 ff.] If the opinion were true, the effect on the present topic would be to reduce Inductive Philosophy to Inductive Logic.

We will next compare Logic and Inductive Philosophy in respect of their aim and value. Logic was at one time considered to be an art, namely, the art of right (deductive) reasoning or thinking. It was further thought, or at any rate implied, that whoever mastered the rules of this art would be able to reason correctly, as a result of which the value of the discipline was rated highly. The modern view, however, differs from this on two scores. First, Logic is now thought of as a science rather than as an art. The contrary opinion arose perhaps from the fact that Logic was, and to some extent still is, expressed in rules. For this is certainly a conspicuous feature of books of art, e.g. manuals of instruction on how to grow roses, play the guitar, or reduce one's handicap at golf. The second difference is more important. It is now appreciated that a mastery of Logic is not even a necessary, still less a sufficient, condition of being able to reason aright. In this sphere, as in others, correct practice precedes and is independent of theory; the latter does but make explicit after the event the principles implicit in the former. Some philosophers, indeed, saw this clearly quite early on; e.g. Locke, who writes: '. . . God has not been so sparing to men to make them barely two-legged creatures, and left it to Aristotle to make them rational. God has been more bountiful to mankind than so. He has given them a mind that can reason, without being instructed in methods of syllogizing. The understanding is not taught to reason by these rules; it has a native faculty to perceive the coherence or incoherence of its ideas, and can range them right, without any such perplexing repetitions. I say not this in any way to lessen Aristotle, whom I look on as one of the greatest men amongst the ancients. . . .' [Locke, 347]

Consequently, Logic is now prized on different grounds. Most philosophers would say, I think, that it just is a good thing to know what these principles implicit in sound argument are; this being simply a special case of the general truth that it is a good thing to possess theoretical knowledge irrespective of whether it has or has not any strikingly useful practical application. Add to this that the study also possesses value on account of its function, just noticed, of explaining in part the meanings of certain words. And this is just a special case of the general truth that it is a good thing to understand the meanings of, not indeed all, but all interesting words. Seen in this light, the question of the value of Logic, the part, is sunk in the question of the value of Philosophy itself, the whole; for the office of the philosopher is to explain the meanings of interesting words.

Much of this applies to Inductive Philosophy also. Here too it was once thought that mastering the rules of 'Inductive Logic' would make a man a good judge of evidence. The author who pitches the claims of the discipline highest is Bacon; but this is chiefly because he believes that knowing the 'aphorisms' in which he delivers his 'new instrument' will make a man a good scientific inventor. For he conceives himself to be formulating the principles not so much of scientific proof as of scientific discovery. Like other great figures at the beginning of Modern Philosophy, he is obsessed by the problem of 'method', and supposes that by adhering to his precepts one may make fruitful discoveries even though he has no great intelligence. 'For my way of discovering sciences goes far to level men's wits, and leaves but little to individual excellence; because it performs everything by the surest rules and demonstrations.' [Bacon, 297] But such a claim is even less plausible in the case of inventive resource than in that of good judgement.

However, philosophers soon came to recognize that knowledge of Inductive Philosophy was neither a sufficient nor a necessary condition of possessing good judgement of evidence; that, as God did not leave it to Aristotle to make men reasonable in the deductive sense, so neither did he leave it to Philodemus or Bacon to make them reasonable in the inductive sense. As Mill notes: 'Mankind judged of evidence, and often correctly, before logic was a science, or they never could have made it one'. [Mill, 6] Bentham makes the point more circumstantially in the following characteristic passage: 'Domestic management turns upon evidence. Whether the leg of mutton now on the spit be roasted enough, is a question of evidence; a question of which the cook is judge. The meat is done enough; the meat is not done enough: these opposite facts, the one positive, the other negative, are the principal facts—the facts sought: evidentiary facts, the present state of the fire, the time that has elapsed since the putting down of the meat, the state of the fire at different points during that length of time, the appearance of the meat, together with other points perhaps out of number, the development of which might occupy pages upon pages, but which the cook decides upon in the cook's way, as if by instinct; deciding upon evidence, as Mons. Jourdan talked prose, without having ever heard of any such word, perhaps, in the whole course of her life.' [Bentham, 18 f.] Connected with this is another point of some importance. Since men learn to judge of evidence by practice, they tend to become better at it as they do it more. Also, their skill in doing it becomes specialized when they regularly apply themselves to certain orders of problems only. The cook may have a very nice judgement about when the meat is done, but a very poor one about the racing form of a horse. These are the considerations which constitute the strongest objection to trial by jury; for this institution rests on a tenet which is democratic in the Athenian or Jacksonian sense, namely, that everybody is at least as good at everything as everybody else.

Hence, a different view must be taken of the value of Inductive Philosophy as well. The plain truth is that it is a good thing to know the principles implicit in sound inductive, no less than in valid deductive, reasoning. But I also submit that the interest of Inductive Philosophy when considered as an explanation of meaning is greater than that of Logic. To put the same point another way, I should claim that the value of this book, if any, lies in its illumination of the concept of Inductive Probability rather than in its explication of the principles on which right inductive reasoning proceeds. There are two reasons for this difference between the two studies.

First, 'probable' is a more interesting word than any of the 'logical' words. I mean by this that Probability is a very prominent and commanding feature on the conceptual map, in the following sense. As explaining its meaning involves describing its relation to a large number of other words, so explaining the meaning of any of these words involves describing their relations to it. Thus, in the course of this essay I have found it necessary to chart the relations of 'probable' to numerous other expressions, some of which stand in fairly close and obvious connexion with it, such as 'evidence', 'generalization', 'hypothesis' and 'chance'; others of which, however, are more remotely and less obviously connected with it, such as 'believe', 'assert', 'random', 'true' and 'reliable method'. Second, the analysis of meaning which inductive philosophers undertake is more thorough than that undertaken by logicians. The reason for this is one just noticed, namely, that logical analysis is confined to pointing out entailments, whereas philosophical analysis is subject to no such restriction. In short, whereas logicians aim at providing partial explanations of the meanings of a few fairly interesting words, inductive philosophers aim at giving a complete explanation of the meaning of a very interesting word.

In comparing the methods by which logicians and inductive philosophers attain their aims, it is desirable to consider three matters: rules and fallacies, the systematization of rules, and formalization. Logic possesses all three features. Consider Syllogistic, a simple and self-contained small sub province of Logic. This theory is characterized by the presence of rules, such as *A term which is distributed in the conclusion must be distributed in the premiss.* A fallacy is simply the obverse of such a rule, and it is indifferent whether one says that a syllogism is invalid when it does not conform to the above rule, or when it involves the fallacy of illicit process. Further, the rules of Syllogistic can themselves be deductively systematized. Thus, it is a rule that a syllogism with two particular premisses can have no valid conclusion. But it is possible to avoid laying this down as a separate rule, by deducing it from other rules. [Black, C, 126 f.] Again, Logic is formalized. In Syllogistic, logicians discuss, not statements such as 'All men are mortal', but statement-formulas such as fAg. The formalization of Syllogistic was initiated at the same time as the study itself by Aristotle. The point of employing variables, as f, g, h, etc., is that it enables us to ignore the irrelevant variety of content that is found in statements.

The first of these features characterizes Inductive Philosophy too. That this study is naturally expressed in rules is apparent from the presence of Rules 1–14 in the foregoing discussion. [2.1–3.2] Yet there is a difference of some importance between the rules of

Inductive Philosophy and those of Logic. The latter are precise, whereas the former are mostly rather vague. Cp. e.g. the syllogistic rule just cited, *A term which is distributed in the conclusion must be distributed in the premiss*, with my Rule (1), *An universal subject-predicate generalization is more probabilified as the observed sample is more varied.* Whether a term is distributed can be settled unequivocally; it manifestly either is or is not. But 'more varied' and 'more probabilified' are vague expressions; there may well be disagreement about how much a sample is varied, or about the degree in which the generalization is probabilified by the degree in which the sample is varied.

There are also inductive fallacies. Some indeed deny this, and maintain that a leading difference between deductive and inductive reasoning is that in the latter there are no fallacies, whereas in the former there are. But this seems to be a mistake. Nor is it an universally held opinion: Mill e.g. explicitly recognizes 'fallacies of generalization' as a sub class of fallacies. [Mill, 487, 514 ff.] As I have just pointed out, the existence of inductive fallacies is a logical consequence of the existence of inductive rules, since 'rule' and 'fallacy' are correlative terms. However, not all breaches of inductive rules are inductive fallacies, only those which are so to say systematic. As Mill well says of fallacies of generalization: 'If the attempt made in the preceding Books to define the principles of well-grounded generalization has been successful, all generalizations not conformable to those principles might, in a certain sense, be brought under the present class: when, however, the rules are known and kept in view, but a casual lapse committed in the application of them, this is a blunder, not a fallacy. To entitle an error of generalization to the latter epithet, it must be committed on principle; there must lie in it some erroneous general conception of the inductive process; the legitimate mode of drawing conclusions from observation and experiment must be fundamentally misconceived.' [Mill, 514] I subjoin examples of inductive fallacies, some of which have been mentioned earlier in this book. Strictly speaking, they should rather be called fallacies of ampliative, not merely of inductive, reasoning, since some of them are committed when the reasoning is not inductive, but hypothetic.

First, the opinion that a proposition is probabilified when the amount of evidence for it is large, even though the individual pieces of evidence are severally worthless evidence for it. Earlier

[4.1], I gave the example of the juryman's judgement that there must be 'something in' the great mass of evidence composing the case against the prisoner, even though counsel for the defence has shown that every single item in that mass is worthless evidence for the guilt of his client. Second, the belief that a generalization is probabilified in some degree, however slight, by a single confirmatory instance, because it is probabilified in an appreciable degree by a number of such instances. [4.1] Third, the belief that generalizations are never true but only in some degree, however high, probable. [5.2] Fourth, the opinion that a proposition is more (or less) probabilified accordingly as the evidence for it is of a certain kind. The classic instance of this is an inveterate tendency among lawyers and others to believe that all circumstantial evidence has greater probabilificatory power than all testimonial evidence, or conversely. [Wigmore, 635 ff.] The fact is, of course, that some circumstantial evidence has greater probabilificatory power than some testimonial evidence, and conversely. Those who rate circumstantial evidence as such lower than testimonial evidence do so, it seems, because they are impressed by the more marked tendency of tribunals to go astray when evaluating the former kind of evidence than when evaluating the latter kind. On the other hand, those who rate circumstantial evidence as such higher than testimonial evidence do so because they are impressed by the consideration that 'facts or circumstances (unlike witnesses) cannot lie'. Both arguments are too threadbare to call for refutation here.

On the other hand, it appears to me that nothing can be effected in the way of systematizing the rules of Inductive Philosophy, as can be done in the case of the rules of Logic. It is instructive to contrast with this finding the view of Carnap; for no other philosopher assimilates Inductive Logic to Deductive Logic so closely as he. [Carnap, iii, 192 ff.] In outlining the programme of his 'Inductive Logic', he claims that its rules are no less exact than those of Deductive Logic, and that the former is a system in the same sense as are modern systems of Formal Logic. The method of systematization is predominantly deductive; i.e. the formulas of the system are proved by being deduced as theorems, as in the *Principia Mathematica* of Whitehead and Russell. But we are also told that, in some but not all cases, the formulas can be proved by a testing-method, as truth-functional formulas are proved by the truth-table method; and that as the latter task can be performed by a deductive machine, so the former task can be performed by an inductive machine.

In rebuttal of this claim, I can only repeat that it does not seem to me that any such systematization of the rules of inductive probabilification is at all possible. The point may be put slightly differently thus. It is doubtless possible to construct a deductive system called 'theory of degree of confirmation' which possesses the features that Carnap describes. But the inevitable result is that the inductive logical constant 'degree of confirmation' ceases to bear any resemblance to our everyday notion, 'degree of probabilification'. And this is as much as to say that constructing the system would have no point; for logical calculi, whether deductive or inductive, lose all purpose if they cannot be interpreted at least partially in ordinary language. To make the obvious comparison, the position here is quite different from what it is with respect to the deductive logical constant 'material implication' of modern Formal Logic. For whereas there is a large area of meaning common to the latter and the 'if . . . then . . .' of ordinary language, there is between the 'degree of confirmation' of Carnap's system and the 'if . . . then probably . . .' of ordinary language no area of common meaning whatever.

Another important resemblance between Logic and Inductive Philosophy lies in the fact that both can be formalized. The advantage gained by doing so is the same in both cases, namely, as already mentioned, that of enabling us to neglect the irrelevant differences of matter or content that are to be found in statements and judgements. [1.2, end] The first person to formalize Inductive Philosophy in some degree was Mill. But he does not proceed very far with it. His use of symbolism is restricted to the exposition of his Experimental Methods and Canons, and consists simply in representing antecedent events by the upper-case letters A, B, C, etc., and 'corresponding' subsequent events by the lower-case italic letters a, b, c, etc. [Mill, 253 ff.; Venn, P, 400 ff.] It scarcely needs to be pointed out that symbolism is used in the present essay for a different purpose and in a much more extensive way.

However, some propose an objection to the thesis that Inductive Philosophy can be formalized. It may be rendered as follows. Cp. the judgement 'All observed copper is malleable ∴ All copper is probably malleable' with the judgement 'All observed blue things are light ∴ All blue things are probably light'. The former is correct, but the latter is not. And the reason is that the former is about copper whereas the latter is about blue things. For copper is a natural kind, i.e. a stable collection of properties such as being heavy, ductile, reddish, an electrical conductor, etc.; whereas blue things are not. This indeed is why we have a name for the former, namely 'copper', but not for the latter. For the fact that all observed copper, which has the properties of being heavy, etc., is also malleable, makes it probable that all copper, which has the properties of being heavy, etc., is also malleable. By contrast, the fact that all observed blue things, which have no other common properties, are light, does not make it in any degree probable that all blue things, which have no other common properties, are light. Hence, the probability of generalizations depends on their content, on what they are about; so that Inductive Philosophy cannot be formalized. For if we attempt to exhibit the principles of inductive probabilification by considering formulas such as $\gamma PF(fAg, f'Ag)$, we obscure the essential point, that some substitutions on this formula are sound whereas others are not, depending precisely on what expressions ('copper' or 'blue things') are substituted for the variable f.

But it is not hard to answer this objection. It evidently rests on a theory about the probabilification of generalizations which bears some resemblance to what I earlier called the traditional doctrine of inductive reasoning by analogy. [4.1] It will be remembered that, according to the latter doctrine, if of two observed so-and-so's one is such-and-such, the probability that the other is such-and-such is greater accordingly as the number of properties common to both so-and-so's is greater. According to the theory now being considered, if all (or most, etc.) observed so-and-so's are such-and-such, the probability that all (or most, etc.) so-and-so's are such-and-such is greater accordingly as the number of properties common to both observed and unobserved so-and-so's is greater. But neither theory is correct. So far as the latter is concerned, what actually makes the generalization probable is the variety of the observed so-and-so's. And this fact does not preclude the formalization of Inductive Philosophy, since it is no part of the connotation of any word that may be substituted on a predicate-variable (f, g, etc.) that it is in a greater or less degree varied.

6.2.2 *Criticism of some Other Views*

I come now to my last theme, some critical observations on the opinions of authors who regard the philosophical study of induction as falling within the province of Logic, beginning with a consideration of the views of Mill.

Mill defines Logic thus: 'Logic is . . . the science of Proof, or Evidence'. [Mill, 5; Venn, L, vii, x f.] I.e., it is defined in terms of its province, what it is about, namely evidence. He subdivides Logic, again on the basis of subject-matter, into Formal Logic or the Logic of Consistency or Deductive Logic, and the Logic of Truth or Inductive Logic. [Mill, 136 f.] As to the method by which the matter of Logic is to be handled, he tells us that his object is to '. . . frame a set of rules or canons for testing the sufficiency of any given evidence to prove any given proposition'. [Mill, 7] We are told further that his Experimental Methods (or rather, the corresponding Canons) are such rules, and that they stand in the same relation to inductive reasoning as do the rules of syllogism to deductive reasoning. Connected with this is the idea that the golden rule which inductions should satisfy is that they should be deducible from a true induction of wider scope, in particular the law of causation. [4.2] It is in these terms that he solves 'the problem of induction', as he defines it; namely, the problem why sometimes a single instance verifies an induction, whereas at other times hosts of instances do not even appreciably probabilify it. [Mill, 206] Consequently, his Inductive Logic is deductivist, in that it regards the supreme test of merit in an induction as its deducibility from some wider induction; and it is also a Logic of Inductive Truth rather than a Logic of Inductive Probability, since the test is that the lower inductions shall be deducible from a higher induction that is true and not merely probable.

The point that I wish to concentrate on now is the first one, namely, the influential thesis that Logic is the Science of Evidence. For the thesis is developed as follows. It is maintained that the upper limit of good, very good, etc., evidence is 'demonstrative evidence', q being demonstrative evidence for p when it entails p. Evidence is thus divided into demonstrative and inconclusive, and Logic divided accordingly; Deductive Logic being the science of demonstrative evidence and Inductive Logic being the science of inconclusive evidence.

But this is fallacious. The upper limit of good, very good, etc., evidence is conclusive, not 'demonstrative', evidence. Though evidence can properly be divided into conclusive and inconclusive, it cannot properly be divided into inconclusive and demonstrative. Again, the difference between probabilification and entailment is not, as the theory implies, one of degree; they are propositional relations of quite different kinds. And yet again, when q entails p it is quite wrong to speak of q as evidence for p at all. We do not rightly say that fAg is evidence that $f'Ag$. The expression 'demonstrative evidence' is illogical and incorporates a serious type-fallacy.

It is not difficult, however, to surmise how being conclusively evidenced by a true evidencing-statement comes to be confused with being entailed by a true premiss. For contrast e.g. the formula, $VF(fAg, f'Ag \cdot \alpha C_2)$, with the formula, $VF(f'Ag, fAg)$. The striking resemblance between the two is, of course, that in both the fact that the reason is true makes the conclusion true, so that both may be regarded as special cases of the formula, $VF(p, q)$.

Erroneous though it be, the notion that demonstrative proof is the upper limit of probabilification is widely current, and may indeed be added to my list of fallacies of ampliative reasoning, above. It is natural to compare it with Keynes' notion of probabilification. For as Keynes regards probabilification as partial entailment, entailment that is imperfect or of an inferior degree; so the patrons of 'demonstrative evidence' regard entailment as the perfection of probabilification or probabilification in the highest degree.

The notion occurs in Ancient Philosophy. According to Sextus Empiricus, some philosophers after Aristotle held that ἀπόδειξις is τῷ γένει σημεῖον, that 'demonstration is generically a sign'. Stocks comments: 'The word σημεῖον had in fact come to be used of all proof or inference, of which the main subdivisions were σημεῖον proper and ἀπόδειξις'. [Stocks, 194]

In an interesting passage, Reid writes: 'That we may not be embarrassed by the ambiguity of words, it is proper to observe that there is a popular meaning of *probable evidence* which ought not to be confounded with the philosophical meaning. . . . In common language probable evidence is considered as an inferior degree of evidence, and is opposed to certainty; so that what is certain is more than probable, and what is only probable is not certain. Philosophers consider probable evidence not as a degree, but as a species of evidence which is opposed, not to certainty, but to another species of evidence called demonstratio.. Demonstrative evidence has no degrees; but probable evidence, taken in the philosophical sense, has all degrees from the very least to the greatest, which we call certainty.' [Reid, 433]

My comments on this are as follows. Evidence is not called 'probable'. That which is probable is, not the evidencing-, but the evidenced-statement, provided the evidence be good. 'Probable evidence', like 'probable reasoning' (a locution which Reid also uses, as do e.g. de Morgan and Peirce), is an illogical expression worth noting for the sake of the mistake it incorporates about what is (called) probable. The distinction which Reid attributes to common language is correctly stated as that between good evidence which makes p probable and conclusive evidence which makes p certain or true. And this, as he says, is a difference of degree. Further, the distinction which he attributes to philosophers is correctly stated as that between good or very good or conclusive evidence on the one hand and premiss on the other. But he is mistaken in calling this a distinction between different kinds of evidence, namely, probable and demonstrative; since a premiss, we have seen, is not (rightly called) evidence at all. The distinction he has in mind is indeed one of kind and not merely of degree; but it is not a distinction between two kinds of *evidence*. It is a distinction between good, etc., evidence and quite a different kind of *thing*, namely, a premiss.

Among contemporary philosophers, it will suffice to mention Wittgenstein and Hempel. The former writes: 'If p follows from q, the proposition q gives to the proposition p the probability 1. The certainty of logical conclusion is a limiting case of probability.' [L. Wittgenstein, *Tractatus Logico-Philosophicus*, London, 1922, p. 110] His second sentence neatly summarizes the fallacy now under discussion. Hempel's view of the matter is contained in the following passages: 'Entailment is a special case of confirmation. Thus, e.g., we want to say that the observation report "*a* is black" confirms the sentence (hypothesis) "*a* is black or grey"'; '. . . entailment . . . might be referred to as the special case of *conclusive* confirmation'; and '. . . we have . . . an extreme case of confirmation in the case when B *conclusively confirms* H; this case is realized if, and only if, B entails H. We shall then also say that B *verifies* H. Thus, verification is a special case of confirmation; it is a logical relation between sentences; more specifically, it is simply the relation of entailment with its domain restricted to observation sentences.' [Hempel, II, 102, 107, 112]

My criticisms of these remarks of Hempel's are as follows. As we saw earlier [1.2] in discussing Carnap's and Hempel's key concept, 'degree of confirmation', they seem to mean by 'confirms' sometimes 'is evidence that', but at other times 'is good evidence that' or 'makes it probable that'. In these passages, Hempel seems to mean by it the former. Then, it is incorrect to say, as he does in the first two extracts, that entailing is a special case of evidencing, namely, conclusive evidencing, because entailing is not any sort, case or kind of evidencing. In the third extract, he implies that q verifies p only when it entails it (and is itself true). But, as I have shown earlier [5.2], q also verifies p when it conclusively evidences it (and is itself true). Now, in this latter sense of 'verification', it is indeed true that 'verification is a special case of confirmation'— assuming 'confirms' to mean 'probabilifies' rather than 'evidences'. But unfortunately it is the former sense of 'verification' that Hempel intends.

Finally in this connexion, it is instructive to notice another misconception of the difference between being entailed by a true premiss and being probabilified by a true probabilifying-proposition. Nicod calls the corresponding inferences 'certain inference' and 'probable inference' respectively, and distinguishes them thus: '. . . certain inference transfers to its conclusion the totality of the certainty or probability of its premisses taken together, and . . . probable inference transfers to the conclusion a part of its certainty'. [Nicod, 208] But neither claim can stand. As against the first, there are cases where, though a proposition entails another proposition, the second proposition is less probable than the first. Witness e.g. the polysyllogistic formula $\gamma PF(gx, \beta P(fAh \cdot hAg) \cdot fx)$, discussed in 2.2. As against the second, there are other cases where, though a proposition probabilifies another proposition, the second proposition is no less probable than the first. This is so in the upper limiting case of probabilification, namely, verification; for consider e.g. the formula, $VF(fAg, f'Ag \cdot \alpha C_2)$, where the verified-no less than the verifying-proposition is true or certain.

6.2.3 *The Meaning of 'Evidence'*

These remarks on good, conclusive and (allegedly) 'demonstrative' evidence conveniently introduce a discussion of evidence in general. This book is about inductive probabilification and verification, i.e. the notions of being good and conclusive evidence for; but some systematic treatment of the notion of evidence is also required. What follows is in part a collection and arrangement of observations on this topic that have been made in passing throughout this book.

'Evidence', Bentham truly observes, 'is a word of relation'. [Bentham, Bk. I, Ch. I] Our first question therefore is, What is (said to be) evidence that what? The answer is, in a categorical evidential-statement a putative fact or true proposition is said to be evidence for or against another proposition. Hence the categorical evidential-statement-formula, (1), E(p, q), read 'The fact that q is evidence that p'. [1.1] We also saw that there are hypothetical evidential-statements as well as categorical ones. As with probabilification-judgements, it is not wrong to say that it is events which are evidence for or against events. We also saw that sensation-statements are usually not called evidence, evidencing-statements generally being about common objects; but that memory-experience-reports are called evidence. [1.2, 4.3]

The next question is, When is a putative fact (said to be) evidence for or against another proposition? It will be helpful to dispose of three wrong answers to this question before giving the right one. The first claims that the fact that q is evidence that p if and only if it suggests to me (the speaker) that p. I pointed out earlier [6.1] that this is the view of Hume, and criticized it on a number of grounds. Others besides Hume hold to this psychological view of the nature of evidence. Bentham e.g. opens his treatise on judicial evidence with the following definition: 'By the term evidence . . . seems in general to be understood,—any matter of fact, the effect, tendency or design of which, when presented to the mind, is to produce a persuasion concerning the existence of some other matter of fact . . .' [Bentham, 17]

It is of some interest that this psychological definition of 'evidence' is suggested by the derivation of the word, of which an early legal authority gives the following account: 'Evidence, *evidentia* . . . is called evidence, because thereby the point in issue is to be made evident to the jury'. [*Coke upon Littleton*, 282, b, 1628] The Oxford English Dictionary supports Coke's statement. I.e., when one says that the fact that q is evidence that p, he is saying that q is that which makes it evident (to him) that p. This reveals the connexion between 'evidence' and 'evident' (or 'obvious', 'clear', 'plain'); the latter notion figures in 'self-evident', an adjective applied by Descartes and Locke to certain truths or propositions. [Locke, 299 f.] The derivation of 'evidence' suggests the psychological definition of it, because saying that the fact that q suggests to me that p, persuades me that p, or makes it obvious to me that p, are different ways of saying pretty much the same thing. A lesson to be learnt from this is, incidentally, that the derivation of a word is not a reliable guide to its present meaning. The most that can be claimed is that the former sometimes provides a useful clue to the latter. As we saw earlier [1.2], this is so in the case of the derivation of 'probable' from the Latin *probabilis*; but it is not so in the case of the derivation of 'evidence' from the Latin *evidentia*.

The second wrong answer asserts that the fact that q is evidence that p if (but not only if) q is true and entails p. This is the fallacious belief in 'demonstrative' evidence which I have just criticized. The third asserts that an event is evidence of another event if and only if it is the (or a) cause (or effect) of it. Like the first, it is found in Hume. I showed earlier [5.1] why this contention is mistaken; but it is desirable to add that there is indeed a connexion, though not an equivalence, between evidencing and causing. Briefly, it is that any causal statement entails a corresponding evidential-statement, but not conversely. E.g., '*Anopheles* is the cause of malaria' entails 'The presence of *anopheles* is evidence of the presence of malaria'; but 'The fact of being a ruminant is evidence of dividing the hoof' does not entail 'The fact of being a ruminant is the cause of dividing the hoof'. Hence, causal evidence is only one sort of evidence among others.

Passing now to the right answer, the fact that q is said to be evidence that p under different conditions. What the most important of these are is revealed by the evidential-statement-formulas, (6), $E(gx, fMg \cdot fx)$; (2), $E(fAg, f'Ag,)$; and also $E(p, (p \supset q) \cdot q)$. In other words, the most important division of evidence from a philosophical point of view is that into casual, inductive and hypothetic evidence. Connected with these distinctions are two more;

for we saw [1.2] that primitive inductive evidence is always instantial, and that hypothetic evidence is always consequential.

There are the following additional philosophically interesting distinctions in evidence besides the causal vs. non-causal distinction: dependent vs. independent; direct vs. indirect evidence; and moral vs. natural evidence. I discussed the first in 1.2, where I distinguished logical from causal (in)dependence, and showed that the condition of independence of evidence, C_5, is involved in compositive formulas such as $\gamma PF(gx, \delta P(gx) . \delta P(gx) . C_5)$. I discussed (in)direct evidencing and probabilification in 2.2, when I distinguished two types of indirect probabilification: the two corresponding cases of indirect evidencing are illustrated respectively by the formula, (12), $E(p, (r \supset p) . E(r, q))$, and by the statement 'Since the presence of smoke here would be evidence of the presence of fire here, and the presence of soot here would be evidence of the presence of smoke here, and there is soot here, that is evidence that there was fire here'. Hume's distinction between natural and moral evidence was mentioned in 1.1: notice that he draws this distinction on the basis of what the evidenced-statement is about, namely, a physical and overt phenomenon on the one hand and a mental and inward phenomenon on the other.

There are plenty of other divisions of evidence which, however, are less important from the philosophical point of view. The best-known of them is probably the jurists' distinction between testimonial and circumstantial evidence, which I alluded to above as being the source of a popular fallacy of ampliative inference. When the evidencing-statement is about what someone says, it is testimonial; but in all other cases it is circumstantial. Cp. 'The fact that C says that A killed B is evidence that A killed B' with 'The fact that A's fingerprints are on the gun is evidence that A killed B'. These two classes can of course be subdivided, and Bentham e.g. carries the process of division a considerable distance. [Bentham, Bk. I, Ch. IV] A curiosity worth notice in passing is that down to the middle of the eighteenth century 'an evidence' actually meant 'a witness', and indeed we still speak of people 'turning Queen's evidence'.

Again, historians and critics distinguish internal from external evidence. Thus, when the authorship of a document is disputed, facts about the document itself, such as its vocabulary, style and calligraphy, are called internal evidence, and all other relevant facts are called external evidence, e.g. a statement in another document about the authorship of the first document.

Unlike the natural *vs.* moral distinction, the testimonial *vs.* circumstantial and the internal *vs.* external distinctions are drawn in terms of what the evidencing-, not the evidenced-, statement is about. In general, evidence can be and is divided in indefinitely many ways according to our interests and purposes. Sometimes, indeed, the qualifying adjectives are inept. This is the case with the title of Bentham's treatise; for it implies that evidence can usefully be divided into judicial and non-judicial in the same way as it can into, say, statistical and non-statistical. But this is untrue and misleading, since there is in fact no property or set of properties, possession of which marks off a given item or lot of evidence as 'judicial', i.e. as falling within the cognizance of a court of law. (Cp., however, my remarks on the legal admissibility of evidence, below.)

A word the meaning of which is closely connected with 'evidence' is 'relevance'. Some, indeed, attempt to define the latter in terms of the former, contending that 'p and q are mutually relevant' means 'q would be evidence for or against p or conversely'. Hempel, e.g., writes: '. . . an empirical finding is relevant for a hypothesis if and only if it constitutes either favourable or unfavourable evidence for it; in other words, if it either confirms or disconfirms the hypothesis. Thus, a precise definition of relevance presupposes an analysis of confirmation and disconfirmation'. [Hempel, I, 3]

However, this is too narrow a definition, since relevance is a wide notion which embraces demonstrative as well as evidential relations between propositions. fAg and $f\bar{I}g$ are (called) mutually relevant although neither is evidence for or against the other. We must rather say that p and q are mutually relevant if and only if p entails q or conversely, or they are inconsistent, or p would be evidence for or against q or conversely. It follows that p and q are mutually relevant if p probabilifies q or conversely, since probabilifying or evidencing well is a special case of evidencing. It is proper to remember, however, that since Hempel regards demonstrative as a species of evidential relations, he doubtless does not disagree with this account of relevance.

Relevance is both a symmetrical and a transitive relation. If p is relevant to q, then q logically must be relevant to p. And if p is relevant to q and q is relevant to r, then p logically must be relevant to r. We saw earlier [2.2] that 'evidences' and 'probabilifies' are transitive relations, and that the existence of indirect evidencing and probabilifying is connected with this fact. There is also direct and indirect relevance. This distinction is explicable in terms of either direct and indirect evidencing or direct and indirect entailing; for q may be said to entail p indirectly when it entails r which entails p. On the other hand, evidencing and probabilifying are not symmetrical relations; though they are not asymmetrical either. 'q would be (good) evidence that p' does not entail 'p would be (good) evidence that q': the two-way relation holds between some statements but not between others. Thus, it is true both that 'He understands Latin pronounced in the Italian manner' is evidence that 'He is a R.C. priest', and conversely. But though it is true that 'This BU is H' is evidence that 'All BU are H', the converse is false, since the latter statement entails, and so does not evidence, the former. Being a transitive and non-symmetrical relation is an important point of resemblance between entailing on the one hand and evidencing and probabilifying on the other, and an important point of difference between these three on the one hand and the transitive and symmetrical relation of being relevant to on the other.

There is, however, a *prima facie* objection to the foregoing account of the meaning of 'relevance', in that we sometimes speak of 'irrelevant evidence'. For if 'q is evidence for or against p' is compatible with 'q is irrelevant to p', then I was wrong in saying that the former entails or is a sufficient truth-condition of 'q is relevant to p'. The reply to this objection is, I think, that strictly speaking the expression 'irrelevant evidence' *is* self-contradictory; and that when an alleged fact is so called, this is to be understood as meaning 'an alleged fact which is claimed to be evidence for or against the statement at issue, but which in fact is not so'.

Finally, an expression related to 'relevance' and so to 'evidence' is 'legal admissibility'. Relevance is not, however, identical in meaning with legal admissibility. By the trial rules of English legal practice, one of the grounds on which the judge may exclude facts offered in evidence is their irrelevance. But it is not the only ground, as witness e.g. the rule excluding hearsay evidence. 'Admissible' and 'relevant' are therefore not equivalent expressions: 'All admissible evidence must be relevant, but all relevant evidence is not therefore admissible'. [J. F. Stephen, *The Principles of Judicial Evidence*, London, 1872, Pt. I, Ch. I] However, the two expressions are sometimes confused. E.g., it is said 'Hearsay is not evidence'. This is a misleading ellipsis of '(In English legal practice) hearsay is not admissible evidence'. Yet I suspect that the existence of the ellipsis betrays a conflation of 'inadmissible' with 'irrelevant': hearsay, it is thought, is inadmissible, and being inadmissible is the same thing as being irrelevant, and being irrelevant is the same thing as not being evidence. But it is not true that being inadmissible is the same thing as being irrelevant. Nor indeed is it true that not being relevant is the same thing as not being evidence, since, as I have just pointed out, '*q* is evidence for or against *p*' entails but is not entailed by '*q* is relevant to *p*'.

The reasons for the rules of inadmissibility which compose the so-called Law of Evidence appear to be of two types. First, practical, to ensure that cases shall not be protracted indefinitely by the introduction of an immense mass of evidence. Second, theoretical, to exclude from the jury's consideration either (*a*) what purports to be evidence but is not so at all, or (*b*) what is evidence but of trivial value. The irrelevance rule excludes (*a*), and the hearsay rule illustrates (*b*); for the reason for the latter rule is what is considered to be the low evidential value of testimonial statements that are not made on oath, either in court where they can be further tested by interrogation, or before a suitable official. [Wigmore, 970 f.] It is the thesis of Bentham in his treatise that only the first of these two types of reason is good, that: '. . . merely with a view to rectitude of decision, to the avoidance of the mischiefs attached to undue decision, no species of evidence whatsoever, willing or unwilling, ought to be excluded: for that although in certain cases it may be right that this or that lot of evidence, though tendered, should not be admitted, yet, in these cases, the reason for the exclusion rests on other grounds; viz. avoidance of vexation, expense and delay'. [Bentham, Prospective View]

6.2.4 *Criticism of some Other Views (concluded)*

So much for the concept of evidence. I return now to a consideration of the views of a few more authors who wish to include Inductive Philosophy in Logic, beginning with the doctrine that Logic is Semiotic or the Theory of Signs, which originates with the Stoics, but which is reproduced by later authors such as Locke and Peirce. [Locke, 370; Peirce, 98 ff.] One might think that this doctrine is equivalent to Mill's view that Logic is the Theory of Evidence, and is accordingly open to the same objections. But this would be a mistake. For, although all evidences are signs, the converse is not true. Signs, like evidences, may be divided in many different ways. But there is one distinction which is vital for present purposes, namely, that between signs-of and signs-for. Some of the chief differences between them are as follows. Signs-of are evidences, whereas signs-for are not. Signs-for are symbols, whereas signs-of are not. The relation between a sign-for and that for which it is a sign is artificial, whereas the relation between a sign-of and that of which it is a sign is natural. A sign-for can be right or wrong, whereas a sign-of cannot. But a sign-of can be good or bad, whereas a sign-for cannot. The intimate connexion between this last consideration, the goodness of evidences, and Probability, has been repeatedly emphasized throughout this book. There are a number of words besides 'evidence' which mean more or less the same as 'sign-of', e.g. 'mark', 'indication', 'symptom', etc.

Some philosophers confuse these two sorts of signs. Berkeley mistakenly thinks that signs-of are a sort of signs-for—specifically, a certain sort of signs-for, namely words—and accordingly calls Nature a Divine Language. Conversely, certain modern philosophers, e.g. C. K. Ogden, I. A. Richards and L. S. Stebbing, erroneously maintain that signs-for are a sort of signs-of—specifically, a certain sort of signs-of, namely inductive evidences. Price formulates their thesis thus: 'Symbols are a species of inductive signs, distinguished from others by the fact that they are produced by human beings'. [Price, 198] He calls this doctrine 'the sign-theory of symbolization' and, as applied to the special sort of signs-for that are words, 'the inductive sign theory of language'. The reader is referred to his thorough discussion of it. [Price, 144 ff., 198 ff.] It is a reasonable surmise that a leading reason for both of these false doctrines is their patrons' failure to notice a crucial ambiguity in the verbs 'mean' and 'signify'. For we say both 'Smoke means (i.e. is a sign of) fire' and '"Smoke" means (i.e. is a sign for) smoke'.

It follows from these considerations on signs-of and signs-for that the doctrine that Logic is the Theory of Signs is objectionable on two scores. First, for the reasons given earlier, it is undesirable to include in Logic the study of inference from evidences or signs-of under some such name as Inductive Logic. Second, it also seems to me to run counter to what is traditionally understood by Logic to include in it a study of symbolism or signs-for. It is true that many, perhaps most, Logic texts include under some such heading as 'names and propositions', 'language' or 'meaning', discussion of such topics as the 'denotation' of 'names'; but on the view of the province of Logic taken here, all this is as foreign to Logic as is a discussion of inference from evidence. In fact, the standard form of Logic texts during the past century reflects the influence of Mill's *Logic*, not only in the inclusion of a book or part on induction and methodology, but also in the inclusion of a book or part on language and symbolism.

Johnson's position on the philosophical study of induction and Logic is this: '. . . assuming that there is general unanimity as regards the usage of the name logic to denote a science whose central or essential function is to criticize thought as valid or in-valid. That induction should be included in logic thus defined follows from the undeniable fact that we do infer inductively, and that some persons in reference to some problems do infer in-validly.' [Johnson, I, xvi] In other words: Logic is the science of reasoning; induction is reasoning no less than deduction is; there-fore the study of induction is part of Logic. These are certainly the considerations which present the strongest temptation to include Inductive Philosophy in Logic, and to distinguish within the latter the co-ordinate divisions, Deductive Logic and Inductive Logic, the subject-matters of which are deductive and inductive reasoning respectively. It is also true, as we have seen [6.1], that inductive probabilification- and verification-judgements are (called) modes of reasoning, Nevertheless, it will not do to call the general study of them Logic for the reason previously given, that the subject-matter of Logic is entailment and inconsistency.

Keynes approves of Leibniz's project of a Logic of Probability. [Keynes, v, 3] But what Leibniz means by this expression is not altogether clear; according to Couturat, he means simply the Cal-culus of Probabilities, and in particular the principles of Inverse Probability. [Leibniz, 272 ff.] Keynes divides Logic into the Logic of Implication and the Logic of Probability. By the former he means, pre-eminently, the *Principia Mathematica* of Whitehead and

Russell. By the latter he means the philosophical study of 'partial implications' or 'probability relations', conceptions which I have already criticized. [1.2] Thus, he conceives of his treatise as a parallel work to *Principia Mathematica*, doing for partial implication what the latter does for plain implication. Substantially the same is true of Carnap's notion of Inductive Logic; he too regards himself as constructing a theory of degree of confirmation in the same sort of way as modern logicians construct theories of implication. In studying long and hard books like Keynes' *Treatise* and Carnap's *Foundations*, it is helpful to form at the outset, if one can, a clear idea of what their authors suppose themselves to be at; and in this their readers may find that this analogy with modern systems of Formal Logic provides a helpful clue.

In its fundamental ideas, Keynes' book is conspicuously a work of its place and date, namely, of Cambridge in the second decade of this century. For it is manifestly influenced by Moore's *Principia Ethica* as well as by *Principia Mathematica*. It is from the former that he derives his view of 'probable' as an indefinable, simple and unanalysable term—like 'good' or 'yellow'. [G. E. Moore, *Principia Ethica*, Cambridge, 1903, pp. 5 ff.] Unfortunately, as I remarked in my earlier discussion, Keynes' two fundamental ideas are incompatible. If 'probable' is unanalysable, then it really is unanalysable, and not analysable or explicable in terms of 'partial implication' or of anything else.

Mention must next be made of Reichenbach's conception of a Logic of Probability. [Reichenbach, 319 ff.; Nagel, 42 f.] His method is to construct a propositional calculus with infinitely many values, namely, those in the interval 0 to 1 inclusive, and to interpret each value as a degree of probability in the sense of limiting value of relative truth-frequency. For we saw in some earlier remarks on Reichenbach's views [2.2] that he accepts Peirce's analysis of the meaning of probability in terms of relative truth-frequency. It seems that the model here is the work of Łukasiewicz, who first constructed a propositional calculus with three values, true, false, and possible, as opposed to the usual two, true and false. For this naturally suggests the possibility of setting up a calculus with the three values, true, false and probable. Actually, however, Reichenbach's procedure differs from this in two ways. First, true and false are not among the values of his calculus, but rather probable in the degree 1 and probable in the degree 0.

For we saw earlier [5.2] that Reichenbach holds that 'true' and 'false' are useless words, since all propositions are only in varying degrees probable and never true. Second, his system has not just one third value, namely, probable, but an infinite number of values, namely, tne infinitely numerous degrees of probability between o and 1; for probability is regarded as a continuous quantity.

Reichenbach's object in all this, it seems, is to merge the Calculus of Probabilities in a general logic of propositions. But from this we can, I think, reasonably conclude that his enterprise can shed no light on inductive probability, only at best on casual probability; since it is of course with this latter type of probability that the Calculus of Probabilities is concerned. [2.2]

Lastly, a few words on the opinions of certain of the followers of Wittgenstein. I shall take Strawson as their spokesman, and shall discuss what seem to me to be the vital points without entering any further than is unavoidable into the rather deep question of the proper definition of the province of Logic.

The gist of Strawson's view is this. [Strawson, 26 ff., 211 f.] Logic divides into two severally exclusive and (presumably) collectively exhaustive branches, Formal or Deductive Logic on the one hand and Informal Logic or the Logic of Language on the other. The basis of the distinction is as follows. The subject-matter of Formal Logic is the entailment-relations of logical words or constants (or, more exactly, of statements containing them); whereas that of Informal Logic is all philosophically interesting relations of all philosophically interesting non-logical words. By 'philosophically interesting non-logical words' is meant words, explaining the meaning of which poses a philosophical problem: such are 'pleasure', 'time', 'right', etc. Of course, the great majority of non-logical words are philosophically uninteresting: no philosophical problems are posed by, say, 'breakage', 'yodel' or 'deciduous'. By 'philosophically interesting relations' is meant relations, consideration of which is necessary to a complete explanation of the meanings of philosophically interesting non-logical words. Such are, besides entailment, the relations of referring to the world, the relation between evaluative words and the descriptive words which constitute their criteria, etc. We have seen in this book that consideration of the last relation in particular is indispensable in explaining the meaning of 'probable'. Consequently, a philosopher inquiring into a certain aspect of the Philosophy of Perception is described by authors of this persuasion as 'investigating the informal logic of "sensation"', and a philosopher inquiring into a certain problem of the Philosophy of Politics as 'charting the informal logic of "liberty"', and so on.

This being their notion of Logic in general, we can readily infer what view these thinkers would take of what I call Inductive Philosophy. They would call much the greater part of it Informal Inductive Logic, since 'probable' is not a logical word and since the relations involved in primitive and non-deductive derivative probabilification-judgements are not entailment-relations. And the small part which I call Inductive Logic, i.e. the study of deductive derivative judgements, they would call Formal Inductive Logic, since the relation involved here is entailment. But since Formal and Informal Inductive Logic are (presumably) collectively exhaustive as well as severally exclusive, and so jointly compose Inductive Logic, this is tantamount to saying that they would call what I call Inductive Philosophy, Inductive Logic.

These philosophers in effect equate all Philosophy with Logic, for they regard all philosophical investigations as falling within either Formal or Informal Logic, i.e. within Logic. Their nomenclature has the advantage of making it explicit that all Philosophy is about language. But it is a slight advantage. For who disputes, or has ever disputed, that Philosophy is in some sense about words —or, as many and perhaps most prefer to say, about the 'ideas' or 'concepts' that they suppose words to stand for?

On the other hand, their manner of speaking has the substantial disadvantage of going against the traditional use of the name 'Logic' in three ways. First, to repeat a point already made, 'Logic' is traditionally equivalent to 'Formal Logic', so that the name 'Informal Logic' is on this ground alone unorthodox. More important, to speak of explaining the meanings of such words as 'sensation' and 'liberty' as doing Logic, is to go against tradition in another way. For Logic has always been thought to be concerned with the form rather than the matter of propositions and inferences, whereas such words as 'sensation' and 'liberty' are descriptive, not formal, words. I.e., anyone hearing a discussion in which they occurred would have some general idea of what it was about. Logical words, on the other hand, are topic-neutral: from the fact that a discourse contains the words 'all', 'and', etc., no conclusion can be drawn respecting what it is about. This is why Logic is formal; being concerned with these logical words or constants and their entailments, subject-matter can be ignored; so that instead of treating of propositions and arguments containing descriptive words, logicians can treat of formulas containing variables, or in other words can formalize their study. But though all inferences which hinge on the entailments of logical words can be formalized, the converse is not true. For we have seen that inductive probabilification- and verification-judgements, which do not so hinge, can also be formalized. The rules or principles implicit in correct judgements of these types are also quite independent of what the judgements are about, be it balls in an urn, human births, periods of pendulums or pressures of gases. Consequently, the philosophical study of these too can be formalized and conducted in terms of formulas rather than judgements.

Finally, Logic is traditionally regarded as part of Philosophy, not as co-extensive with it, as these thinkers make it out to be. Their position, notice, is much more extreme than that of others who take a broad view of the province of Logic and include in it, besides the study of deductive reasoning, that of meaning, induction and methodology. Russell indeed now maintains, surprisingly, that Logic is not even part of Philosophy. [Russell, H, 5] I say surprisingly, not so much because his present opinion is unorthodox, as because it is directly opposed to his earlier opinion that 'all philosophy is logic'. [*Our Knowledge of the External World*, London, 1926, p. 42] This last formula does, however, render succinctly the view of the philosophers I am discussing; though it must be remembered that their notion of Logic is quite different from any ever held by Russell, who has never employed the concept of Informal Logic.

Since, then, none of these reviewed opinions on the relation of the philosophical study of induction to Logic is acceptable, I conclude that the inquiry which I here close is rightly called an essay in, not Logic, but Philosophy.

APPENDIX:
TABLE OF FORMULAS

The following table comprises the main probabilification-judgement-formulas discussed in the text. The table is intended to serve three purposes. First, to provide a glossary of the symbolism: this is effected by giving a judgement exemplifying each formula. Second, to remind the reader of the chief distinctions between the formulas and of the nomenclature in terms of which they are drawn: this is effected by classifying the formulas and by indicating the type of each formula. Third, to give a synopsis of the constructive part of the argument of the book: here, the illustrations of the meanings of the conditions C_1 to C_7 are crucial.

1. INDUCTIVE (HOMOGENEOUS) FORMULAS

A. Primitive

Formula $(2')$: $\gamma PF(fAg, f'Ag \cdot \gamma C_2)$

Exemplifying judgement: 'The fact that all observed balls in this urn are hollow and varied makes it probable that all the balls in this urn are hollow (abbr., all BU are H)'.

Type: Universal subject-predicate probabilification-judgement-formula.

Formula: $VF(fAg, f'Ag \cdot \alpha C_2)$

Exemplifying judgement: 'The fact that all observed BU are H and very, very varied makes it true that all BU are H'.

Type: Universal subject-predicate verification-judgement-formula.

Formula (10'): $\gamma\text{PF}(fMg, f'Mg \cdot \gamma C_2 \cdot \gamma C_6)$

Exemplifying judgement: 'The fact that most observed BU are H and varied, and that this proportion is stable, makes it probable that most BU are H'.

Type: Non-numerical proportional subject-predicate.

Formula (11'): $\gamma\text{PF}(fm/ng, f'm/ng \cdot \gamma C_2 \cdot \gamma C_6)$

Exemplifying judgement: 'The fact that m-$n$ths of observed BU are H and varied, and that this proportion is stable, makes it probable that m-$n$ths of BU are H'.

Type: Numerical proportional subject-predicate.

Formula (7'): $\gamma\text{PF}((Aa)(Ab)\ b = a, (Aa')(Ab')\ b = a \cdot \gamma C_2 \cdot \gamma C_3)$

Exemplifying judgement: 'Since, for all observed values of the length and breadth of this leaf, its breadth in cms. is equal to its length in ins., and the observations have been made under varied conditions, and the observed values of the variables are numerous and evenly distributed over the range of observation; it is probable that, for all values of the length and breadth of this leaf, its breadth in cms. is equal to its length in ins.'.

Type: Functional.

B. Derivative

Formula (3'): $\gamma\text{PF}(gx, \gamma P(fAg) \cdot fx)$

Exemplifying judgement: 'The fact that all BU are probably H and that this ball is a BU, makes it probable that this ball is H'.

Type: Singular subject-predicate deductive.

Formula (9'): $\gamma\text{PF}(b_n, \gamma P((Aa)(Ab)\ b = a) \cdot a_n)$

Exemplifying judgement: 'Since it is probable that, for all values of the length and breadth of this leaf, its breadth in cms. is equal to its length in ins., and its present length is 3·5 ins., it is probable that its present breadth is 3·5 cms.'.

Type: Functional deductive (Interpolation).

Exemplifying judgement: 'Since it is very probable that, for all values of the breadth of this leaf and all values of its length between 2·5 ins. and 9·5 ins., its breadth in cms. is equal to its length in ins.; and since its present length is 9·55 ins., so that the degree of extrapolation is small (ϵC_7); it is fairly probable that its present breadth is 9·55 cms.'.

Type: Functional non-deductive (Extrapolation).

II. PARTLY INDUCTIVE (HETEROGENEOUS) FORMULAS

All the following formulas are derivative.

Formula (5'): $\delta PF(gx, \alpha P(fMg)) . fx . C_1)$

Exemplifying judgement: 'The fact that most BU are very, very probably H, and that this ball is a random BU, makes it fairly probable that this ball is H'.

Type: Non-numerical singular subject-predicate casual and inductive non-deductive.

Formula (16'): $\gamma PF(m/nP(gx), \gamma P(fm/ng)) . fx . C_1)$

Exemplifying judgement: 'The fact that m-$n$ths of BU are probably H, and that this ball is a random BU, makes it (inductively) probable that there is a (casual) probability of m-$n$ths that this ball is H'.

Type: Numerical singular subject-predicate casual and inductive non-deductive.

Formula (18'): $\eta PF(gx, \alpha P(hMg . fMh)) . fx . C_1)$

Exemplifying judgement: 'Since it is very, very probable that most holders of absolute power become tyrants and that most successful revolutionary leaders become holders of absolute power, and N is a random successful revolutionary leader, there is an appreciable probability that N will become a tyrant'.

Type: Casual and inductive non-deductive.

Formula (17'): $\delta PF(gx, fMg . fx . \alpha P(C_1))$

Exemplifying judgement: 'The fact that most BU are H and that this ball is very, very probably a random BU, makes it fairly probable that this ball is H'.

Type: Casual and inductive non-deductive.

III. NON-INDUCTIVE FORMULAS

A. *Primitive*

Formula (6'): $\gamma PF(gx, fMg \cdot fx \cdot C_1)$

Exemplifying judgement: 'The fact that most BU are H, and that this ball is a random BU, makes it probable that this ball is H'.
Type: Non-numerical casual.

Formula: $m/nPF(gx, fm/ng \cdot fx \cdot C_1)$

Exemplifying judgement: 'The fact that m-$n$ths of BU are H, and that this ball is a random BU, makes it probable in the degree m-$n$ths that this ball is H'.
Type: Numerical casual.

Formula : $\gamma PF(gx, (gx \supset fx) \cdot fx \cdot \beta C_4)$

Exemplifying judgement: 'The fact that if this man is a Roman Catholic priest then he understands Latin pronounced in the Italian manner, and that he does understand Latin so pronounced, and that this property is very selective of being a R.C. priest, makes it probable that he is a R.C. priest'.
Type: Hypothetic.

B. *Derivative*

Formula: $1PF(fx \vee gx, 1/2\ P(fx) \cdot 1/2P(gx))$

Exemplifying judgement: 'The fact that it is probable in the degree one-half that this penny will fall heads uppermost and that it is probable in the degree one-half that it will fall tails uppermost, makes it probable in the degree one that it will fall either heads uppermost or tails uppermost'.
Type: Numerical casual deductive.

Formula: $\gamma PF(p, (p \supset \gamma P(q)) \cdot q)$

Exemplifying judgement: 'Since, if m-$n$ths of BU are H and the observed sample of BU is large and random and stable in respect of the proportion, then it is (casually) probable that about m-$n$ths of observed BU are H; and m-$n$ths of

observed BU are H and the observed sample is large and random and stable in respect of the proportion; it is (hypothetically) probable that about *m-n*ths of BU are H'.
Type: Casual and hypothetic (heterogeneous) non-deductive.

IV. INDETERMINATE FORMULAS

The following formulas may be wholly inductive, or partly inductive, or wholly non-inductive. They are all derivative.

Formula (15'): $\delta PF(fAg, \alpha P(f'Ag) \cdot \gamma C_2)$

Exemplifying judgement: 'The fact that all examined boys in the school very, very probably have chicken-pox, and that they are a varied sample, makes it fairly probable that all the boys in the school have chicken-pox'.
Type: Non-deductive.

Formula: $\gamma PF(gx, \delta P(gx) \cdot \delta P(gx) \cdot C_5)$

Exemplifying judgement: 'The fact that there are two independent evidences, each of which makes it fairly probable that Smith is the culprit, makes it probable that Smith is the culprit'.
Type: Additive compositive non-deductive.

Formula: $\gamma PF(gx, \beta P(gx) \cdot \epsilon P(\bar{g}x) \cdot C_5)$

Exemplifying judgement: 'The fact that there are two independent evidences, one of which makes it very probable that Smith is the culprit and the other of which makes it slightly probable that Smith is not the culprit, makes it probable that Smith is the culprit'.
Type: Subtractive compositive non-deductive.

Formula (14'): $\gamma PF(fAg, \beta P(hAg \cdot fAh))$

Exemplifying judgement: 'Since all mammals are very probably vertebrates and all porpoises are very probably mammals, all porpoises are probably vertebrates'.
Type: Syllogistic deductive.

Formula (12'): $\gamma PF(p, (r \supset p) \cdot \gamma PF(r, q))$

Exemplifying judgement: 'Since, if all metals are malleable, all gold is malleable, and the fact that all observed silver, copper, lead and iron are malleable makes it probable that all metals are malleable, it is probable that all gold is malleable'.

Type: Type 1 indirect deductive.

Formula (13'): $\gamma PF(p, (r \supset \beta P(p)) \cdot (q \supset \beta P(r)) \cdot q)$

Exemplifying judgement: 'Since, if there was smoke here there was very probably fire here, and if there is soot here there was very probably smoke here, and there is soot here, there was probably fire here'.

Type: Type 2 indirect deductive.

Formula: $\delta PF(p, \alpha P(q \vee p) \cdot \gamma P(\sim q))$

Exemplifying judgement: 'Since it is antecedently very, very probable that either this die is true and the observed fact of 400 out of 600 throws with it being ace is fortuitous, or it is not true and this is the explanation of the observed fact; and it is improbable that it is true since the observed fact would be improbable if this were so; it is fairly probable that it is not true and that this is the explanation of the observed fact'.

Type: Mixed alternative syllogistic deductive.

INDEX

Note.—The Index does not cover the References [pp. xiii ff.] or the Table of Formulas [pp. 323 ff.]

INDEX

logic of casual probability, 111 f., 114
logic of consistency; *see* deductive logic
logic of implication, 318
logic of inductive probability, 108, 111, 114 f., 296, 307
logic of inductive truth, 108, 111, 114 f., 296, 307
logic of language; *see* informal logic
logic of probability, 111 f., 113, 234, 318 ff.
logic of truth, 111, 113 ff., 234, 238, 307; *see also* inductive logic
logical consequence, 280
logical constant; *see* logical word
logical form, 321
logical word, 281, 297 f., 301, 320 ff.
logically independent evidence, 56, 313
lottery sampling, 97, 121, 173, 218
Łukasiewicz, 319

Mace, 3, 13 f., 144, 283
Mach, 21, 275
material implication, 305
mathematical description, 18, 248; *see also* colligation of facts
mathematical expectation, 37
mathematical induction, 5 f.
mathematical probability, 8, 118, 129, 131; *see also* casual probability
maturity of the chances, 211
meaning, 27 ff., 66 f., 209 f., 275, 282 f., 298 ff., 317, 320; *see also* descriptive meaning, evaluative meaning, philosophy, significance
meaninglessness; *see* significance
measurement of probability, 8, 37, 51 f., 77, 118, 129 ff., 138 f., 198, 200, 207, 239; *see also* degree of probability
medical diagnosis, 115, 124
memory-experience, 223
memory-experience report, 224 f., 311
memory-inference, 223
memory, reliability of, 223 ff.
memory-statement, 32
method of agreement, Mill's, 189 ff., 228
method of concomitant variations, Mill's, 15, 142, 189 ff.
method of curves, 149
method of difference, Mill's, 105, 189 ff.
method of differences, 149 f.
method of inquiry, 270 f., 300; *see also* scientific method
method of least squares, 146 ff.
method of maximum likelihood, 239
method of means, 147 f.
Mill, x, 2, 6, 11, 15 f., 18, 20, 29 f., 83, 85, 87 ff., 101 f., 104 f., 107, 128, 142, 152, 154 f., 157 f., 161 ff., 185, 187 ff., 198, 200, 221 f., 227 ff., 242, 251, 269, 274 f., 288 ff., 296 f., 300, 305, 307, 317 f.
Milne, 186
miracle, 221 f.
Mises, von, 45, 101, 120, 133 f., 136, 173
mistaken claim, 257
modal syllogism, 112
modal word, 266, 295
mode of ampliative inference, 205 ff., 214
model of a theory, 74
Moivre, de, 125 f., 129
Moore, 45, 319
moral evidence, 23 f., 313 f.
Morgan, de, 309
most, 123, 125

Nagel, 205, 263, 319
naming, 84 f.
natural class, 87 f.
natural evidence, 23 f., 313 f.
natural kind, 87, 198, 306
natural sign, 64 f.
naturalistic fallacy, 45 ff., 123, 206 f.
necessary condition, 176 f., 191

necessary truth, 34, 86, 195 f., 259, 266 f.
necessity, 282, 284, 295
negative analogy; *see* variety of observed instances
negative instance; *see* exception
Newton, 194, 275
Neyman, 9, 218
Nicod, 3, 98, 107, 110, 112, 155, 179, 226, 232 f., 247, 274, 310
Nisbet, ix, 117
nomenclature, 87
non-deductive derivative probabilification-judgement(-formula), 81, 296, 321
non-deductive inductive derivative probabilification-judgement(-formula), 89, 151
non-empirical explanation, 277
non-empirical generalization, 7, 274
non-empirical hypothesis, 53, 237, 267 f., 271 ff.
non-empirical principle, 19 f., 273, 277
non-empirical proportional hypothesis, 74 ff.
non-empirical universal hypothesis, 59 ff.
non-homogeneous population, 97, 173, 175
non-numerical casual primitive probabilification-judgement(-formula), 50, 117 ff.
non-numerical preponderant induction(-formula), 15 f.
not probable, 49, 258
number of conditions, 246 f.
number of observed instances, 127 f., 142 f., 145, 167, 195, 197, 210, 228, 232, 283, 307; *see also* size of sample
number of observed values of variables; *see* number of observed instances
numerical casual primitive probabilification-judgement(-formula), 50, 117 ff., 125
numerical difference, 90 ff.
numerical hypothetic probabilification-judgement(-formula), 77
numerical preponderant induction(-formula), 15 f.

objectivity of probability, 287
observation, 84, 244, 254
observation-statement, 32, 225, 260, 275 f.
Ogden, 317
opinion; *see* belief
other minds, knowledge of, 62 ff., 224, 260
otiose statement, 267 f.

parapsychology, 237
part of the truth, 263
partial elimination, 232 ff.
partial implication, 47 f., 132, 204, 207, 262, 280, 296, 308, 319; *see also* probabilification-relation
partial material implication, 48
partly true, 263
pattern of ampliative inference; *see* mode of ampliative inference
pattern of inference, 234, 238 f., 288; *see also* mode of ampliative inference
Pearson, 21, 275
Peirce, x, 9, 12, 28, 48, 52 f., 66, 118, 131 ff., 137, 172 f., 205 ff., 214, 217, 260, 262, 274, 280, 298, 309, 317, 319
perfect analogy, 202 f., 245 f.
performative utterance, 37 f.
persuasion; *see* suggestion
persuasive definition, 272, 278
phenomenalism, 32, 148, 225, 260, 265
Philodemus, 14, 123 ff., 140, 182 f., 279, 300
philosophical analysis; *see* philosophy
philosophical probability, 131
philosophy, xi, 27, 41, 44, 46, 113 f., 296, 302, 321 f.; *see also* logic, philosophy of science
philosophy of (inductive) probability; *see* philosophy
philosophy of science, 276
place, inductive irrelevance of, 92 ff., 184, 192, 250; *see also* uniformity of nature

INDEX